MW00488737

Medical and Legal Aspects of Neurology

By
Jeffrey Wishik, M.D., J.D.

Lawyers & Judges
Publishing Company, Inc.
Tucson, Arizona

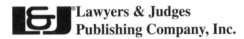

Lawyers & Judges Publishing Company, Inc.

P.O. Box 30040 • Tucson, AZ 85751-0040
(800) 209-7109 • FAX (800) 330-8795
e-mail: sales@lawyersandjudges.com

Library of Congress Cataloging-in-Publication Data

Wishik, Jeffrey.
  Medical and legal aspects of neurology / by Jeffrey Wishik.
    p. cm.
  ISBN-13: 978-1-930056-30-5 (hardcover)
  ISBN-10: 1-930056-30-3 (hardcover)
  1. Neurology. 2. Forensic neurology. I. Title.
RC346.W579 2005
614'.1--dc22

                    2005010018

ISBN 1-930056-30-3
ISBN 978-1-930056-30-5
Printed in the United States of America
10 9 8 7 6 5 4 3 2 1

www.lawyersandjudges.com

Contents

Preface

This book exists thanks to the vision of my incredibly patient publisher, Steve Weintraub. Initially, we envisioned a mere updating of Dr. WJ Ken Cumming's 1998 *Neurology* volume in the Medico-Legal Practitioners Series published in England. However, the rapid pace of advances in neurology meant that much of the material in that older volume was out of date. I have extensively revised or rewritten some material and added a great deal of other information. Nevertheless, I was very fortunate to be able to build on Dr. Cumming's work. Any errors are, regrettably, my own.

In speaking to my attorney colleagues I realized this was also an opportunity to help them understand how physicians, or at least neurologists, think when they are evaluating patients. Since neurologic diagnosis relies on neuroanatomy and neurophysiology I present some basic information about these subjects. Furthermore, I also explain what neurology is and who neurologists are—our education, training, clinical work, organizations, and certifications. I hope this helps attorneys when they look at medical reports and evaluate neurologists' credentials.

Physicians and attorneys look at the world in very different ways. All too often, when they interact the result is misunderstanding and distrust. While some physicians go to great lengths to avoid such interactions, for many clinicians they are unavoidable. Neurology is one of the medical specialties with a high likelihood of cases with legal ramifications. Unfortunately, many—perhaps, even most—neurologists do not have much understanding of the legal system. They may not present clinical information to the lawyer in a clear and usable manner. When this occurs the attorney is left to her own devices. One of my goals for this book is to help bridge this gap.

There are many excellent neurology textbooks available. However, these are written for clinicians. This book is written with attorneys (and other nonphysician readers) in mind. My intention is not to cover every detail of every aspect of neurology, impossible for a one-volume work. Indeed, if any reader comes away from this book believing that he or she has a total understanding of a particular topic then I have failed to convey a sense of the richness and complexity of this field. Instead, I try to give concise presentations on major areas of clinical concern and to highlight topics likely to have legal significance.

Many of my attorney and physician colleagues have encouraged me in this seemingly endless endeavor. I particularly want to thank Barry Levin, M.D., for his helpful and incisive comments.

Writing a book is an enormous challenge for which I was not entirely prepared. Fortunately, I was inspired and encouraged by my sister, Debra Englander, an author and book editor. I now have much greater respect and appreciation for what she has accomplished professionally and thank her for being such a good example. I would never have attempted this project were it not for a love of learning and respect for the written word; for that, I sincerely thank my parents, Harriet and Julius Wishik.

For their invaluable help in keeping our practice afloat while I took time off for this project, I thank my office manager Tracey Ellison and nurse practitioner Sally Davidson.

Finally, I thank Susan Bridges for her deep devotion and constant support while I was engaged in this project.

Chapter 1

Introduction: Neurology and Neurologists

1.1 The Specialty of Neurology

Neurology is the field of clinical medicine concerned with the diagnosis and treatment of diseases of the nervous system. This includes illnesses affecting the brain, spinal cord, spinal nerve roots, peripheral nerves, neuromuscular junction, muscles, and the blood supply and supportive structures of all of these. Clinical evaluation of patients with neurologic disease requires a thorough understanding of neuroanatomy and neurophysiology—subjects of great complexity. Thus, neurology is often regarded as one of the most difficult fields in all of medicine. Nevertheless, nonphysicians can understand the essentials of neurologic diagnosis and nervous system disease.

Many neurologic disorders are quite rare but others are exceedingly common. Historically, there were few effective therapeutic options for many of these illnesses, contributing to the view that neurologists spend their time making accurate diagnoses of obscure untreatable diseases. However, in recent years there have been major treatment advances for several neurologic diseases such as migraine, epilepsy, and stroke. Neurologic conditions include:

- amyotrophic lateral sclerosis (Lou Gehrig's disease),
- dementias including Alzheimer's disease,
- epilepsy,
- meningitis and other nervous system infections,
- migraine and other headaches,
- muscular dystrophies and myopathies,
- multiple sclerosis,
- Parkinson's disease,
- radiculopathy ("pinched nerve"),
- spinal cord injury,
- stroke and other cerebrovascular diseases, and
- traumatic brain injury.

There are no rigid barriers between neurology and other fields of medicine. Many patients with neurological symptoms will see non-neurologists for evaluation and treatment of their neurological complaints. For example, most people with headaches do not see a neurologist. Also, many neurologists treat conditions that might not, strictly speaking, be considered neurological. These include chronic pain, sleep disorders, depression, and attention deficit hyperactivity disorder.

Neurologists work in a variety of settings and capacities. Most provide clinical care in solo or small neurology group practices.[1] A neurologist can be the principal caregiver for a patient with a neurological disease or serve as a consultant to the patient's primary care physician. Some neurologists pursue academic careers, devoting much of their time to research and education. Many neurologists—both in private practice and academia—will specialize even further, working in one of the many neurological subspecialties (see §1.2C).

Neurologists are often involved in medicolegal activities. Automobile accidents, work injuries, and other traumas often produce brain, spine, and peripheral nerve injuries. The neurologist is well-suited to evaluate the impact of such injuries. Some develop particular expertise in disability medicine—evaluating pain complaints, calculating impairment ratings, and performing independent medical evaluations.

1.2 The Making of a Neurologist
A. College and medical school

The process of becoming a neurologist is a long one. It begins with an undergraduate college degree, often with a major in one of the sciences. However, medical and osteopathy schools certainly do enroll non-science majors as long as they have completed the prerequisite biology, chemistry, and other courses. Prospective neurologists must then graduate from a medical or osteopathy school, usually after a four-year course of study. The education leading to the doctor of medicine (M.D.) and doctor of osteopathy (D.O.) degrees is similar. There is no reason to discriminate between the two, a change from generations ago.

The first half of the medical curriculum typically is devoted to basic sciences, subjects such as anatomy, physiology, biochemistry, microbiology, and pathology. Instruction takes place in lecture halls and laboratories. Before the end of the second year there may be some preliminary exposure to clinical medicine, especially courses in physical diagnosis.

The second half of the curriculum emphasizes clinical training. Students evaluate and treat patients under the supervision of physicians-in-training (interns, residents, and fellows) and the senior attending physicians. This portion of undergraduate medical education is organized around rotations, several weeks or a few months spent in a particular medical specialty. The core rotations usually include internal medicine, general surgery, pediatrics, obstetrics-gynecology, and psychiatry. There is also time for elective rotations such as neurology.

B. Neurology training

Following graduation from medical school a physician interested in becoming a specialist ordinarily enters into a period of postgraduate education. *Residency* training programs prepare medical school graduates for independent careers in medical specialties. In order to become board-certified (see §1.3) most medical school graduates will enroll in a residency program that has been accredited by the Accreditation Council for Graduate Medical Education[2] (ACGME).

The ACGME is a private organization that accredits residency programs in 110 different specialties and subspecialties. There are specialty-specific Residency Review Committees responsible for revising standards and reviewing accredited programs. Members of these Committees are physicians with expertise in medical education. They are appointed by organizations including the American Medical Association, member boards of the American Board of Medical Specialties (ABMS) and other academic specialty organizations.

An adult neurology residency lasts forty-eight months and includes a preliminary year of training with at least eight months in general internal medicine. This first postgraduate year is often known as an *internship*. Some neurology programs provide this first year of training; others accept trainees who complete it elsewhere. Physicians specializing in child neurology have a longer training period. They first spend either two years in general pediatrics, or a year each in pediatrics and internal medicine, or a year each in research and pediatrics. Next, they complete at least one year in an adult neurology program and two years in child neurology training. The adult and child neurology residency programs must provide supervised clinical training as well as educational opportunities in basic neuroscience.

The ACGME neurology residency requirements are quite detailed and can be reviewed on that organization's website. The requirements include standards for faculty qualifications, hospitals and other facilities, patient resources, medical libraries, educational programs, and trainee evaluations.

C. Subspecialties

Some neurologists decide to pursue additional training beyond residency in a subspecialty of neurology. This postresidency education is known as a *fellowship*. These programs usually last one or two years. There are fellowships in several neurology subspecialties. Some provide expertise in specific diseases or conditions such as headache, epilepsy, or stroke—the three most common areas of clinical focus for neurologists.[3] There are fellowships available in movement disorders, behavioral and cognitive neurology, dementia, neuro-oncology, otoneurology, and other fields. Other fellowships focus on technical areas such as *clinical neurophysiology*, also known as *electrodiagnostic medicine*, the field devoted to techniques for assessing the electrical activity of the nervous system.

1.3 Recognition of Competency: Certification

There are many credentialing bodies that promulgate educational and training standards and assess physicians' clinical skills. Board certification in neurology and its subspecialties is not a requirement for medical licensing. Nevertheless, most neurologists do seek certification as a means of demonstrating their expertise.

The twenty-four major clinical medical and surgical fields have certifying boards that are members of the American Board of Medical Specialties.[4] This organization assists individual boards "in their efforts to develop and utilize educational standards for the evaluation and certification of physician specialists."

A. American Board of Psychiatry and Neurology (ABPN)[5]

The ABPN is a nonprofit corporation founded in 1934 "as a method of identifying the qualified specialists in psychiatry and neurology." The impetus to establish the ABPN came from the American Psychiatric Association, the American Neurological Association, and the American Medical Association's Section on Nervous and Mental Diseases.

The Board has eight psychiatry members nominated by the American College of Psychiatrists, American Psychiatric Association, and the American Medical Association, and eight neurology members nominated by the American Neurological Association and the American Academy of Neurology. The ABPN offers ten certifications including neurology, neurology with special qualification in child neurology, pain medicine, clinical neurophysiology, and neurodevelopmental disabilities. Since October 1, 1994, all certificates are issued with a ten-year limit; to avoid expiration the neurologist must pass a recertifying examination.

General eligibility requirements for board certification include:

- completion of an ACGME-accredited residency program,

- M.D. or D.O. degree from an accredited school, and
- unrestricted license to practice medicine.

Certification in neurology is a two-part process. First, there is a daylong written examination covering both basic and clinical neuroscience. If successful, the neurologist then must pass an oral examination. This includes observation of the physician with an actual patient and quizzing by several senior neurologists. The examination takes place in a hospital or clinic setting. It is a very stressful process.

B. Other certifications

The member boards of the ABMS are from large general specialties such as anesthesiology, internal medicine, surgery, pediatrics, and radiology. Smaller subspecialty groups have established certifying boards independent of the ABMS. These boards are also designed to evaluate the skills of physicians practicing in these specialized areas. There is considerable variation in standards and academic rigor among these independent boards. Nevertheless, in certain areas the certification process may be even more rigorous than an ABMS-approved certification. A few of these independent boards are described.

The American Electroencephalographic Society (now known as the American Clinical Neurophysiology Society) founded the American Board of Clinical Neurophysiology (ABCN)[6] in 1950. There are eight board members. One each is appointed by the American Academy of Neurology, the American Neurological Association, and the American Psychiatric Association. The Board itself elects the five other members. The ABCN examination focuses on "functional evaluation of the central nervous system."

The American Board of Electrodiagnostic Medicine (ABEM)[7] is an autonomous credentialing body operating as a committee of the American Association of Neuromuscular & Electrodiagnostic Medicine. It defines electrodiagnostic medicine as "the medical subspecialty that applies neurophysiologic techniques to diagnose, evaluate and treat patients with impairments of the neurologic, neuromuscular, and/or muscular systems." The written examination evaluates clinical knowledge as well as "special knowledge about electric signal processing, including waveform analysis, electronics and instrumentation, stimulation and recording equipment, and statistics." As of late 2002, there were 2,834 ABEM diplomates.[8]

The American Medical Electroencephalographic Association established the American Board of Electroencephalography in 1972 "to identify qualified electroencephalographers who are physicians." The Board renamed itself the American Board of Electroencephalography and Neurophysiology (ABEN)[9] in 1986 to reflect the increased usage of newer testing modalities including evoked potentials, EEG brain mapping, and computerized EEG analysis. The ABEN tests physician candidates for certification in electroencephalography and in four areas of special competence:

- evoked potentials,
- pediatric EEG,
- quantitative EEG, and
- sleep disorders.

More and more neurologists are expanding their practices by performing a variety of medicolegal services. Independent medical evalautions or examinations (IMEs) are important in the workers' compensation field and in many liability and disability cases. A clinician who is not treating the examinee performs the IME. Unfortunately, there is a wide range of quality in these examinations and examiners. A group of physicians concerned about this problem incorporated the American Board of Independent Medical Examiners (ABIME)[10] in 1994 "to establish and maintain standards of conduct and performance among independent medical examiners." The certification process includes educational requirements and a written examination. Certification is for five years and may be renewed either by re-examination or satisfaction of expanded continuing education requirements.

1.4 Professional Organizations

There are many neuroscience professional associations. Most do not have exclusionary or particularly restrictive membership policies. However, some of these organizations do have membership categories that reflect a higher level of achievement or recognition by peers. Such credentials might serve to distinguish one neurologist from another. Membership in a professional organization is not a requirement for a medical license. Among the different types of associations are those devoted to:

- general neurology,
- specific disease categories such as movement disorders, headache, or epilepsy, and
- subspecialties such as clinical neurophysiology or behavioral neurology.

Many neurologists belong to general interest medical societies (e.g., American Medical Association, state or local medical associations). Depending on their interests neurologists may also join associations devoted to fields outside of traditional neurology including sleep medicine, pain management, or disability evaluation. A few of the hundreds of societies are described briefly.

A. American Academy of Neurology (AAN)[11]

The AAN is the largest general interest professional association for neurologists and other neuroscience clinicians. The AAN was established in 1948 "to advance the art and science of neurology, and thereby promote the best possible care for patients with neurological disorders." It has more than 18,000 members, both in this country and abroad. Roughly 80 percent of American neurologists are AAN members. The Academy produces several publications including the widely-read journal *Neurology*, and provides a variety of educational material for clinicians and patients. This includes technology assessments and clinical practice guidelines. The AAN also provides guidance on ethical issues.[12] Much of this material is available at its website.

In addition to its regular membership categories, the AAN offers a *Fellow* membership. Qualifications for this include:

- achievement in the clinical neurosciences,
- attendance at five annual meetings as an active member,
- seven years or more of active membership status, and
- sponsorship by two AAN Fellows.

The highest membership category, *honorary* membership, recognizes individuals who have made exceptional contributions to neurology. They need not be members of the Academy. Nominees must be sponsored by letters from two Fellows of the Academy.

B. American Neurological Association (ANA)[13]

Unlike the AAN, membership in the ANA is not automatic. The ANA "is a society of academic neurologists and neuroscientists devoted to advancing the goals of academic neurology; to training and educating . . . and to expanding both our understanding of diseases of the nervous system and our ability to treat them." The ANA publishes a respected journal, *Annals of Neurology*, and holds an annual meeting.

The ANA has about 1,400 members.[14] Candidates for election to *Active* (United States and Canada) and *Corresponding* (elsewhere) *Membership* must:

- have a doctoral level degree,
- have at least nine years of training and experience in clinical neuroscience,
- have published at least ten scientific papers, and
- present evidence of excellence in teaching and research.

C. American Clinical Neurophysiology Society (ACNS)[15]

The ACNS was founded in 1946 as the American EEG Society and now has more than 1,200 members. Its mission is "fostering excellence in clinical neurophysiology and furthering the understanding of central nervous system function in health and disease through education, research, and the provision of a forum for discussion and interaction."

Educational courses and materials cover electroencephalography, evoked potentials, quantitative neurophysiological methods, sleep technology, and related areas. The Society holds an annual course and publishes the *Journal of Clinical Neurophysiology*. Besides neurologists, members include psychiatrists, neurosurgeons, and clinical neurophysiologists.

D. American Headache Society (AHS)[16]

The AHS is a professional organization "dedicated to the study and treatment of headache and face pain." Membership is not restricted to neurologists. The AHS was established in 1959 and has more than 2,500 members worldwide. These include physicians, dentists, psychologists, pharmacists, and mid-level practitioners. Approximately 1,000 are neurologists.[17] The AHS sponsors a range of educational programs for clinicians and the general public. It also publishes the journal *Headache*.

E. American Association of Neuromuscular & Electrodiagnostic Medicine (AANEM)[18]

With 4,902 members the AANEM is the largest organization in the world devoted to "advancing neuromuscular, musculoskeletal, and electrodiagnostic medicine." Most members are either neurologists or physiatrists.

Physicians who are board-certified by one of the member boards of the ABMS are eligible for *Active* membership. *Fellow* membership requires additional certification by the American Board of Electrodiagnostic Medicine (see §1.3B). *Associate* members are not board-certified and *Junior* members are in residency or fellowship training.

1.5 Practice Standards and Guidelines

The AAN, AAEM, and other neuroscience organizations are in the forefront of what is known as *evidence-based medicine*. This refers to clinical practice guidelines designed to help clinicians and patients determine a course of treatment based on the best available scientific evidence or expert consensus. The National Guideline Clearinghouse has 1,176 such guidelines available online.[19]

Guidelines come from many sources including:

- federal, state, and local governments,
- health insurance companies,
- hospitals,
- medical associations,
- research companies such as the RAND Corporation, and
- volunteer organizations such as the American Cancer Society.

These entities each have agendas that may influence their guidelines.

Evidence-based medicine shifts the emphasis from an individual clinician's experience and personal knowledge to information derived from more systematic and unbiased studies. Evidence-based medicine requires:[20]

- clearly defined clinical questions,
- critical appraisal of the evidence,
- evaluation of the entire process,
- gathering the best available evidence to answer the questions, and
- implementation of recommendations derived from the evidence.

Each of these elements should be examined to determine the validity and usefulness of a guideline. These disease management recommendations are not meant to be followed rigidly in all cases since it is impossible to take into consideration all of the factors that go into treatment decisions by individual physicians and their patients. AAN guidelines go through a rigorous review process to avoid undisclosed bias and provide valid recommendations.[21]

There are several general criticisms of clinical practice guidelines:

- guidelines may stifle research into less favored treatments;
- guidelines suggest greater uniformity of patients and illnesses than is warranted;
- most guidelines will be out-of-date within a few years given the rapid pace of research;
- over reliance on recommendations may be harmful in some situations; and
- they create the impression that medicine is practiced in a "cookbook" fashion.

It is unclear how well clinicians follow the various guidelines. Reasons for not adopting a guideline include ineffective dissemination or inadequate understanding. Also, there may be disagreements about the recommendations. It is important to remember that existence of a practice guideline does not necessarily indicate a broad consensus about what constitutes usual and customary practice in a particular field. Nevertheless, clinical practice guidelines have been used by courts as evidence of the standard of care.[22] Ideally, therefore, they should be derived from high quality peer-reviewed studies and produced by unbiased credible sources.

1.6 The Literature of Neurology
A. Learned treatises
The surge in our understanding of neurologic disease is reflected in the plethora of books devoted to neurology and neuroscience. There are many highly regarded single and multi-volume general neurology textbooks available. There are also numerous monographs devoted to specific diseases or subspecialty areas. Some texts and monographs are listed in Additional Reading; others are cited throughout this volume.

B. Journals
Medical journals contain more recent information than textbooks. The most rigorous require peer review of all submissions. In this process one or more anonymous reviewers critique articles and suggest corrections or ask for clarifications. The reviewers may also recommend to the editor whether publication is warranted or not. There are hundreds of journals that publish articles of neurologic interest. A few of the most important are listed here.

- *Acta Neurologica Scandinavica*
- *American Journal of Neuroradiology*
- *Annals of Neurology*
- *Archives of Neurology*
- *Brain*
- *Canadian Journal of Neurological Sciences*
- *Cephalalgia*
- *Cerebrovascular Diseases*
- *Cognitive and Behavioral Neurology*
- *Epilepsia*
- *European Journal of Pediatric Neurology*
- *Headache*
- *Journal of Child Neurology*
- *Journal of Clinical Neuropsychiatry*
- *Journal of Neurological Science*
- *Journal of Neurology, Neurosurgery, and Psychiatry*

- *Journal of Neuropathology and Experimental Neurology*
- *Journal of the American Medical Association*
- *Journal of the Neurological Sciences*
- *Lancet*
- *Muscle & Nerve*
- *Neurologic Clinics*
- *Neurology*
- *New England Journal of Medicine*
- *Pain*
- *Pediatric Neurology*
- *Revue Neurologique*
- *Seminars in Neurology*
- *Sleep*
- *Sleep Medicine*
- *Spine*
- *Stroke*
- *The Neurologist*
- *Trends in Neuroscience*

Endnotes

1. Swarztrauber K, Lawyer BL, AAN Practice Characteristics Subcommittee. *Neurologists 2000: AAN Member Demographic and Practice Characteristics.* St. Paul: American Academy of Neurology; 2001.

2. Accreditation Council for Graduate Medical Education: www.acgme.org, accessed December 24, 2004.

3. Swarztrauber K, Lawyer BL, *supra* note 1, at 10.

4. American Board of Medical Specialties: www.abms.org, accessed December 24, 2004.

5. American Board of Psychiatry & Neurology: www.abpn.com, accessed December 24, 2004.

6. American Board of Clinical Neurophysiology: www.abcn.org, accessed April 10, 2004.

7. American Board of Electrodiagnostic Medicine: www.abemexam.org, accessed December 24, 2004.

8. Hockert K. American Association of Electrodiagnostic Medicine. E-mail to author. October 16, 2002.

9. American Board of Electroencephalography and Neurophysiology: www.abeninfo.com, accessed December 24, 2004.

10. American Board of Independent Medical Examiners: www.abime.org, accessed December 24, 2004.

11. American Academy of Neurology: www.aan.com, accessed December 24, 2004.

12. Bernat JL, Goldstein ML, Ringel SP. "Conflicts of interest in neurology." *Neurology* 1998;50:327-331.

13. American Neurological Association: www.aneuroa.org, accessed December 24, 2004.

14. Wilkerson L. American Neurological Association. E-mail to author. October 9, 2002.

15. American Clinical Neurophysiology Society: www.acns.org, accessed December 24, 2004.

16. American Headache Society: www.ahsnet.org, accessed December 24, 2004.

17. Baldwin M. American Headache Society. E-mail to author. October 14, 2002.

18. American Association of Neuromuscular & Electrodiagnostic Medicine: aanem.org, accessed December 21, 2004.

19. National Guidelines Clearinghouse: www.guideline.gov, accessed December 24, 2004.

20. Tandon R, Goldman M. "Principles of evidence-based medicine." *CNS News* 2004;6(7):11-12.

21. Franklin GM, Zahn CA. "AAN clinical practice guidelines: Above the fray." *Neurology* 2002;59:975-976.

22. Sokol AJ, Molzen CJ. "The changing standard of care in medicine: E-health, medical errors, and technology add new obstacles." *J Legal Medicine* 2002;23:449-490, at 483-486.

Additional Reading

Aminoff MJ, Daroff RB, eds. *Encyclopedia of the Neurological Sciences*. New York: Academic Press; 2003. This is a four-volume publication.

Asbury AK, McKhann GM, et al., eds. *Diseases of the Nervous System*. New York: Cambridge University Press; 2002.

Bradley WG, Daroff RB, et al., eds. *Neurology in Clinical Practice*, 4th ed. Boston: Butterworth-Heinemann; 2003.

Evans RW, ed. *Saunders Manual of Neurologic Practice*. Philadelphia: Saunders; 2003.

Goetz CG, ed. *Textbook of Clinical Neurology*, 2nd ed. Philadelphia: Saunders; 2003.

Pryse-Phillips W. *Companion to Clinical Neurology*, 2nd ed. New York: Oxford University Press; 2003.

Rowland LP, ed. *Merritt's Neurology*, 10th ed. Philadelphia: Lippincott Williams & Wilkins; 2000.

Samuels MA, Feske S, eds. *Office Practice of Neurology*, 2nd ed. New York: Churchill Livingstone; 2003.

Victor M, Ropper AH, Adams RD. *Adams & Victor's Principles of Neurology*, 7th ed. New York: McGraw-Hill; 2000.

Vinken PJ, Bruyn GW, series eds. *Handbook of Clinical Neurology*. New York: Elsevier. This is a seventy-eight volume collection as of 2002, thirty-one in the revised series. Publication dates vary.

Chapter 2

The Diagnostic Process

2.1 Introduction

The purpose of taking a history and performing an examination is to reach a diagnosis in order to help the patient. This can be a very difficult process because much of the nervous system is hidden from direct observation. Also, different neurologic conditions may produce identical symptoms and a single disease may present in different ways. Furthermore, the nervous system cannot be evaluated in isolation from the rest of the body. Many systemic diseases have neurologic manifestations and sometimes these are the first signs of the illness.

Destructive processes usually lead to loss of function, producing negative signs such as weakness. Conversely, positive signs indicate irritation or excessive function. For example, when certain areas of the nervous system are destroyed they lose their inhibitory function over intact structures. This leads to abnormal excessive activity reflecting this loss of control—such as spasticity following a stroke. Other examples of *positive* signs due to irritation or overexcitation of nerve cells include epileptic seizures and *hyperkinetic* movement disorders.

Some diseases produce widespread or *diffuse* dysfunction. Others cause anatomically localized or *focal* damage. Still other pathologic processes affect only certain systems or functional units within the nervous system such as amyotrophic lateral sclerosis (commonly know as Lou

17

Gehrig's disease) with its destruction of motor cells but little else. The initial focus in the diagnostic process is localization—determining which anatomical part or functional unit of the nervous system is abnormal. Next, the neurologist will generate a *differential diagnosis*—a list of possible causes of the presenting problems.

2.2 General Organization of the Nervous System

The building blocks of the nervous system are the nerve cells—*neurons*—and the far more numerous supportive glial cells—*glia*. Approximately one hundred billion neurons produce the electrical signals that underlie communication within the nervous system. There are several types of neurons but most share some common features. There is a cell body or *soma* that is the metabolic center of the cell and contains its genetic material. Electrical signals from other neurons reach the soma via a network of receptive fibers called *dendrites*. Outgoing messages leave the soma via a larger fiber, the *axon* (Figure 2.1). Axons may split into numerous branches, allowing transmission to many cells. Axons can be as long as two meters.

Near the end of each axonal branch are specialized regions known as *presynaptic terminals*. These contain vesicles filled with chemicals called *neurotransmitters* that are released into the space or *synapse* between the transmitting axon and the dendrite of the receiving neuron. There are several types of synapses besides the prototypical axon-dendrite type. These serve to fine tune neurotransmission.

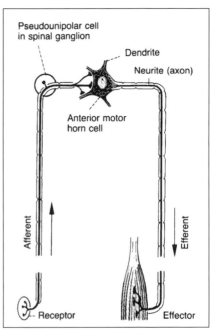

(From Duus P. Topical Diagnosis in Neurology, 2nd rev. ed. New York: Thieme; 1989:6. Reprinted by permission.)

Figure 2.1 Simple reflex cicuit. Input from a sensory neuron and its receptor connecting with a motor neuron. The motor axon's output goes to the effector, in this case a muscle.

The glia come in several varieties. Central nervous system (CNS) *oligodendrocytes* and peripheral nervous system (PNS) *Schwann* cells produce *myelin*, the insulating substance that surrounds the axons. *Astrocytes* help maintain proper extracellular ion concentrations and have other structural and nutritive roles. They may also have a role in learning and memory. *Microglia* are immune system cells located in the central nervous system. They produce substances involved in battling inflammatory and infectious processes. Unfortunately, malfunctioning microglia can cause CNS damage. Our understanding of the importance of glial cells in both health and disease is growing.[1]

The nervous system can be divided into central and peripheral portions. The brain and spinal cord make up the central nervous system or *neuraxis* (Figure 2.2). The peripheral nervous system includes the spinal nerve roots, groups of nerve cells known as *ganglia*, peripheral nerves, neuromuscular junctions, and muscles.

The *autonomic nervous system* regulates homeostatic functions throughout the body and traverses both central and peripheral nervous systems (Figure 2.3). It is involved in respiratory, circulatory, metabolic, gastrointestinal, and other functions. There are two divisions of the autonomic system—*sympathetic* and *parasympathetic*. The former helps the body during times of stress; sympathetic activation

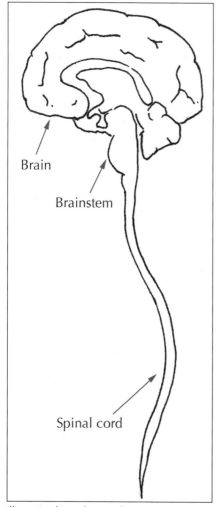

Brain

Brainstem

Spinal cord

Illustration by Beth Lutynski

Figure 2.2 *Neuraxis*

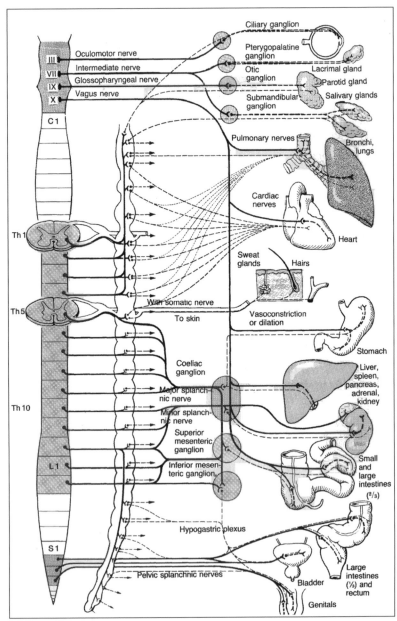

From Duus P. Topical Diagnosis in Neurology, 2nd rev. ed. New York: Thieme; 1989:209. Reprinted by permission.

Figure 2.3 *Autonomic nervous system. Parasympathetic fibers arise in brainstem nuclei and sacral spine. Sympathetic fibers arise in the thoracic and upper lumbar spine.*

raises blood pressure, increases blood flow, elevates blood sugar, and slows digestive movements. Parasympathetic activation enhances rest and recovery. Most autonomic functions occur without any conscious intervention.

Though the CNS and PNS can be separated structurally they are functionally connected. The PNS sends information into the CNS via the peripheral nerves and segmental nerve roots. This input reaches the brain via ascending pathways (see §4.1). Motor commands to the periphery travel from the brain through the spinal cord via descending pathways (see §4.2). Sensory information from the head and face reaches the brain via the cranial nerves (see Chapter 5). Motor commands to the head and face also travel through the cranial nerves.

Most of the cranial nerves connect to the portion of the brain known as the brainstem. The cranial nerves and spinal nerve roots intersect the brainstem and spinal cord respectively, forming segmental or horizontal pathways. Brainstem and spinal cord damage can disrupt both ascending and descending pathways, as well as horizontal pathways. Identifying the latter helps determine the anatomic level or site of injury.

Some frequently used anatomic terms are:

- Anterior or ventral—front side
- Posterior or dorsal—back side
- Superior or cranial—toward the top
- Inferior—toward the bottom or lower end
- Caudal—toward the tail
- Rostral—toward the front
- Medial—toward the midline
- Median—at the midline
- Lateral—away from the middle
- Bilateral—both sides
- Ipsilateral—same side
- Contralateral—other side

2.3 Localization and Diagnosis

The key to diagnosis is linking the symptoms and signs of a disease to the underlying anatomy and physiology. The neurologist must obtain the necessary clues and interpret them properly. Neurology lends itself to this localization process more than most fields in medicine. The different structures and systems of the nervous system are highly specialized. Therefore, damage or disease may produce a set of abnormalities that can only arise from a particular location. However, it requires a methodical, thorough, and orderly approach in order to derive this information. An accurate anatomic localization narrows the range of diagnoses and avoids unnecessary testing.

The first step is to elicit symptoms and signs of the disease process. The former are obtained through a history, the latter from examination. The second step is the interpretation of the relevant symptoms and signs in terms of underlying anatomy and physiology. In other words, the neurologist determines which function of the nervous system is disturbed. This will usually permit localization to one of the following structures: muscle, neuromuscular junction, peripheral nerve, spinal nerve root, spinal cord, brainstem, cerebellum, or cerebral hemispheres. Some neurologic signs themselves are virtually diagnostic of particular diseases. Subsequent chapters will include details about the symptoms and signs of dysfunction in relation to the relevant anatomy and physiology. Characteristic clusters of symptoms and signs comprise syndromes. A syndrome is not itself a disease but a construct used to facilitate diagnosis.

The next step in the diagnostic process is to make an anatomic or structural diagnosis—the actual localization of the disease to a particular structure, region, or functional unit of the nervous system. Finally, the neurologist combines the anatomic diagnosis with other relevant medical data including the mode of onset and course of the illness, the existence of any nonneurologic organ system involvement, past and family histories, and laboratory results in order to reach a more specific pathologic or etiologic diagnosis.

2.4 The Neurologic History

"Ninety percent of neurologic diagnosis depends on the patient's medical history."[2] Although it may be tempting to rely on MRI and other advanced diagnostic techniques a thorough history will usually lead to a correct anatomic localization and an accurate clinical diagnosis. Sometimes laboratory or imaging results are diagnostic of a particular illness. However, it is essential that the clinician know enough to order the proper tests. An incomplete or inaccurate history can cause diagnostic confusion, unnecessary testing, and therapeutic mayhem. It is much more difficult and time-consuming to obtain a good history than to perform the actual neurologic examination.

Taking a history requires a relaxed and empathetic approach. As much information as possible should be obtained directly from the patient. Leading questions should be avoided and the process should not be rushed. Some physicians will take notes during the history-taking to aid their recollection. Others do not, potentially a problem if they do not generate a report immediately after seeing the patient when memory is freshest.

Demographic information is part of the history. Sex, age, occupation, socioeconomic data, and ethnicity can be relevant in particular clinical situations. There are neurological diseases with a predilection for one sex or the other. Many illnesses have a typical age of onset. Some diseases tend to occur in certain ethnic groups. Evidence about the impact of ethnicity on the expression of genetic disease is accumulating rapidly.[3,4]

The main portion of the history is the description of the present illness. The patient should be allowed to describe in his or her own words the chief—or presenting—complaint. The neurologist needs to clarify any unclear terminology used by the patient. For example, "I feel dizzy" might indicate vertigo, lightheadedness, loss of balance, incoordination, confusion, or something else entirely. Each symptom of the present illness must be described and analyzed in detail. This will include details about the onset of the symptom. Was it sudden or gradual? What is the course of the illness? Are the symptoms intermittent, progressive, stable, or fluctuating? Are there diurnal or seasonal variations in the symptoms? The neurologist will ask about precipitating or exacerbating factors as well as responses to treatment.

A complete neurologic history also includes a general medical and surgical history. The nervous system cannot be separated from the rest of the body. Many systemic diseases have neurologic manifestations. Neurological side effects from medications used to treat other illnesses are quite common. Tobacco, alcohol, and illicit substance intake should be explored since all may have a role in producing illness. In some cases, details about the patient's birth and developmental history will be relevant to the present illness. Since many neurological diseases have a genetic basis a family history should also be obtained.

The length of medical reports varies considerably. A young person with an isolated symptom and no other complaints will have a shorter history than someone with a lengthy list of complaints and numerous past illnesses. Also, physicians differ in the amount of detail they record. Some focus almost exclusively on the neurologic issues while others delve more deeply into other areas. If the patient's diagnosis is already well established and extensive medical records are available the physician may produce a less comprehensive report than when faced with a patient without prior evaluation.

Endnotes

1. Kurosinski P, Götz J. "Glial cells under physiologic and pathologic conditions." *Arch Neurol* 2002;59:1524-528.

2. Rowland LP. "Signs and symptoms in neurologic diagnosis." In: Rowland LP, ed. *Merritt's Neurology*, 10th ed. Philadelphia: Lippincott Williams & Wilkins; 2001:50.

3. Gwinn-Hardy K. "Editorial: When is ataxia not ataxia?" *Arch Neurol* 2004; 61:25-26.

4. Lu C-S, Chou Y-H W, et al. "The parkinsonian phenotype of spinocerebellar ataxia type 2." *Arch Neurol* 2004;61:35-38.

Additional Reading

Blumenfeld H. *An Interactive Online Guide to the Neurologic Examination with Video Demonstrations*. www.neuroexam.com, accessed December 24, 2004.

Brazis PW, Masdeu JC, Biller J. *Localization in Clinical Neurology*, 4th ed. Philadelphia: Lippincott Williams & Wilkins; 2001.

Haerer A. *DeJong's The Neurologic Examination*, 6th ed. Philadelphia: Lippincott Williams & Wilkins; 2005.

Patten JP. *Neurological Differential Diagnosis*, 2nd ed. London: Springer; 1996.

Poolos NP. *Handbook of Differential Diagnosis in Neurology*. Boston; Butterworth-Heinemann; 2001.

Spillane JA, ed. *Bickerstaff's Neurological Examination in Clinical Practice*, 6th ed. Malden, MA: Blackwell Science; 1996.

Chapter 3

Diagnostic Testing

3.1 Introduction

After obtaining a detailed history and performing a neurological examination the neurologist can usually make an anatomical diagnosis. Sometimes, the pathologic or etiologic diagnosis is also obvious at this point without further investigation. Often, though, additional investigation is required to identify the pathology underlying the patient's symptoms and signs. Useful techniques in neurology include:

- Biopsy—brain, muscle, nerve
- Genetic testing
- Imaging—X-ray, CT, MRI, angiography, myelography, functional
- Lumbar puncture

- Neurophysiology—EEG, EMG and NCS, evoked potentials
- Neuropsychology

3.2 Imaging

CT (computed or computerized tomography) and MRI (magnetic resonance imaging) techniques greatly enhance the ability to image the brain and spinal cord. MRI is the modality of choice for most conditions because it does not expose the patient to any radiation hazard and it provides a higher resolution image.

A. X-ray

Plain radiology of the skull and spine is still important even though more sophisticated imaging modalities are available (Figure 3.1). Plain x-rays sometimes delineate fractures much more clearly than CT or MRI. Special views of the skull can identify the openings (*foramina*) at the base of the skull. In the cervical spine plain x-rays can measure canal diameter. Views of the spine in flexion and extension are also important in determining spinal stability.

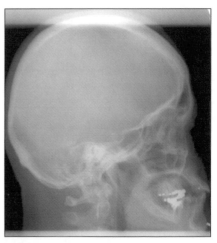

Figure 3.1 *Normal Skull X-Ray. Courtesy of Dr. Roman Klufas.*

B. Computerized tomography (CT)

CT scanning has been used since the early 1970s. CT is derived from x-ray imaging and does require exposure to small amounts of radiation. CT can image the brain rapidly and reveal stroke, bleeding, tumor, and atrophy. With subdural bleeding it is possible to identify the age of the hemorrhage by measuring its density (Figure 3.2). Spiral CT is a recent enhancement used for more rapid or detailed images of ischemia, aneurysms, and narrowed blood vessels.

CT can identify foraminal disorders in the cervical and, to a lesser extent, thoracic spine. CT techniques provide less detailed images of the

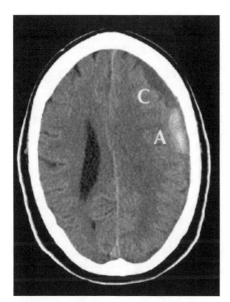

Figure 3.2 *CT Scan of Subdural Hematoma. Note obliteration of a ventricle and shift of the midline away from the hematoma. Acute (A) bleed superimposed over chronic (C) bleed. Courtesy of Dr. Roman Klufas.*

spinal cord compared to MRI, but the latter is not always available or feasible. To image the spinal cord and nerve roots contrast media is introduced into the spinal canal by lumbar puncture before scanning—*CT myelography.*

C. Magnetic resonance imaging (MRI)

MRI is the preferred test for most neurological diseases because it provides greater detail. MRI images require applying powerful magnetic fields to the body part being examined. This produces changes in the spin of various atomic particles. As the particles return to their normal state there are measurable energy changes. MRI uses a series of different scanning sequences to highlight different properties of neural tissue. There is no radiation.

Limitations of MRI include cost, the time needed to obtain a scan, and the fact that the technique can be very claustrophobic. Some patients require sedation to tolerate a scan. There are MRI machines that do not completely enclose the patient, producing less claustrophobia. However, these machines have weaker magnetic fields and less resolution power. Even so, the images from these "open" MRI units are superior to CT images. MRI cannot be performed in patients with pacemakers and other magnetically active metal implants. This often eliminates this modality from consideration in critically ill patients on life-support.

MRI readily identifies vascular disease, multiple sclerosis, and tumors. It is greatly superior to CT scanning in imaging the structures in the posterior portion of the cranium—namely brainstem and cerebellum (Figure 3.3). MRI can easily reveal disc herniation and nerve root compression. Modern MRI scanners can image the blood vessels in the neck and in

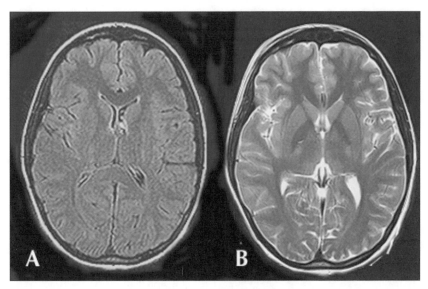

Figure 3.3 *Normal Brain MRI. A. Axial fluid attenuation inversion recovery (FLAIR) image. B. Axial T2-weighted image. Courtesy of Dr. Roman Klufas.*

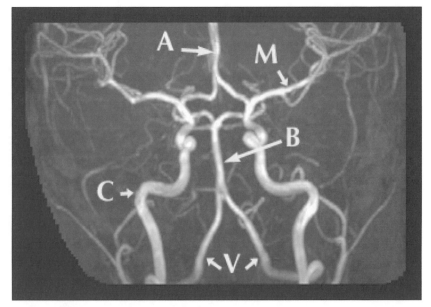

Figure 3.4 *Magnetic Resonance Angiography. Arrowheads indicate main arteries: anterior cerebrals (A) superimposed, basilar (B), carotid (C), middle cerebral (M), vertebrals (V). Courtesy of Dr. Roman Klufas.*

the brain, a procedure known as magnetic resonance angiography, *MRA* (Figure 3.4). The current level of sophistication with this technique is such that it is supplanting the riskier conventional angiography.

D. Angiography

Cerebral angiography is an x-ray technique used to assess the brain's blood supply. The most common method is for a catheter to be passed through the femoral artery to the arch of the aorta; a contrast agent is then injected directly into each carotid artery and into the vertebrobasilar system by selective catheterization. Images can reveal fatty deposits along the blood vessel walls, aneurysms, arteriovenous malformations, and arterial spasm.

Angiography carries a significant risk of mortality and morbidity. Up to 5 percent of patients suffer a transient or permanent neurological deficit following angiography; fatal strokes can occur, particularly in patients with arteriosclerosis.

E. Myelography

In this technique a lumbar puncture or *cisternal tap* (at the base of the skull) is performed to introduce a radio-opaque dye around the spinal cord. Then, x-rays of the spine are taken. Nerve root entrapment and spinal cord deformities may be revealed. MRI techniques have, for the most part, supplanted myelography but it may still be useful. For example, a patient who cannot undergo MRI scanning—whether because of uncontrollable claustrophobia or the presence of implanted metal susceptible to magnetic fields—may need a myelogram to delineate the nature of the lesions (Figure 3.5).

Risks of myelography include those for lumbar puncture (see §3.4), plus the added risk of the dye. Currently, water-soluble contrast mediums are preferred. Seizures are a rare complication linked to these agents. Older oil-based contrast agents have considerable potential to cause inflammation in the tissue around the spinal cord, known as *arachnoiditis.*

F. Functional neuroimaging

The techniques described above reveal structure. Increasingly, neurologists are using additional tools to assess neurological function in conjunction with structural images. Functional neuroimaging studies are per-

formed while the patient performs a specific cognitive task. In simple terms increased metabolic activity or blood flow
indicates the areas of the brain that are
activated by the cognitive activity. Currently, functional neuroimaging is more
of a research tool than a routine diagnostic aid. However, the various techniques
have proven useful in presurgical evaluation of epilepsy patients and in detecting abnormalities in patients with cognitive decline.

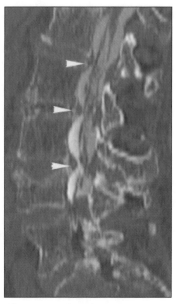

Positron emission tomography (PET)
measures radioactivity following injection of a radioactive tracer molecule. A
nearby cyclotron is needed to produce
the tracer. The tracer decays by emitting
a positron; when the positron collides
with an electron both are annihilated and
produce photons that the equipment detects. PET scanners are sensitive to cerebral blood flow or metabolism. However, the spatial resolution of the image
is not as good as MRI.

Figure 3.5 *Myelogram.
Sagittal image of lumbar
spinal stenosis. Note
narrowing of the dye column
at arrowheads. Courtesy of
Dr. Roman Klufas.*

Single photon emission computed tomography (SPECT) also uses a
tracer to measure cerebral blood flow. However, SPECT measures gamma
radiation; the tracer does not require a cyclotron. Therefore, SPECT studies are more readily available than PET. Unfortunately, resolution is even
poorer than PET.

Functional MRI (fMRI) has better spatial resolution than PET or
SPECT and does not require injections of tracers. The best-known fMRI
technique measures oxygen levels in hemoglobin. Changes that take place
in a matter of seconds can be measured, allowing fMRI to be used in
memory studies.

3.3 Clinical Neurophysiology

Clinical neurophysiologic assessment can confirm suspected diagnoses or detect unsuspected dysfunction. These tests can be used to monitor progression of illness or response to therapy, and provide information regarding prognosis. During certain surgical procedures or in the intensive care unit particular tests can monitor neurologic function.

Neurophysiologic studies measure function of the nervous system rather than structure. Individual tests are selected based on the patient's symptoms and signs. The most widely used procedures are electroencephalography, evoked potential studies, electromyography, and nerve conduction studies.

A. EEG (electroencephalogram)

The EEG is widely used and often misunderstood. This test does not have high sensitivity or specificity for all neurologic conditions. Altered consciousness, impaired cognition, and episodes of neurologic dysfunction are common problems requiring neurological evaluation. MRI and other neuroimaging procedures may be normal in patients with such problems. The EEG can provide information about brain function that would not otherwise be available. The EEG is particularly useful in the diagnosis and management of patients with known or suspected epilepsy and in those with brain dysfunction due to a range of toxic, metabolic, or infectious causes. EEG is less important nowadays for identification and localization of blood clots, strokes, tumors, and other structural lesions.

The EEG records spontaneous electrical activity originating in the brain. Electrodes are attached to particular locations on the scalp and connected to the EEG equipment. Considerable amplification and filtering is required to record the electrical activity. The neurologist interpreting the record must understand the limitations of the equipment and be able to identify artifact. Extracellular current flows derived from large populations of neurons in the cortex beneath the recording electrodes produce the recorded waves. A routine EEG usually records twenty to thirty minutes of brain activity. Both normal and abnormal wave patterns can be identified.

An EEG report should include some clinical information about the patient, especially level of consciousness and behavior during the test and whether medications had been taken. The report will contain a description of the electrical activity that is seen. The brain waves are usually described in terms of their frequencies. Alpha activity refers to waves occurring at a frequency of eight to thirteen cycles per second or hertz (Hz). Posterior regions of the head in a relaxed, awake adult usually exhibit a dominant rhythm in the alpha frequency range. Significant asymmetries in the alpha rhythm may be pathologic.

Beta activity refers to frequencies of thirteen Hz or more; certain medications can increase the amount of beta activity. Delta waves are those of less than four Hz; during wakefulness these almost always indicate dysfunction. Theta waves are in the four to seven Hz range. They are markers of drowsiness. Excessive theta activity during wakefulness is abnormal.

EEG abnormalities can be specific or nonspecific; distribution can be focal, lateralized, or generalized. A nonspecific abnormality can be produced by many different conditions. Diffuse slowing in the background of the EEG is the commonest nonspecific abnormality. Deep or midline structural lesions and conditions causing generalized brain dysfunction (*encephalopathy*) produce diffuse slowing. Focal or localized EEG slowing is likely to reflect damage or dysfunction to a particular region. Brief runs of generalized synchronous discharges known as *triphasic waves* occurring in a slow background usually indicate a toximetabolic encephalopathy, especially from liver or kidney failure. Generalized periodic sharp waves can occur with Creutzfeldt-Jacob disease, anoxia, or lithium intoxication.

Epileptiform activity refers to particular discharges known as spikes, sharp waves, and spike and slow wave complexes. Most EEG studies do not record seizures. The electrical activity recorded between seizures is known as *interictal* activity. The nature of any epileptiform discharges recorded during an interictal EEG aids the diagnosis of specific epilepsy syndromes (Figure 3.6). However, normal EEGs are not unusual in epilepsy patients and do not exclude the diagnosis. Repeat studies are often necessary before an abnormality is finally recorded. Rarely, a patient will experience a typical episode during the recording and specific EEG patterns will confirm whether this was a seizure or not.

Activation procedures to induce an EEG abnormality are used frequently. These include hyperventilation, where a patient is asked to over breathe for a few minutes. This can induce instability in the record and

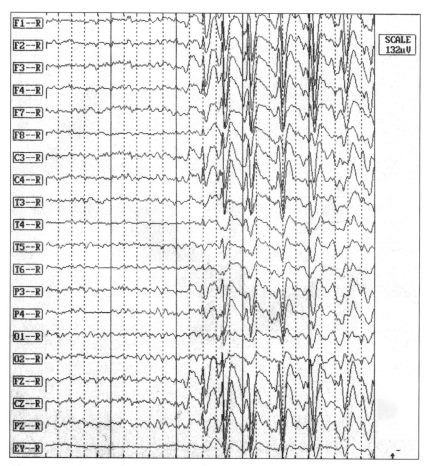

Figure 3.6 Abnormal EEG. Interictal epileptiform discharges in a five-second EEG segment. The patient was alert and there were no convulsive movements.

may also accentuate suspicious waveforms seen in the resting record. Photic stimulation is another common activation technique. A light is flashed at frequencies between three and twenty cycles per second. This may cause generalized discharges or even a seizure in susceptible individuals. In some EEG laboratories special electrode placements (sphenoidal, nasopharyngeal) are used to increase the diagnostic yield of the test by recording from parts of the brain that are "hidden" from standard scalp electrodes.

Sleep deprivation is another activation technique. It can increase the likelihood of eliciting an epileptiform discharge. It also increases the chance that the patient will fall asleep, desirable because certain seizure types are more likely to produce abnormalities during sleep. However, there are the added burdens to the patient of staying awake overnight and being exposed to an increased risk of a seizure. Also, in light of the expected drowsiness patients will need someone to transport them to and from the laboratory. There is no clear consensus about when and how to perform sleep-deprived studies.[1]

The ideal situation when attempting to diagnose epilepsy is to record a typical episode. This rarely happens during the course of the relatively brief routine EEG. Therefore, prolonged EEG monitoring is often helpful. With ambulatory EEG equipment the patient can carry a small recording unit and have the brain wave activity recorded for one or more days. The patient will keep a log and make entries to indicate any suspicious episodes. Later, the log is reviewed in conjunction with the EEG recording to determine whether or not a spell was epileptic.

Prolonged EEG recording may be supplemented by simultaneous video recording. This usually takes place in a specialized inpatient epilepsy center. The patient is observed for twenty-four hours or longer. The EEG is monitored continuously so that behavioral concomitants of any EEG abnormalities can be identified. This procedure is a standard part of the assessment process for epilepsy surgery. Since it is critical that the anatomic source of the seizures be identified, antiepileptic medication may be discontinued during the inpatient video EEG monitoring. Often, video EEG monitoring is done for diagnostic purposes in patients who are having nonepileptic episodes—frequently termed *pseudoseizures*, though that label is discouraged because of its disparaging connotation.

Traditionally, the EEG was recorded on paper with analog equipment. Now, many EEG machines use digital recording techniques. Digital EEG simplifies storage and retrieval of the data. Furthermore, digital EEG equipment facilitates advanced mathematical analysis of the raw EEG data. This is often referred to as *quantitative EEG* (*qEEG*). Such techniques are utilized more for research than routine clinical purposes. Some qEEG systems allow for topographic map displays of the EEG data, or brain mapping. Only experienced electroencephalographers should perform the quantitative manipulation of EEG data because these advanced techniques are more susceptible to misinterpretation than conventional EEG. Brain mapping and qEEG are not used by most neurologists, but in the hands of skilled neurologists in particular situations these techniques can provide additional useful information.[2]

There is considerable variation in how neurologists interpret EEG, leading to wide ranges in sensitivity and specificity estimates for this test.[3]

B. EMG (electromyography) and NCS (nerve conduction studies): Uses and limitations

Weakness, loss of sensation, muscle cramping, easy fatigability, and other neuromuscular symptoms and signs often require investigation beyond the standard neurologic examination. These tests can provide considerable information about neuromuscular illnesses. Conditions where electrodiagnostic evaluation is useful include:

- Focal or compressive nerve damage such as carpal tunnel syndrome
- Guillain-Barré syndrome and related diseases
- Motor neuron diseases (e.g., amyotrophic lateral sclerosis)
- Muscle diseases
- Myasthenia gravis
- Peripheral nerve dysfunction (neuropathy)
- Radiculopathy or "pinched nerve"
- Traumatic nerve lesions

EMG and NCS testing (often "EMG" is used to refer to both) are part of an electrodiagnostic medical consultation. This is an extension of the clinical neurologic evaluation and should be performed by a physician with both technical skill and knowledge of neuromuscular disease. These tests are not mere laboratory procedures done in a rote manner like an electrocardiogram or a chest x-ray. The electrodiagnostic consultant reviews referral data, obtains a history, and examines the patient with emphasis on the neuromuscular system. The test protocol is designed for each patient based on the examiner's clinical impression of the problem. During the testing unexpected findings can require alterations or additions to the planned testing. The need for such a dynamic approach can only be met by a physician who understands the equipment and knows the relevant anatomy, physiology, and pathology.

Some neurologists will train a technician to perform the NCS. The physician should review these results, repeat any questionable studies, and add additional tests if indicated. The physician will then perform the needle EMG testing. In a few jurisdictions, some nonphysicians—notably chiropractors and physical therapists—are allowed to perform needle EMG. The AAEM has a position statement about qualifications for these tests that includes recommendations for the education, training, and experience needed by electrodiagnostic consultants.[4]

When muscles contract they generate electrical activity. *Electromyography* involves recording this electrical activity from muscles. This is usually accomplished by inserting a thin recording needle directly into the muscle—the *needle electrode examination*. The electrical activity is displayed on a screen and broadcast on a loudspeaker. Some abnormalities are easier to hear than to see. EMG, almost always in conjunction with NCS, is performed to evaluate a wide range of neuromuscular diseases. *Surface EMG* is a very different procedure. Electrical signals are recorded only from the skin overlying skeletal muscles. The amount of information obtained is limited and there is little evidence that this procedure is useful in the diagnosis of peripheral nerve and muscle disease.[5]

By examining the patterns of *insertional*, *spontaneous*, and *voluntary* activity the electromyographer usually can distinguish between muscle and peripheral nerve diseases. *Fibrillation potentials* and *positive sharp waves* are the commonest forms of abnormal spontaneous activity. These indicate an active disease process—*acute denervation*. The presence of acute denervation in a particular nerve root distribution helps to distinguish a symptomatic disc herniation from the commonplace asymptomatic disc abnormalities detected in many individuals by MRI scanning.

EMG is not infallible. Muscle tissue is under the control of peripheral nerves. If there is no damage to the motor nerve fibers supplying the muscle or to the muscle itself the needle EMG examination will be normal. Damage restricted to the sensory portion of the nerve will not produce EMG abnormalities no matter how much pain or sensory dysfunction is present. Thus, a large herniated disc compressing only the sensory portion of the nerve root—and not the motor—will produce symptoms of radiculopathy without EMG findings. Furthermore, even if the motor fibers are compressed and dysfunctional because the insulating layer of myelin is disrupted the EMG will still be normal unless the axons themselves are damaged.

A reliable EMG study requires accurate interpretation by the examiner. There are normal discharges such as *endplate potentials* that can be confused with signs of disease. Some clinicians correctly identify *polyphasic potentials* in the muscle but misinterpret these as abnormal even though small numbers are normal. Newer EMG equipment allows for storage and printout of the electrical activity. However, older machines do not have this capability and it is not standard practice to include such printouts with a report. Therefore, it can be difficult or impossible to know whether or not the interpretation is correct. Repeat testing elsewhere might be useful in chronic or progressive diseases with persistent abnormalities but not in conditions where the natural history of the disease can be one of improvement.

Studies of nerve conduction (motor and sensory) are complementary to the needle examination of muscle. NCS can identify subclinical or unsuspected disease, localize the site of a focal nerve injury, and assess the severity of peripheral nerve dysfunction. In simple terms, these tests require stimulating a motor or sensory nerve with electrical impulses and recording from a distant site.[6] Stimulation of a motor nerve produces contraction of a muscle. The resulting *compound muscle action potential* is recorded from an electrode placed over the muscle. Sensory nerve stimulation produces a *nerve action potential* that is recorded with an electrode placed over the nerve at a different location.

Measurements include size and latency of the response and the transmission velocity through the nerve. Faulty distance and latency measurements are the most likely sources of error. The NCS report should include information about measurement techniques such as whether the latency is measured at the onset or the peak of the waveform. Interpretation of results also requires valid normative data.[7] If need be, the raw data should be available for independent review.

Standard NCS assess only the fastest conducting, larger myelinated nerve fibers. Pain and other sensory modalities such as temperature sense are served by smaller myelinated and unmyelinated fibers. Thus, routine testing can miss *small-fiber* neuropathies, such as the common diabetic polyneuropathy. Quantitative sensory testing with different devices and techniques is used to measure these smaller fibers.[8]

There are potential risks and complications with EMG and NCS.[9] Needle examination is invasive. Bleeding, infection, pneumothorax (punctured lung), and nerve or muscle injury are possible rare complications. There are also electrical hazards with NCS, especially in patients with pacemakers or in those connected to electrical equipment.

C. Evoked potential (EP) studies

EMG and NCS assess function in the peripheral nervous system. Central nervous system motor and sensory pathways also can be evaluated using electrophysiologic techniques. Major sensory pathways in the CNS can be activated and the electrical response thereby evoked can be recorded from the scalp. The commonly recorded EP tests measure the auditory, somatosensory, and visual pathways. The electrical signal measured at the scalp is quite small. Therefore, EP testing requires summation of hundreds or thousands of responses in order to separate the desired signal from background interference. Although occasionally unpleasant these techniques are not risky.

Brainstem auditory evoked potentials or responses (BAEPs or BAERs) measure function in both peripheral and central auditory pathways. BAEPs are elicited by an auditory stimulus, usually a click, presented to an ear. The sound activates a variety of structures in the auditory pathway—cranial nerve VIII, cochlear nucleus, superior olive, lateral lemniscus, and inferior colliculus. Usually, five waveforms are recorded. Abnormalities include prolonged latencies, diminished amplitudes, and excessive asymmetries. Acoustic nerve tumors almost always produce abnormal BAEPs. Multiple sclerosis and brainstem lesions including strokes and tumors are other common causes of abnormality. Significant hearing loss can prevent acquisition of the BAEP.

Visually evoked potentials (VEPs) evaluate the visual pathways. The usual stimulation technique is to present a shifting black and white checkerboard pattern to each eye. The main measurement is the latency of an electrically positive signal recorded in the occipital region of the scalp—the *P100* wave. The commonest abnormality is a delayed P100 following stimulation of one eye. This indicates an abnormality in the visual pathway on that side, anterior to the optic chiasm. This is extremely common in multiple sclerosis, even in patients who have not had a clinically obvious episode of optic neuritis.

Somatosensory evoked potentials (SEPs or SSEPs) are recorded over the scalp, neck, and spine. These are produced by stimulating peripheral nerves, usually the median or ulnar in the arm, tibial or peroneal in the leg. The responses travel mainly in the dorsal columns of the spinal cord, then through the brainstem to the contralateral somatosensory cortex.[10] SEPs may be helpful in evaluation of *myelopathy* due to multiple sclerosis or other spinal cord diseases. Diseases affecting the somatosensory cortex of the brain will also produce abnormal results though neuroimaging procedures identify and localize such lesions more accurately. SEPs are often used for intraoperative monitoring of the spinal cord to warn the surgeon of impending neurologic injury. They are not generally useful in evaluation of acute radiculopathy.[11]

Dermatomal SEPs (DSEPs) are elicited by stimulation of the skin and recorded on the scalp overlying the contralateral primary somatosensory cortex. These are sometimes used to measure the sensory component of the spinal nerve roots, especially in the lumbar region. However, there are neither clear-cut criteria for abnormality nor sufficient data regarding sensitivity and specificity. Furthermore, "there is no evidence that DSEP findings provide any reliable information beyond the routine clinical examination and there is no evidence to suggest DSEPs are superior to already established neurophysiologic techniques."[12]

Motor evoked potential (MEP) studies, usually performed with magnetic stimulation, are not as widely used as the sensory EP tests. The clearest utility of MEP testing is in evaluation of multiple sclerosis. Cognitive function is sometimes evaluated with the P300 cognitive evoked response. Abnormalities are seen in conditions characterized by impaired attention and stimulus processing.

3.4 Lumbar Puncture

It is often necessary to examine the cerebrospinal fluid (CSF) that surrounds the brain and the spinal cord. This is essential in infectious disease of the nervous system (meningitis and encephalitis). CSF examination is a valuable aid in the diagnosis of subarachnoid hemorrhage. It can also be helpful in some forms of neuropathies and radiculopathies, in multiple sclerosis, in vasculitis and inflammatory diseases, and in some malignancies. The chemical, bacteriologic, cellular, physical, and serologic components of the CSF are assessed.

Measurement of the spinal fluid pressure is useful in conditions such as pseudotumor cerebri (benign intracranial hypertension) and certain types of hydrocephalus. Occasionally, clinicians perform therapeutic lumbar punctures to reduce intracranial pressure by removing spinal fluid. Lumbar puncture is used to introduce contrast material around the spine, as in myelography, and to administer chemotherapy.

In adults the spinal cord usually terminates above the level of the second lumbar vertebra. Access to the CSF is by lumbar puncture (spinal tap) at a lower lumbar interspace (2-3, 3-4, or 4-5). Unless absolutely critical, this should not be undertaken in the presence of abnormal neurological signs, since these suggest structural pathology and increased intracranial pressure within the brain or the spinal cord. In such instances an appropriate imaging technique to evaluate for a mass effect is necessary before the procedure. If the tap must be performed despite such abnormality special precautions are followed—use of a small diameter needle and slow removal of the minimal amount of fluid needed for testing. Lumbar puncture ordinarily should not be performed if there are infections present in the skin near the intended site. Low platelet counts and coagulation abnormalities are other relative contraindications to the procedure.

The decision to perform lumbar puncture is based on an assessment of the potential benefits versus possible side effects. The more likely that information from the test will be used to determine treatment, the more important the test. Complications of lumbar puncture include headache, back pain, double vision, brain herniation, spinal cord compression, bleeding, and infection. Fortunately, serious complications are rare with modern needles and proper technique.

A. Postlumbar puncture headache

Headache is by far the most frequent complication of lumbar puncture, probably occurring in at least one-quarter of patients, though estimates vary. Spinal fluid leakage at the site of the puncture causes the headache. Postlumbar puncture headache begins within forty-eight hours of the test in most patients though onset can be delayed for several days. Most patients recover within a week or two.

The headache can be frontal, occipital, or generalized. It worsens when the patient is upright and improves or resolves when the patient is lying down. The headache is worse with movement, coughing, straining, and sneezing. The longer the patient is upright, the longer it takes for the headache to subside when the patient lies down.

Postlumbar puncture headache is more common in women and in young adults. A history of headaches or a prior postlumbar puncture headache increases the risk. The size and orientation of the needle is also important. Narrower modern needles reduce the incidence. Treatment includes bed rest, hydration, and simple analgesics. In severe cases the dural tear is repaired with an epidural blood patch.

B. Other complications of lumbar puncture

The most ominous complication of lumbar puncture is brain herniation. Tumors and other causes of increased intracranial pressure can literally push the brainstem or cerebellum down through the foramen magnum when the spinal fluid is removed. Increased intracranial pressure can produce an abnormality of the retina—*papilledema*—and other clinical findings. If there is any question of a mass lesion, neuroimaging should be performed before the spinal tap. Fortunately, the ready availability of CT scanners helps to reduce the risk of herniation.

Abnormalities of the cranial nerves have been reported following lumbar puncture. These are usually transient and are thought to be due to lowered CSF pressure producing traction on the nerve. A sixth nerve palsy producing double vision is the commonest of these infrequent complications. During a lumbar puncture some patients complain of transient electric shocks or pins and needles; this indicates contact between the spinal needle and the sensory portion of a spinal nerve root. Infrequently, permanent sensory or motor loss can occur. Many individuals complain of back ache following a lumbar puncture but this usually resolves within a few days. Rarely, there are injuries to the vertebrae, intravertebral discs, or even the spinal cord itself. Bacterial meningitis, vertebral osteomyelits, extradural abscess, and disc infection are all rare complications. These can follow a spinal tap done in the presence of local infection or with poor sterile technique.

Paraspinal and intracranial subdural blood clots are very rare complications. The former cause severe low back pain or radicular pain, followed within hours or days by progressive leg weakness and other signs of spinal cord compression. Intracranial subdural clots, either unilateral or bilateral, can develop weeks or months after the lumbar puncture. The presumed mechanism is traction on the blood vessels with tearing due to low CSF pressure. A subdural hematoma should be suspected when postlumbar puncture headache lasts for much more than one week or a headache without a postural component develops after a headache-free interval.

3.5 Biopsies

In some situations biopsies of nerve, muscle, or brain may be needed. Biopsies are only necessary when other less invasive means of investigation do not lead to a diagnosis. Increasingly, genetic and biochemical tests are used to diagnose neuromuscular diseases. Biopsies are not infallible. The tissue sample may not include a lesion, the abnormalities may be too mild to detect, or the condition is too far advanced for diagnosis.

Muscle biopsy is used for evaluation of weakness, abnormal muscle tone, cramping, and other symptoms suggestive of muscle disease. The biopsy may be taken by a direct surgical approach or with a percutaneous needle. The muscle is examined under a microscope with specialized histochemical staining techniques. There are diagnostic features for both inherited and acquired neuromuscular disorders (muscular dystrophies, myopathies, neuropathies, and motor neuron diseases).

A nerve biopsy is taken from a sensory nerve, leaving only an area of absent sensation and not weakness. The terminal branch of the radial nerve in the arm and the sural nerve in the leg are common targets. Such biopsies allow the differentiation of demyelinating from axonal neuropathies. Nerve biopsy may reveal evidence of inflammation or invasion of nerve by abnormal substances or cells. Nerve biopsies are more useful for diagnosis of focal and multifocal neuropathies—particularly when due to vasculitis—than polyneuropathies.[13]

Brain biopsy is undertaken to determine the nature of cerebral tumors and other masses when neuroimaging and other studies are not diagnostic. Brain biopsy is performed occasionally for diagnosis of cerebral infections and some rare genetic diseases.

3.6 Neuropsychology

Brain injuries and diseases often produce changes in behavior and cognition. These abnormalities can have significant medicolegal implications. Neurologists have a working knowledge of higher cortical function and can and do evaluate these problems with a mental status examination. However, there are many situations where a more detailed, precise, and formal assessment is needed.

Cognitive functions can be defined and measured. The neuropsychologist is able to identify and characterize both cognitive defects and capacities. Neuropsychological testing can demonstrate abnormalities when neurophysiological and neuroimaging techniques are normal. This is particularly important when there are only mild deficits or a patient exhibits inconsistent cognitive performance.

The neuropsychological evaluation differs from the "bedside" mental status testing performed by neurologists. Neuropsychologists use a battery of tests designed to assess particular cognitive domains including attention, learning and memory, language, visuospatial and visuoconstructive abilities, and executive (frontal lobe) functions. Most of these tests are standardized, have normative values, and have known rates of reliability and validity.

Detailed neuropsychological testing can take many hours though briefer test instruments are available. The content of the neuropsychological test battery may vary according to the clinical issue being assessed. Many neuropsychologists follow a flexible approach, screening the major areas of cognitive function and then examining the most critical in more depth. Others use a fixed test battery for all patients. The more specific the referral questions, the more useful the evaluation.

Generally, neuropsychologists are doctoral level psychologists (Ph.D. or Ed.D.) with additional postdoctoral training in neuropsychology. There are several professional organizations and certification boards in neuropsychology. The best-known of the latter are the American Board of Professional Neuropsychology[14] and the American Board of Clinical Neuropsychology.[15] Some neuropsychologists will use lesser-trained technicians to administer some or all of the tests; this should be made clear in the report.

Neuropsychological assessment plays a major role in the preoperative evaluation of prospective epilepsy surgery patients. It is also of particular importance for evaluation and treatment planning in traumatic brain injury patients. The American Academy of Neurology suggests neuropsychological consultation in seven situations:

(1) there are only mild or questionable deficits on mental status testing and more precise evaluation is needed to establish the presence of abnormalities or distinguish them from changes that may occur with normal aging; (2) there is a need to quantify the patient's deficits, particularly when the information will be useful in predicting or following the course of a disorder (recovery or decline); (3) when there is a need to characterize the strengths and weaknesses of the patient as part of constructing a management or rehabilitation plan . . . ; (4) when the neuropsychologist can provide the specific rehabilitation or other therapeutic services required; (5) when neuropsychological data can provide a more comprehensive profile of function that . . . may assist in diagnosis; (6) when the patient is being considered for epilepsy surgery; and (7) when there is litigation that concerns the patient's cognitive status.[16]

Neuropsychological data can be of paramount importance when there is litigation about cognitive impairment. This is often the case in personal injury claims for traumatic brain injury or toxic exposure. Neuropsychologists may be called on to evaluate various competencies including driving, medical decision-making, testamentary capacity, control of financial affairs, and professional or vocational activities. The neuropsychological report will be scrutinized closely. A competent neuropsychologist will not overstate test results or ignore confounding factors such as age, education, medication effects, psychiatric illness, and other psychosocial issues.

The neuropsychologist can play an important role when there are questions about malingering, symptom magnification, or poor motivation. There are tests of effort that can identify deliberate attempts to feign cognitive dysfunction. Furthermore, neuropsychologists are able to compare a patient's results to those of individuals with known disease to see if the pattern of test results is consistent with the presumed diagnosis.

3.7 Neurogenetics

Genetic testing refers to analysis of DNA, RNA, and other substances to detect inherited diseases or predispositions to disease.[17] Genetic testing for neurological disease is not new. However, the recent sequencing of the human genome is having a significant impact on clinical neurology. The number of neurologic diseases linked to specific gene abnormalities is rising rapidly. DNA testing increases diagnostic accuracy and reduces the need for other tests such as biopsy. Ultimately, better understanding of the genetic mechanisms of neurological disease should lead to better treatments and preventative efforts.

Genetic microarray techniques are particularly promising. These can assess thousands of genes at a time. Microarrays can help to identify abnormalities, predispositions to disease, and variations in an individual's response to medication.[18] Polymerase chain reaction (PCR) analysis is one DNA identification technique. It is especially useful in detecting infectious agents quickly. For example, PCR testing has supplanted brain biopsy, tissue culture, and immunohistochemical analysis for diagnosis of herpes encephalitis.[19]

However, genomic medicine also raises many complex issues about discrimination and the physician-patient relationship.[20] Who will have access to the genetic information and what will be done with it? Can employers and insurers use genetic information? Do physicians have a duty to warn a patient's family members of their risk for an inherited disease? Many states have addressed some of these questions[21] but there is no nationwide consensus. Since genetic testing only reveals the potential to develop a disease the Americans with Disabilities Act, which covers only existing conditions, is inapplicable.[22]

Endnotes

1. Glick TH. "The sleep-deprived electroencephalogram." *Arch Neurol* 2002; 59:1235-1239.

2. American Academy of Neurology and the American Clinical Neurophysiology Society. "Assessment of digital EEG, quantitative EEG, and EEG brain mapping." *Neurology* 1997;49:277-292.

3. Gilbert DL, Sethuraman G, et al. "Meta-analysis of EEG test performance shows wide variation among studies." *Neurology* 2003;60:564-570.

4. American Association of Electrodiagnostic Medicine. "Who is qualified to practice electrodiagnostic medicine?" *Muscle Nerve* 1999;22(suppl 8):S263-265.

5. Haig AJ, Gelblum JB, et al. "Technology assessment: The use of surface EMG in the diagnosis and treatment of nerve and muscle disorders." *Muscle Nerve* 1996;19:392-395.

6. Kimura J. "Facts, fallacies, and fancies of nerve conduction studies: Twenty-first annual Edward H. Lambert lecture." *Muscle Nerve* 1997;20:777-787.

7. Dorfman LJ, Robinson LR. "AAEM minimonograph #47: Normative data in electrodiagnostic medicine." *Muscle Nerve* 1997;20:4-14.

8. Chong PST, Cros DP. "Technology literature review: Quantitative sensory testing." *Muscle Nerve* 2004;29:734-747.

9. Al-Shekhlee A, Shapiro BE, Preston DC. "Iatrogenic complications and risks of nerve conduction studies and needle electromyography." *Muscle Nerve* 2003;27:517-526.

10. Aminoff MJ, Eisen AA. "AAEM minimonograph 19: Somatosensory evoked potentials." *Muscle Nerve* 1998;21:277-290.

11. AAEM Somatosensory Evoked Potentials Subcommittee. "Somatosensory evoked potentials: Clinical uses." *Muscle Nerve* 1998;21:252-258.

12. Therapeutics and Technology Assessment Subcommittee of the American Academy of Neurology. "Assessment: Dermatomal somatosensory evoked potentials." *Neurology* 1997;49:127-1130.

13. Said G. "Indications and usefulness of nerve biopsy." *Arch Neurol* 2002; 59:1532-1535.

14. American Board of Professional Neuropsychology: www.abpn.net, accessed December 24, 2004.

15. American Board of Clinical Neuropsychology: www.theabcn.org, accessed December 24, 2004.

16. Therapeutics and Technology Assessment Subcommittee of the American Academy of Neurology. "Assessment: Neuropsychological testing of adults. Considerations for neurologists." *Neurology* 1996;47:592-599.

17. Burke W. "Genetic testing." N Engl J Med 2002;347:1867-1875.

18. Sturla L-M, Fernandez-Teijeiro A, Pomeroy SL. "Application of microarrays to neurological disease." *Arch Neurol* 2003;60:676-682.

19. Crumpacker CS, Gonzales RG, Makar RS. "Case 26-2003: A 50-year-old Colombian man with fever and seizures." *N Engl J Med* 2003;349:789-796.

20. Clayton EW. "Ethical, legal, and social implications of genomic medicine." *N Engl J Med* 2003;349:562-569.

21. *Id*. at 564-565.

22. Krumm J. "Genetic discrimination: Why Congress must ban genetic testing in the workplace." *J Legal Med* 2002;23:491-521.

Additional Reading

Aminoff MJ. *Electrodiagnosis in Clinical Neurology*, 4th ed. New York: Churchill Livingstone; 1999.

Boller F, Grafman J, eds. *Handbook of Neuropsychology*, 2nd ed. Vols. 1-9. New York: Elsevier; 2000-2003.

Chiappa KH. *Evoked Potentials in Clinical Medicine*, 3rd ed. New York: Lippincott Williams & Wilkins; 1997.

Daube JR. *Clinical Neurophysiology*. Philadelphia: F.A. Davis; 1996.

Dumitru D, ed., Amato AA, Zwarts MJ. *Electrodiagnostic Medicine*, 2nd ed. New York: Lippincott Williams & Wilkins; 2001.

Ebersole JS, Pedley TA. *The Current Practice of Clinical Electroencephalography*, 3rd ed. New York: Lippincott Williams & Wilkins; 2002.

Fisch BJ. *Fisch and Spehlmann's EEG Primer*, 3rd ed. New York: Academic Press; 1999.

Fishman RA. *Cerebrospinal Fluid in Diseases of the Nervous System*, 2nd ed. Philadelphia: Saunders; 1992.

Kimura J. *Electrodiagnosis in Diseases of Nerve and Muscle: Principles and Practice*, 3rd ed. New York: Oxford University Press; 2001.

Misulis KE, Fakhoury T. *Spehlmann's Evoked Potential Primer*, 3rd ed. Boston: Butterworth-Heinemann; 2001.

McQuillen MP, Beresford HR, et al., eds. *Ethical Issues for Neurologists* (American Academy of Neurology, *Continuum*, Volume 9, Number 4). Philadelphia: Lippincott Williams & Wilkins; 2003.

Niedermeyer E, Lopes da Silva F. *Electroencephalography: Basic Principles, Clinical Applications, and Related Fields*, 5th ed. Baltimore: Lippincott Williams & Wilkins; 2004.

Chapter 4

Sensory and Motor Function

4.1 Sensory System

Sensory pathways convey information from the external and internal environments to the brain. Sensation requires activation of a receptor and transmission of nerve impulses to the CNS. Sensory input is needed for perception, to maintain arousal and alertness, to regulate internal systems, and for control of movement and posture. Most conscious sensation requires three groups of neurons. Sensory receptors are connected to *first-order neurons*. These transmit *afferent* impulses into the spinal cord or brainstem. Next, *second-order neurons* carry the sensory messages into the thalamus. Finally, *third-order neurons* connect to areas of the cortex for processing of the information (Figure 4.1).

Neurologists may refer to *epicritic* and *protopathic* sensations. The former refers to stimuli that are better differentiated and more precisely localized (position sense, fine touch). The latter refers to coarser, less precisely localized sensations (dull pain, temperature sense). There are dif-

51

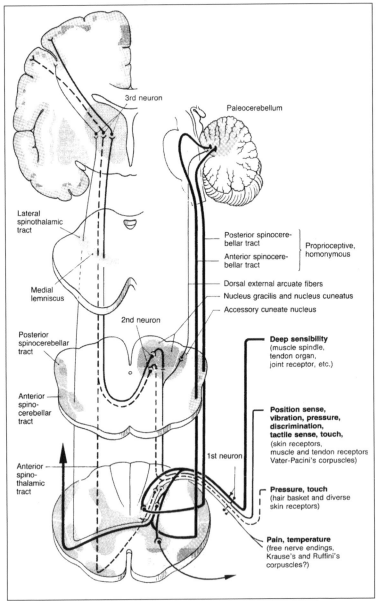

Source: Duus P. Topical Diagnosis in Neurology, 2nd rev. ed. New York: Thieme; 1989:18. Reprinted by permission.

Figure 4.1 *Sensory Pathways. Note how different types of sensations reach the cortex via different pathways. This is the basis for dissociated sensory loss—damage affects certain modalities while sparing others.*

ferent pathways for these and it is possible for disease to affect one but spare the other, a useful diagnostic clue.

A. Peripheral receptors

Sensory receptors are specialized structures with the ability to respond to certain stimuli. Activation of a receptor generates electrical impulses that are carried by sensory nerve fibers. *Exteroceptors* in the skin and mucous membranes are sensitive to changes in the environment including touch and pressure (*mechanoceptors*), temperature (*thermoceptors*), and pain (*nociceptors*). *Proprioceptors* provide information about movement, weight, and position. These receptors are located predominantly in deeper tissues—muscles, joints, tendons, ligaments, and bones. We are not conscious of most proprioceptive input. *Visceroceptors* or *enteroceptors* are sensitive to stimuli from the internal organs.

B. Transmission to the brain

The sensory receptors are the terminal points of sensory nerve fibers. Bundles of hundreds or thousands of these fibers make up the peripheral nerves. Nerve fibers are classified according to the thickness of their myelin covering and their conduction velocity. Different fiber types have various functions and pathologic vulnerabilities. Most peripheral nerves also contain motor fibers. Groups of first-order sensory neuron cell bodies comprise the *spinal* or *dorsal ganglia*. These are located near the spinal cord. The sensory fibers transmit their electrical impulses through the spinal nerve's posterior (dorsal) root into the spinal cord. Motor messages leave the spinal cord through the anterior (ventral) root.

Peripheral nerves usually carry fibers from two or more adjacent segmental spinal roots. This is accomplished by nerve plexuses (Figure 4.2). Nerve root fibers divide and recombine in the plexus to form peripheral nerves. The first four cervical nerve roots form the cervical plexus. It divides into sensory and motor nerves that supply the neck (Figure 4.3). The fifth through eighth cervical and first thoracic nerve roots usually make up the complex *brachial plexus*, though variations are common. It sends its nerves into the shoulder and arm. The main terminal nerves of the brachial plexus are the ulnar, radial, and median (Figure 4.4). The *lumbosacral plexus* is actually two plexuses (Figure 4.5). The first four lumbar nerve roots form the *lumbar plexus*. Its largest branches are the femoral and ob-

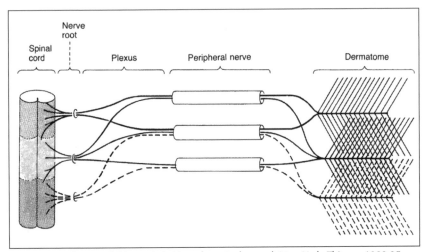

Source: Duus P. Topical Diagnosis in Neurology, 2nd rev. ed. New York: Thieme; 1989:25.
Reprinted by permission.

Figure 4.2 Dermatomes. Each spine segment receives sensory information from an area of skin. However, more than one peripheral nerve may carry the input to the spine.

turator nerves. Fibers from the fourth and fifth lumbar roots and the first three sacral roots comprise the *sacral plexus* (confusingly, sometimes called the lumbosacral plexus). The sciatic nerve is the main branch; it divides into the tibial and peroneal nerves.

The nerve fibers in the dorsal root of the spinal nerves are organized in a particular manner. The medial fibers carry proprioceptive input, the lateral pain and temperature input, and those in the middle of the root other epicritic input. All of these fibers connect with neurons in the spinal cord. Most of the proprioceptive input will travel to the cerebellum. The finely localizable epicritic input travels predominantly in the ipsilateral posterior columns, eventually crossing over to the contralateral thalamus. The protopathic input crosses to the other side of the spinal cord within a few levels of the entry point and travels to the thalamus via different pathways, the spinothalamic tracts (see Figure 4.1).

These fibers maintain a *somatotopic* organization as they ascend in the spinal cord, with fibers from each region of the body traveling together. The somatotopic arrangement is maintained in the parietal lobe of the brain, arrayed there as a sensory *homunculus*. This homunculus is dis-

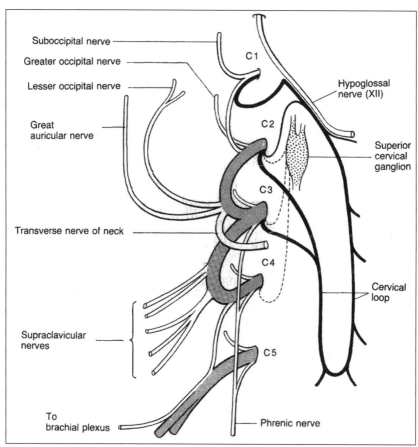

Source: Duus P. Topical Diagnosis in Neurology, 2nd rev. ed. New York: Thieme; 1989:23.
Reprinted by permission.

Figure 4.3 Cervical Plexus. Fibers from the first four cervical roots form this plexus.

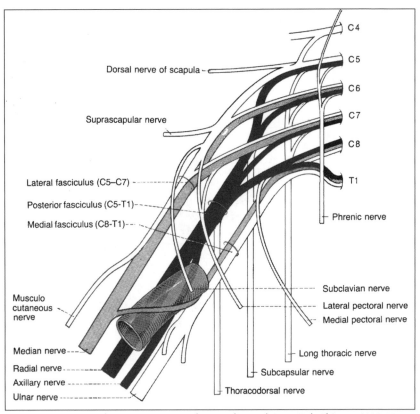

Source: Duus P. Topical Diagnosis in Neurology, 2nd rev. ed. New York: Thieme; 1989:24. Reprinted by permission.

Figure 4.4 Brachial Plexus. The nerve roots forming this plexus first combine to form three trunks—upper, middle, and lower. These divide into anterior and posterior divisions that, in turn, form the three fasciculi, or cords. For simplicity the trunks and divisions are not labeled.

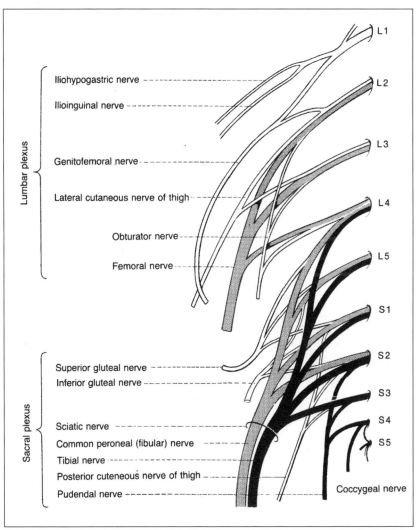

Source: Duus P. Topical Diagnosis in Neurology, 2nd rev. ed. New York: Thieme; 1989:24. Reprinted by permission.

Figure 4.5 *Lumbosacral Plexus. The lumbar plexus is located within the psoas muscle; the sacral plexus rests against the piriformis muscle. Damage to these nerve complexes is less common than individual nerve root lesions.*

torted, with larger areas of cortex devoted to fingers, hands, and face compared to back and legs (Figure 4.6).

C. Central processing

The thalamus is a critical relay station for sensory processing. Pain, temperature, and other stimuli reaching the thalamus can be felt consciously. However, the sensation is indistinct, dull, and poorly localized. Full appreciation of sensation requires transmission to the cerebral cortex, particularly, the parietal lobe. This is where sensory input is analyzed, inte-

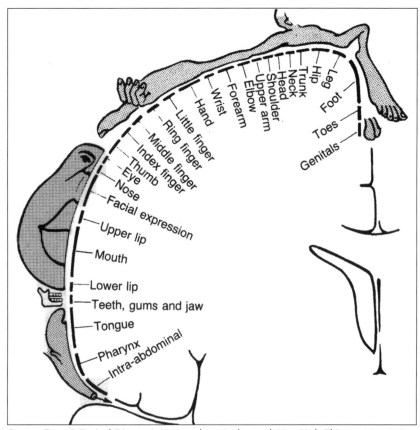

Source: Duus P. Topical Diagnosis in Neurology, 2nd rev. ed. New York: Thieme; 1989:265. Reprinted by permission.

Figure 4.6 *Sensory Homunculus. Note the relatively greater cortical representation for the lower face, lips, and thumb.*

grated, and interpreted. Precise localization and characterization of sensory input requires the cortex.

D. Sensory examination

The purpose of the sensory examination is to detect areas of lost or abnormal sensation. The changes can be anatomically restricted or widespread; deficits can involve one or more sensory modalities while sparing others. Evaluation of sensation is probably the most difficult part of the neurological examination. It can be time-consuming and fatiguing for both patient and examiner. If sensory complaints are prominent this portion of the examination must be especially thorough. To minimize problems with fatigue the sensory testing should be done early in the examination.

Patient cooperation is particularly important because the sensory examination relies almost exclusively on subjective responses. Thus, the patient must understand the examiner and be able to respond appropriately. Critical evaluation by the neurologist is necessary to assess the validity of the results and their significance. Sensory testing can produce confusing and contradictory results. Repeat evaluations to confirm findings are often necessary. Unfortunately, even with the use of quantitative sensory testing techniques[1] patients feigning sensory loss can fool examiners.[2]

If there are no sensory complaints a screening examination can be done quickly. At least one exteroceptive and one proprioceptive sensory modality should be examined in all limbs. The examiner looks for deficits and asymmetries. However, if sensory symptoms or abnormalities are detected during the preliminary screening more detailed testing is needed to determine the nature and location of the dysfunction. Examination is best done moving from abnormal to normal regions.

E. Interpretation of sensory symptoms and signs

Determining the kind of sensory loss and its distribution will usually lead to accurate anatomical diagnosis. There are characteristic distributions for peripheral nerve, nerve root, nerve plexus, spinal cord, and brain lesions producing sensory dysfunction. The type of sensory syndrome depends on where the sensory pathway is damaged.

Each peripheral nerve innervates a particular area of the body, though with some overlap from nearby nerves (Figure 4.7). This distribution is fairly consistent from person to person though not necessarily identical. Loss or damage to a sensory nerve will alter or destroy all sensory modalities in the area supplied by the nerve. Decreased sensitivity to touch, *hypesthesia*, is usually more obvious than diminished pain sensation, *hypalgesia*, because there is greater overlap of pain fibers from adjacent nerves. Overlapping fibers from healthy nerves function normally, thereby preserving perception. Careful examination may reveal transitions from zones of complete loss of touch and pain sense (*anesthesia* and *analgesia*), to areas of marked dysfunction and finally, zones of minimal loss.

Dysfunction restricted to a single peripheral nerve is termed focal neuropathy or *mononeuropathy*. Medical illnesses such as diabetes or vasculitis may impair more than one nerve, producing multifocal neuropathies or *multiple mononeuropathies* (the older term for this is *mononeuropathy multiplex*). More generalized, system-wide peripheral nerve disease is called *polyneuropathy*. Peripheral neuropathies are discussed in Chapter 10.

The sensory fibers of a single spinal nerve root supply a particular area of skin known as a *dermatome* (Figure 4.8). Dermatome maps derived from different physiological methods[3] are available; though these generally are consistent there are variations that can lead to diagnostic confusion. The segmental innervation of the limbs is far more complex than the trunk's and is best appreciated graphically. The dermatomes overlap considerably, more for touch than pain. Loss of sensation in a single dermatome is harder to detect than loss from a single peripheral nerve because of this extensive overlapping. Nevertheless, identification of a dermatomal pattern of loss is a key finding that identifies the level of damage.

Peripheral nerve and nerve root lesions almost always produce very different distributions of sensory loss (compare Figures 4.7 and 4.8). One notable exception is ulnar nerve and eighth cervical root (C8) lesions. However, since both C8 and the ulnar nerve have motor components analysis of the distribution of weakness usually leads to the correct diagnosis. This is because some C8-innervated muscles are supplied by other peripheral nerves. Therefore, weakness in those muscles cannot be due to an ulnar lesion. If clinically obvious weakness is not present electrodiagnostic testing (see §3.3B) is needed to clarify the diagnosis. A

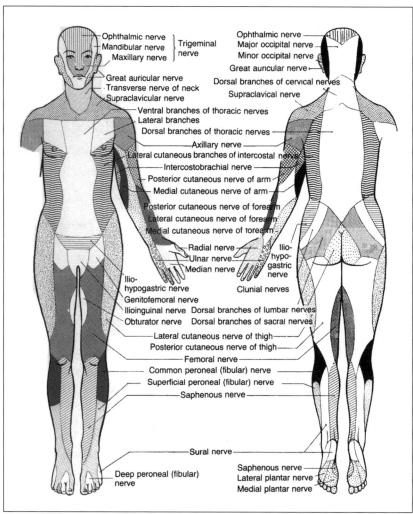

Source: Duus P. Topical Diagnosis in Neurology, 2nd rev. ed. New York: Thieme; 1989:27.
Reprinted by permission.

Figure 4.7 *Peripheral Nerve Innervation of Skin. Compare to Figure 4.8.*

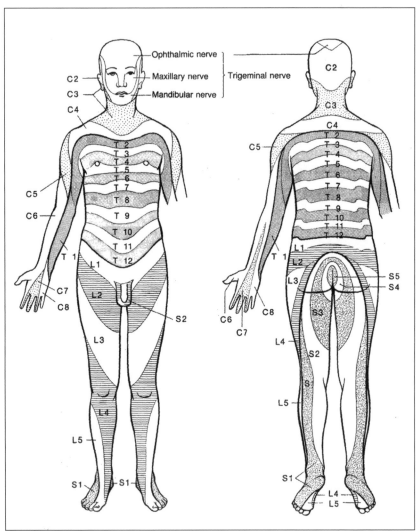

Source: Duus P. Topical Diagnosis in Neurology, 2nd rev. ed. New York: Thieme; 1989:26. Reprinted by permission.

Figure 4.8 *Dermatomal Innervation of Skin. Compare to Figure 4.7.*

similar situation can occur in the lower extremity with peroneal nerve and fifth lumbar (L5) lesions.

Plexus lesions produce more complex patterns of injury than peripheral nerve or nerve root lesions. Accurate diagnosis requires an even more meticulous examination and a very clear understanding of the underlying anatomy and origins of the peripheral nerves.

F. Sensory syndromes by location

Identification of the distribution and nature of sensory dysfunction will usually permit localization of the lesion. Lesions to parietal sensory cortex and underlying subcortical regions produce *contralateral* sensory disturbances. For example, if the damage involves the arm region of the homunculus the contralateral arm is involved. Large areas of sensory cortex must be damaged to produce extensive dysfunction. A smaller *subcortical* lesion, in contrast, can cause more widespread sensory loss because the sensory fibers are much closer together as they travel from the thalamus to the parietal cortex.

Cortical and subcortical sensory lesions produce loss of sensation or abnormal sensation—*paresthesia*. Usually, distal portions of the limbs are most affected. There may be focal sensory epileptic seizures. Since there is some overlap of sensory and motor function in the cortex motor abnormalities are also possible. Extensive damage to the thalamus causes contralateral loss of sensation, particularly deep sensibility. Typical features include slowed sensory perception, poor stimulus localization, and abnormal unpleasant sensations.

Location is critical in understanding sensory deficits due to brainstem damage. A lesion involving the *lateral spinothalamic tract* will produce contralateral loss of pain and temperature in the body. If the lesion is in the upper portion of the pons, pain and temperature fibers from the face will also be involved. If fibers in the *medial lemniscus* are affected there will be loss of fine touch and other epicritic modalities. A *dissociated sensory loss* means only one group of sensations is involved while the other is spared. For example, damage to the medial lemniscus with sparing of the lateral spinothalamic tract produces a dissociated sensory loss involving fine touch but sparing pain and temperature sense.

A unilateral lesion in the lower portion of the brainstem could damage both the lateral spinothalamic tract carrying pain and temperature input from the other side of the body as well as the structures receiving sensory input from the same side of the face—spinal trigeminal nucleus and tract. This creates both a dissociated sensory loss and a *crossed* syndrome—contralateral loss of pain and temperature sense on the body but ipsilateral loss on the face.

Position, vibration, and fine discriminatory sensations ascend in the posterior columns of the spinal cord. A unilateral lesion there produces an ipsilateral dissociated loss sparing pain and temperature sensation. This causes unilateral limb incoordination, *ataxia*. Bilateral posterior column dysfunction can occur as a result of vitamin B12 deficiency. Symptoms include loss of fine discrimination, abnormal gait, and impaired postural reflexes.

The spinal nerve root fibers carrying pain and temperature sensations enter the posterior horn of the spinal cord and synapse with the neurons forming the lateral spinothalamic tract. Thus, damage to a posterior horn produces an ipsilateral dissociated loss of those modalities but spares the posterior column modalities.

4.2 Central Control of Movement

The ability to respond to changes in our surroundings requires movement. The motor system enables us to move our bodies and to maintain our postures. Even apparently simple muscle contractions require complex patterns of nerve and muscle activation, much of which is accomplished unconsciously.

A. Pathways to the periphery

Voluntary muscle contraction requires activation and coordination of two groups of motor structures, the *pyramidal* and *extrapyramidal* systems. Neurons in the *precentral* and adjacent motor cortex of the frontal lobes transmit their impulses via axons that form the *pyramidal* (or *corticospinal*) tract. Like the sensory cortex there is also a somatotopic organization in the frontal lobe motor cortex (Figure 4.9).

With a few exceptions the motor neurons from each hemisphere control voluntary movement on the opposite side of the body. The axonal fibers in the *corticospinal bundle* of the pyramidal tract travel through the posterior limb of the internal capsule and then enter the brainstem. Almost all the corticospinal fibers cross to the other side in the lower medulla,

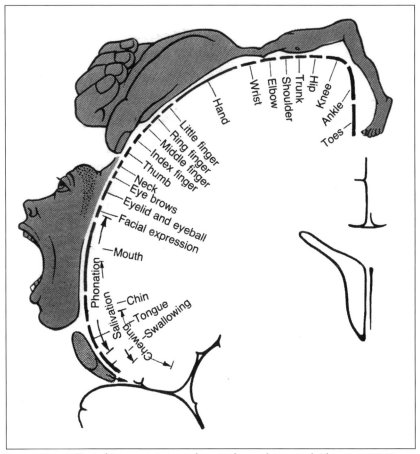

Source: Duus P. Topical Diagnosis in Neurology, 2nd rev. ed. New York: Thieme; 1989:265.
Reprinted by permission.

Figure 4.9 Motor Homunculus. Areas requiring fine gradations of movement have larger cortical representations—hands and face, for example.

enter the spinal cord, and eventually reach the anterior horn motor neurons. Other pyramidal tract axons form the *corticomesencephalic* and *corticonuclear tracts* (together also known as the *corticobulbar bundle*) that connect with motor nuclei in the brainstem (Figure 4.10).

The extrapyramidal motor system includes all nonpyramidal systems involved in voluntary movement. It is deeply interconnected with the pyramidal system and helps to regulate movement by acting at the level of the anterior horn motor neurons. The extrapyramidal system plays an im-

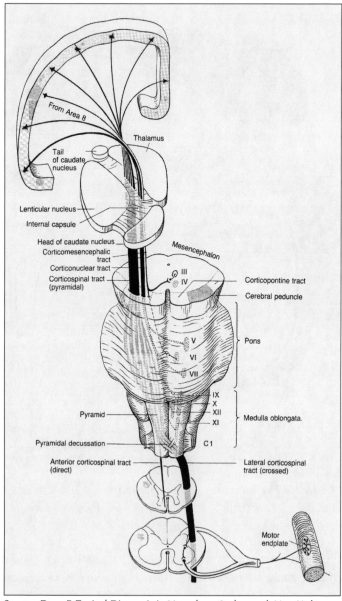

Source: Duus P. Topical Diagnosis in Neurology, 2nd rev. ed. New York: Thieme; 1989:31. Reprinted by permission.

Figure 4.10 Pyramidal Tract. Small internal capsule and other deep lesions can destroy many of the tightly packed motor fibers, producing widespread weakness, whereas much larger cortical lesions are necessary to cause comparable damage.

portant role in regulating coordination, muscle tone, posture, and reflexes. The *basal ganglia*, *subthalamic nucleus*, and several brainstem structures are the main components of the extrapyramidal system. The *cerebellum* can also be considered a part of this system but is usually discussed on its own because of its unique structural and functional properties.

The integration of input from higher centers in the brain takes place at the level of the anterior horn motor neurons in the spinal cord (Figure 4.11). The axons from these neurons travel via nerve roots into peripheral nerves. The neuromuscular junction is the point where the motor neurons activate the muscle by releasing a chemical neurotransmitter.

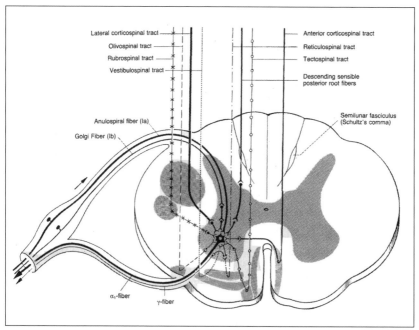

Source: Duus P. Topical Diagnosis in Neurology, 2nd rev. ed. New York: Thieme; 1989:34. Reprinted by permission.

Figure 4.11 *Anterior Horn Motor Neurons. Pyramidal and extrapyramidal inputs converge on the spinal cord motor neurons, the beginning of the final common pathway to muscle—also known as the lower motor neuron. Gamma motor neurons are involved in regulation of muscle tone. The alpha motor neurons are responsible for muscle contraction.*

B. Motor examination

There are several aspects of motor function that must be evaluated for proper diagnosis. These include strength, tone, coordination, muscle bulk, and abnormal movements.

Strength is probably the most obvious aspect of motor function. To test strength, movements at a joint are evaluated and individual muscles assessed. Usually this is done by asking the patient to resist efforts by the examiner to move the body part or to move the limb against the examiner's resistance. Patient cooperation is essential. Most joint movements require simultaneous contraction of several muscles and relaxation of others. The examiner must understand the movement sufficiently to avoid rating the wrong muscle or identifying apparent weakness that is merely the result of improper positioning.

Weakness is often termed *paresis*; complete paralysis is *plegia*. Thus, *monoparesis* is weakness of a single limb. *Paraplegia* indicates paralysis of both legs; *diplegia* may be used for weakness of either both arms or both legs. *Hemiparesis* is weakness on one side of the body. *Quadriparesis* or *tetraparesis* refers to weakness in all four limbs.

A 5/5 rating scheme is standard:

- 0 = No muscle contraction
- 1 = Flicker of contraction
- 2 = Active movement without gravity
- 3 = Active movement against gravity
- 4 = Active movement against both gravity and resistance
- 5 = Normal strength

Some clinicians will further refine the rating by adding a + or - to indicate intermediate levels of weakness. Considerable experience is necessary for proficiency in evaluating strength.

Muscle tone is the resting tension of muscles or the tendency to resist movement when not contracting. Antigravity muscles, which maintain erect posture, have greater resting tone than other muscles. Muscle tone depends on a constant stream of impulses from pyramidal and extrapyramidal brain centers to the spinal cord motor neurons. There are also reflexes generated within the muscle by special fibers (*muscle spindles*) that affect tone.

Tone is evaluated by passive movement of a limb by the examiner. Unlike strength testing the patient is asked not to contract the muscles. Results are difficult to quantify; the examiner makes a judgment based on his or her experience. Decreased tone, *hypotonicity*, is seen with abnormalities in the spinal motor neurons, posterior column, cerebellum, peripheral nerves, or muscle. The muscles feel flaccid and soft.

Hypertonicity is produced by loss of inhibitory input or imbalance in input from higher centers. There are two forms. *Rigidity* is due to lesions in the basal ganglia or other extrapyramidal structures. Resistance to passive movement is increased in both the agonist and antagonist muscles around a joint. The muscles feel tight. *Cogwheel rigidity* is characterized by increased tone with intermittent yielding that causes the muscle to jerk as if attached to a cogwheel. This is common in Parkinson's disease.

Spasticity is the other form of hypertonicity. It develops following lesions of the pyramidal system. The damage produces an imbalance between inhibitory and excitatory input. There is increased muscle tone due to an abnormally active muscle stretch reflex. Unlike rigidity the increased tone is more prominent in only one of the muscles groups around a joint. For example, following a cerebral infarction increased muscle tone will be more prominent in the extensor muscles of the leg and the flexor muscles in the arm.

Proper movement requires coordination of many different muscles. *Agonists* contract to produce the desired movement while *antagonist* muscles must relax. *Synergistic* muscles facilitate the movement. The cerebellum plays a major role in proper coordination but normal pyramidal and extrapyramidal function is also necessary. Coordination can be evaluated by observing the patient while he or she carries out skilled actions such as tying shoelaces or dressing.

Muscle size and shape are assessed by inspection and measurement. Muscle wasting, *atrophy*, has many different causes. It can be due to intrinsic muscle disease or interruption of the motor input to the muscle. Abnormal increased size, *hypertrophy* or *pseudohypertrophy*, suggests the presence of abnormal substances in the muscle.

There are many different kinds of abnormal movements that can be seen during examination. These must be observed and analyzed carefully. Several features should be described including:

- Degree of conscious control if any
- Location of the movements
- Pattern or rhythmicity
- Presence during sleep
- Relationship to anxiety or tension
- Response to heat or cold
- Size and strength of the movements
- Speed and frequency

Abnormal movements include tremors, myoclonus, chorea, tics, athetosis, dystonia, and fasciculations.

C. Motor abnormalities
Motor system dysfunction occurs when there is:

- Defective integration of the pyramidal and extrapyramidal systems
- Irritation or overactivity in a component
- Loss of function in a constituent element of the system

Acute, rapidly progressive generalized weakness is a potential emergency. Neurologists must consider a long list of possible causes.[4] Important information needed for diagnosis includes:

- Distribution of weakness
- History of onset
- Presence or absence of pain, sensory deficits, abnormal reflexes

The spinal cord anterior horn motor neurons, spinal nerve roots, neuromuscular junction, and muscles collectively make up the *lower motor neuron* (LMN). Lesions in this functional system produce weakness, muscle wasting, decreased tone, and reduced muscle stretch reflexes. The pyramidal and extrapyramidal systems comprise the *upper motor neuron* (UMN). Damage produces weakness, exaggerated and pathologic reflexes, increased muscle tone, and impaired fine motor control and coordination.

The pattern of abnormalities allows the neurologist to characterize and localize the problem. Some examples with localization or cause are:

- Bilateral flaccid leg weakness (LMN), distal greater than proximal—polyneuropathy
- Bilateral spastic leg weakness (UMN)—thoracic or upper lumbar spinal cord
- Flaccid quadriparesis (LMN), proximal greater than distal—muscle disease
- Spastic quadriparesis (UMN) of limbs and UMN cranial nerve findings—both cerebral hemispheres
- Spastic quadriparesis (UMN), no cranial nerve abnormalities—cervical spinal cord
- Unilateral spastic limb weakness (UMN) and cranial nerve abnormalities—brainstem
- Unilateral spastic weakness (UMN) of limbs and face—contralateral cerebral hemisphere

When particular muscles are weak the neurologist must rely on knowledge of neuroanatomy to localize the lesion. Just as the sensory portion of a nerve root supplies a region of skin known as the dermatome the motor portion of the root supplies muscles within a *myotome* (Figure 4.12). Many limb muscles are supplied by overlapping myotomes. Along the thoracic wall the spinal nerve roots become intercostal nerves. In the limbs, however, most nerve roots do not form peripheral nerves directly. Instead, the roots divide, branch, and recombine within plexuses, as described earlier. Most limb nerves arise from these plexuses.

Therefore, in order to determine the lesion's location the neurologist must know the source of a muscle's innervation. For arm muscles this includes the nerve roots, peripheral nerve, and brachial plexus derivation. Localizing a lesion requires determining which muscles are weak and then knowing if these muscles are supplied by the same peripheral nerve or the same nerve root.

Easy fatigability is the hallmark of dysfunction at the neuromuscular junction. Normally, there is a considerable safety margin for neurotransmission at the synapse. That is, ongoing activation of the motor nerve results in decreasing quantities of acetylcholine release. However, in normal muscles there is still enough acetylcholine to trigger a full muscle

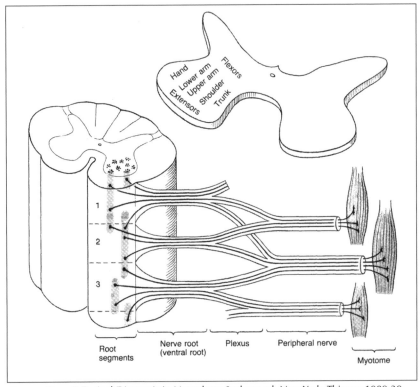

Source: Duus P. Topical Diagnosis in Neurology, 2nd rev. ed. New York: Thieme; 1989:39. Reprinted by permission.

Figure 4.12 *Myotomes. Peripheral nerves innervating a muscle may contain fibers from more than a single spinal level.*

contraction. This is not the case in diseases such as myasthenia gravis (see §17.2).

Disorders of the voluntary muscles are known as *myopathies* (see §17.1). These are distinguished from other neuromuscular disorders by fairly specific clinical and laboratory signs and symptoms. Proximal, symmetric weakness is the most common presentation, but there are myopathies characterized by distal or cranial muscle weakness. A detailed history and examination emphasizing detection of the distribution of weakness usually leads to the correct classification of a myopathy. Laboratory testing will confirm the clinical impression or provide a more specific diagnosis. The three main tests are measurement of serum muscle enzymes, electrodiagnostic studies, and muscle biopsy. Molecular genetics and biochemical testing are becoming increasingly important and often eliminate the need for biopsy.

Myopathies and other muscle diseases may produce some pain but the sensory examination should be normal. A very asymmetric pattern of weakness is inconsistent with a primary muscle disease. The history is of major importance in diagnosing muscle disease, particularly the tempo of the progression of the muscle weakness. Also, a family history of similar problems has considerable diagnostic significance.

4.3 The Cerebellum and Coordination

The cerebellum is located in the posterior portion of the cranium, overlying the brainstem and beneath the cerebral hemispheres. It consists of two hemispheres and the midline *vermis*. There are extensive interconnections with vestibular nuclei, spinal cord, and motor cortex. Functionally, the cerebellum has three divisions:

- Corticocerebellum—coordination of fine limb movements
- Spinocerebellum—gait and station
- Vestibulocerebellum—balance and eye movements

Acute cerebellar damage usually produces *hypotonia* and *ataxia* (incoordination). Lesions restricted to vestibulocerebellar structures cause postural ataxia of the head and trunk that is not worse with eyes closed; patients lose their balance even while seated. However, limb movements are spared. Spinocerebellar damage produces gait ataxia and truncal instability; with eyes closed the patient falls—the *Romberg sign*. Unilateral corticocerebellar damage causes ipsilateral limb ataxia but spares gait and station. Often, more than one functional division of the cerebellum is impaired. There is a long list of conditions, both acquired and inherited, that can cause cerebellar dysfunction.[5] Many also cause brainstem dysfunction.

Endnotes

1. Chong PST, Cros DP. "Technology literature review: Quantitative sensory testing." *Muscle Nerve* 2004;29:734-747.

2. Freeman R, Chase KP, Risk MR. "Quantitative sensory testing cannot differentiate simulated sensory loss from sensory neuropathy." *Neurology* 2003;60:465-470.

3. Greenberg SA. "The history of dermatome mapping." *Arch Neurol* 2003; 60:126-131.

4. Van Doorn P. "Acute flaccid paralysis." *Continuum* 2003;9(3):47-61.

5. Timmann D, Diener HC. "Coordination and ataxia." In: Goetz CG, ed. *Textbook of Clinical Neurology*, 2nd ed. Philadelphia: Saunders; 2003:299-315.

Additional Reading

Goetz CG, ed. *Textbook of Clinical Neurology*, 2nd ed. Philadelphia: Saunders; 2003.

Haerer AF. *DeJong's The Neurologic Examination*, 6th ed. Philadelphia: Lippincott Williams & Wilkins; 2005.

Manto M-U, Pandolfo M, eds. *The Cerebellum and its Disorders*. Cambridge: Cambridge University Press; 2001.

Patten J. *Neurological Differential Diagnosis*, 2nd ed. London: Springer-Verlag; 1996, reprinted with corrections, 1998.

Chapter 5

Cranial Nerves: Organization, Function and Examination

5.1 Introduction

The twelve pairs of cranial nerves are the peripheral nerves of the brain. All but the first two and the spinal portion of the eleventh arise in the brainstem (Figure 5.1). The cranial nerves as a group have both motor and sensory functions. However, an individual nerve can have pure sensory, pure motor, or mixed function. Some of these nerves supply organs far from the head (Figure 5.2).

5.2 Olfactory Nerve (CNI)

The olfactory nerve is a pure sensory nerve that is the receptor for the sense of smell, *olfaction*. Much of what we regard as flavor relies on normal olfaction. Without normal olfaction food loses much of its appeal. Many people who lose their sense of smell develop nutritional problems. Loss of olfaction is *anosmia*, reduced olfaction is *hyposmia* or *microsmia*,

75

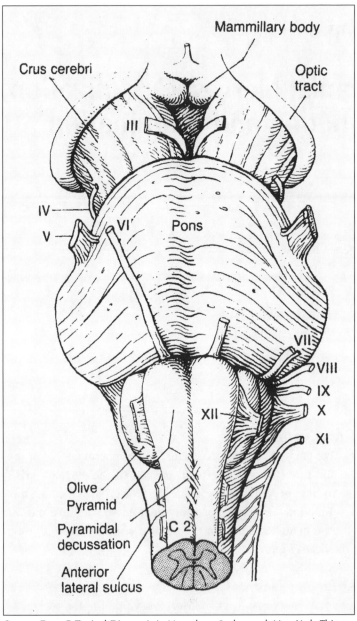

Source: Duus P. Topical Diagnosis in Neurology, 2nd rev. ed. New York: Thieme; 1989:71. Reprinted by permission.

Figure 5.1 Brainstem. *Ventral view showing the origin of cranial nerves III through XII. The optic tracts come from cranial nerve II, the optic nerve.*

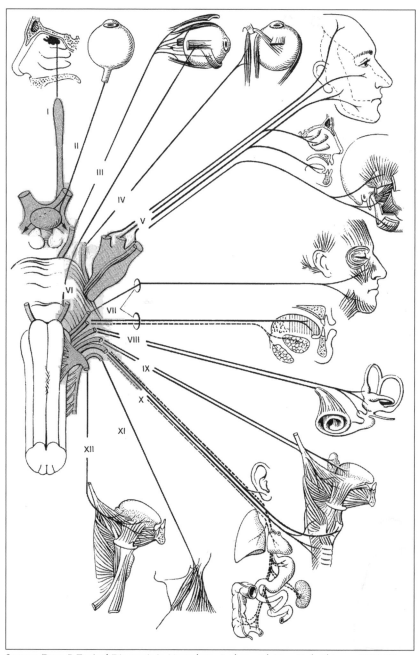

Source: Duus P. Topical Diagnosis in Neurology, 2nd rev. ed. New York: Thieme; 1989:76.
Reprinted by permission.

Figure 5.2 Cranial Nerves. Connections to and from organs shown.

dysosmia is perverted or altered olfaction, and unpleasant or foul dysosmia is known as *parosmia* or *cacosmia*.

The receptive branches of the nerve run from the upper nasal cavity through the cribriform plate of the ethmoid bone into the olfactory bulb. These fibers are susceptible to damage in the upper nasal cavity. More importantly, the fine nerve twiglets passing through the cribriform plate are easily torn, a common occurrence with head trauma. The olfactory tract runs beneath the inferior surface of the frontal lobes from the olfactory bulb back to the olfactory cortex in the temporal lobes. Tumors or other masses on the floor of the anterior skull surface can also damage this nerve. The phylogenetically primitive areas of the brain involved in olfaction are known collectively as the *rhinencephalon*.

Smell and taste combine to produce flavor. Impairment of either sense impairs the ability to discern flavors. With complete olfactory nerve lesions only primary sensations of taste generated in the tongue can be appreciated (bitter, salt, sweet, and sour). Therefore, a report of anosmia with normal taste sensation is physiologically inconsistent; patients with this combination may be dissembling. Head injury is a common cause of complete or partial anosmia. The more severe the trauma, the more likely is anosmia. Persistent dysosmia indicates irritation of the olfactory nerve. Brief episodes of olfactory (or gustatory) *hallucinations* can be a form of epileptic seizure arising in olfactory cortex.

Anosmia can be a very early finding in both Alzheimer's disease and Parkinson's disease.[1] Other common causes of lost or altered smell are upper respiratory infections, nasal and sinus disease, and toxic exposures. Anosmia may occur in association with liver or kidney disease, smoking, and chemotherapy.

Traditionally, CN I is tested by asking the patient to smell and identify various odors (clove, coffee, eucalyptus), a crude method. Ammonia or other noxious substances are sometimes used but these probably activate sensory fibers of the CN V, rather than the olfactory nerve. Since anosmia often has medicolegal significance a quantitative assessment is preferable in order to:[2]

- Characterize the deficits precisely
- Establish the validity of the complaint
- Identify malingering

- Monitor changes over time, including treatment response
- Rate impairment for disability purposes

Several reliable quantitative olfactory tests are available commercially. Perhaps the best known is the University of Pennsylvania Smell Identification Test (Sensonics, Inc., Haddon Heights, New Jersey). This uses a forced-choice paradigm that can identify malingering; there are extensive normative data for the test.[3]

5.3 Optic Nerve (CNII)

The visual pathways start in retinal *ganglion* cells that receive input from the *bipolar* cells. The ganglion cell axons run from the back of the globe to form the optic nerve. The two optic nerves meet at the optic chiasm. They unite, with fibers from the temporal half of the retina remaining on the same side while fibers from the nasal half of each retina cross the chiasm to join the temporal fibers from the opposite side.

The optic tracts run posteriorly from the chiasm. Each is composed of the fibers from the temporal half of the ipsilateral retina and the nasal half of the contralateral retina. Thus, vision for the left half of space travels in the right optic tract, vision for the right half travels in the left tract. These fibers extend posteriorly, with most terminating on the *lateral geniculate body*—a part of the thalamus. Some fibers leave the optic tract and travel to the midbrain where they are involved in controlling the amount of light that passes through the pupils to the retina, the light reflex (see §5.4). The final visual pathway—the *optic radiation* or geniculocalcarine fibers—runs from the lateral geniculate body to the calcarine cortex in the occipital lobe.

Optic nerve lesions may cause partial or total loss of *monocular* vision. Chiasm lesions produce different patterns of visual field loss that depend upon the site of the damage. Behind the chiasm, lesions of the optic tract or radiation may produce *homonymous hemianopia* (literally loss of half the vision). The defect is *binocular*, present in both eyes, and involves the visual fields contralateral to the lesion. Incomplete lesions produce sector or quadrant defects. The field defects can be identical in the two eyes—*congruous*—or different—*incongruous*. Visual cortex lesions also produce a contralateral field defect.

Involvement of the lower part of the optic radiation in the temporal lobe produces a contralateral *superior* quadrantanopia (one-quarter of the field), while lesions in the parietal lobe produce a contralateral *inferior* quadrantic hemianopia. Optic tract lesions are generally the result of compression by tumors or aneurysms. The commonest causes of optic radiation lesions are stroke, hemorrhage, and tumor. Stroke and tumors are the most likely causes of occipital lobe damage.

Depending on the clinical situation CN II evaluation may include:

- Assessing pupillary responses to light and accommodation
- Evaluating color perception
- Funduscopic examination of the retina
- Measuring the visual fields either at the "bedside" by confrontation testing or by more formal *perimetry*
- Visual evoked responses and electroretinography

Many conditions can affect CN II and the visual pathways including acquired metabolic and nutritional disorders, autoimmune diseases, demyelinating diseases, inherited degenerative conditions, infections, migraine, neoplasms, trauma, and vascular disease.[4] Some of these are treatable if identified promptly.

Nonphysiologic visual complaints are not rare. There are several clinical tests or observations that help distinguish these from true lesions of the visual system:[5]

- Fixation of patient's "blind" eyes on his or her image in a mirror— "swinging mirror" test
- Intact opticokinetic response produced by moving target despite alleged visual loss
- Lack of expansion of patient's visual fields with increased target size and distance in tangent screen testing—so-called *tunnel vision*, a common nonphysiological complaint
- Lack of improvement in visual acuity with increasing letter size or decreasing target distance
- Normal color vision in the presence of severely diminished visual acuity
- Normal pupil, retina, and ocular examination in reportedly blind eye

- Poor performance on proprioceptive tasks that patient believes relies on vision—looking away from his or her own outstretched arm, not being able to touch finger tips together
- Responses on tests that surreptitiously rely on binocular vision—patient responds in a way that indicates the "impaired" eye functions well
- Retained blink reflex in response to threat or bright light in reportedly "blind" eye

5.4 Oculomotor, Trochlear, and Abducens Nerves (CN III, IV, and VI)

These three cranial nerves are connected functionally to allow the eyes to move together as a "yoked pair." Horizontal eye movements are either outward (abduction), or inward (adduction). The vertical movements are elevation and depression. Conjugate movement refers to the simultaneous movement of the two eyes in the same direction at the same velocity. There are several types of conjugate gaze requiring input from cerebral cortex, cerebellum, vestibular centers, and brainstem.

Six extraocular muscles move the eyes, the four recti muscles (superior, inferior, lateral, and medial) and the two oblique muscles (superior and inferior). The medial and lateral recti act in the horizontal plane only. The superior rectus and inferior oblique move the eye upwards, the inferior rectus and superior oblique produce downward gaze. These four muscles also produce rotation, or torsion, of the eyeball.

Abnormalities can occur in the brainstem yoking mechanism or in these nerves as they run from the brainstem to the orbit. The extraocular muscles themselves can be damaged. When the eyes do not work together the patient develops double vision—*diplopia*. This is due to a mismatch of image location in the two retinas. The degree of diplopia increases when the affected eye attempts to move in the direction served by the paralyzed muscles.

Diplopia almost always requires vision in both eyes. When either eye closes, only one image remains and the diplopia disappears. Diplopia present in one eye when the other is closed—*monocular diplopia*—is a common nonphysiologic complaint. The physician needs to exclude the rarer cases of true monocular diplopia—ocular problems such as retinal deformity or cataract, or visual cortex lesions. However, most cases of monocular diplopia are not due to such lesions.

CN III, IV, and VI can be damaged individually, as a group, and either unilaterally or bilaterally. The common causes of unilateral, isolated CN III palsies are aneurysms, nerve infarction (common in diabetics), tumor, and trauma. Isolated CN IV lesions are infrequent, but are the most common cause of pure vertical diplopia. The head tends to tilt towards the side of the affected eye in order to compensate for the muscle weakness. A cause for a CN IV palsy is not always identified. Common causes of a VI nerve palsy include demyelination (as in multiple sclerosis), infarction, tumor, subarachnoid hemorrhage, trauma, and skull fracture. The affected eye cannot move laterally from the midline because of the lateral rectus muscle paralysis.

Causes of combined lesions to these cranial nerves vary by location:

- Brainstem—infarction, tumor
- Cavernous sinus—aneurysm, mucocele, tumor
- Orbit—cellulitis, pseudotumor, thyroid eye disease, trauma, tumor
- Subarachnoid space—aneurysm, meningitis, trauma

The eyelid is elevated by two muscles—the levator palpebrae superioris innervated by CN III and Müllers palpebral muscle supplied by cervical sympathetic fibers. Drooping of the upper eyelid is known as *ptosis* and can be due to an abnormality of either muscle. When the former is involved, lid closure is almost complete; with the latter, the droop is milder. Ptosis is common in myasthenia gravis. Lid closure depends upon the orbicularis oculi, innervated by the facial nerve (CN VII).

The pupil is under the control of two antagonistic muscles. The circular muscle of the iris, supplied by the cervical autonomic system, dilates the pupil; the sphincter pupillae, supplied by CN III, constricts the pupil. Up to 0.4 or 0.5 millimeters of pupillary asymmetry is a normal finding termed *anisocoria*. Paralysis of the sphincter pupillae produces a widely dilated pupil (*midriasis*) due to the unopposed action of the iris dilator muscle. The pupil does not constrict to light or accommodation. Conversely, paralysis of the dilator muscle causes a constricted pupil (*miosis*) that does not dilate in the dark.

The light reflex describes the constriction of both pupils in response to light stimulation; the response in the eye in which the light is being shone is the *direct* response, that in the opposite eye, the *consensual* response. The accommodation response describes the combination of pupillary constriction when gaze is changed from far to near plus *convergence* of the pupils to maintain focus on the near object.

Lesions of the optic nerve can impair the pupillary light reflex. With a relative afferent pupillary defect (*Marcus Gunn* pupil) the affected eye shows only a minimal direct response, but a normal consensual response. When the light moves from the normal to the affected eye there is a paradoxical dilation. This is a common finding in multiple sclerosis patients with optic nerve involvement. Syphilis can destroy the light reflex without impairing convergence and accommodation, the *Argyll Robertson pupil.*

In *Adie's tonic pupil*, patients may suddenly realize that one pupil is larger than the other. This condition is due to dysfunction of the parasympathetic nerves responsible for pupillary constriction. The paralysis of the iris muscle is progressive, occurring as the nerve fibers degenerate.[6] The affected pupil is moderately dilated and shows little or no response to light. However, with prolonged accommodation the pupil does constrict, even becoming smaller than the other. The pupillary abnormalities are often accompanied by absent muscle stretch reflexes—*Adie's syndrome.* This is more common in women. The condition is unrelated to trauma or drug ingestion.

Examination of the oculomotor nerves requires careful observation of the head, eyes, and eyelids. The pupil's response to light and accommodation is measured to assess the sympathetic and parasympathetic innervation. Eye movements are examined for signs of individual muscle weakness and conjugate gaze dysfunction. The examiner elicits both smooth pursuit movements and *saccades*—rapid conjugate eye movements that redirect gaze from one target to another. Simple testing of saccades is done by having the patient quickly look in different directions on command. Voluntary saccades are generated in the cortex and are contralateral; that is, saccades to the right require activation of the left hemisphere's *eye fields.* Smooth pursuit is tested by having the patient follow a slowly moving target such as the examiner's finger.

5.5 Trigeminal Nerve (CN V)

CN V is a mixed function nerve. It carries sensory information from the face and the meninges. It also has a motor component supplying the tensor tympani (a middle ear muscle that dampens sound), the tensor veli palatini (active during swallowing), and the jaw's muscles of mastication. As its name suggests the trigeminal nerve is divided into three branches— ophthalmic, maxillary, and mandibular.

There are many causes of CN V lesions. Tumors, arteriovenous malformations, vascular disease, and syringomyelia in the pons, medulla, and upper cervical spinal cord can affect the trigeminal sensory nucleus. Lesions at the lower end of the medulla and upper cervical cord affect the spinal tract of the trigeminal nerve, producing a typical "onion skin" distribution of sensory disturbance that widens progressively from the nose to the ear. Damage to the trigeminal motor nucleus in the brainstem weakens jaw movements.

Trigeminal neuralgia (*tic douloureux*) is characterized by brief, paroxysmal attacks of excruciating pain within the distribution of one or more divisions of the trigeminal nerve. The pain is lancinating, stabbing, burning, or shocklike. Triggers include cold wind on the face, touching or washing the face, applying make-up, shaving, talking, swallowing, and chewing. In many patients the pain is triggered from a specific zone. Sometimes, trigeminal neuralgia is associated with an underlying condition such as multiple sclerosis, a vascular malformation, or tumor. This is especially true in younger patients. However, everyone with trigeminal neuralgia should undergo neuroimaging.

There are several effective treatments for this painful condition. Tricyclic antidepressants, the antispasticity agent baclofen, and the anticonvulsants carbamazepine, oxcarbazepine, and others are useful for many patients. Radiofrequency thermocoagulation of the trigeminal sensory ganglion and nerve transection are necessary in patients with refractory pain, but with a risk of sensory loss. Often, a blood vessel is compressing the nerve where it enters the brainstem; surgical decompression is therapeutic.

Trigeminal sensory neuropathy is a painful condition with either unilateral or bilateral sensory loss. It may be associated with connective tissue diseases such as lupus or Sjögren's syndrome.[7] *Herpes zoster ophthalmicus* affects the ophthalmic division of CN V and is one of the most common causes of postherpetic neuralgia in the elderly. The pain can be so unrelenting and severe that it leads to suicide.[8] *Atypical facial pain* is a label covering several conditions characterized by facial pain, but not otherwise classifiable. The pain is more likely to be constant and dull rather than paroxysmal and shocklike. There may be prominent psychological factors, but these patients need a thorough evaluation to exclude structural causes.[9]

The examiner tests trigeminal sensory function by assessing sensation in the distribution of all three divisions of the nerve. The trigeminal sensory fields overlap the midline. Therefore, with hemifacial sensory loss there should not be an abrupt change at the midline. Nonorganic hemifacial loss often "splits" the midline precisely. Testing vibration sense over the forehead can confirm suspicions of a nonorganic complaint. Since vibration spreads throughout the bone, patients can feel vibration on the unaffected side when the tuning fork is placed over the "numb" side of the face. Patient reports to the contrary are physiologically implausible.

Jaw muscle bulk and strength is evaluated to assess trigeminal motor function. The corneal reflex measures trigeminal sensory function and CN VII motor function. Lightly touching the *cornea* with cotton elicits this reflex. The *jaw jerk* is mediated by trigeminal sensory and motor fibers in the mandibular division. The examiner taps the closed and relaxed jaw. An exaggerated jaw jerk indicates supranuclear dysfunction.

5.6 Facial Nerve (CN VII)

This is a predominantly motor nerve with a small sensory component carrying information from the external ear. The *chorda tympani*, which carries taste sensation from the anterior two-thirds of the tongue to the *nucleus solitarius* in the brainstem, runs with the facial nerve.

Facial weakness due to lesions above the facial nucleus (*supranuclear*) involves movements of the lower face much more than the upper face. There may be complete sparing of the muscles that elevate the eyebrows. This pattern is termed *central weakness* and is explained by bilateral innervation of the upper facial and eyelid muscles. Facial expressions of emotion may be spared as well. This is an upper motor neuron lesion.

In nuclear or infranuclear lesions—lower motor neuron—all muscles supplied by the nerve are affected. The weakness affects the upper and the lower facial muscles, usually equally. Lesions within the pons itself usually impair other nearby cranial nerves and descending motor or ascending sensory pathways.

Within the posterior fossa, CN VII lies close to CN VIII. Both may be affected by an acoustic nerve tumor or other cerebellopontine angle masses such as meningioma, cholesteatoma, chordoma, and glomus jugulare tumors. Within the temporal bone the facial nerve is vulnerable to skull fracture and middle ear or mastoid infections. Outside the skull CN VII is susceptible to parotid gland masses. Facial muscle weakness is common in myasthenia gravis and some myopathies. There are dozens of other causes.[10]

Bell's palsy is an acute-onset facial paralysis of unknown cause, though herpes simplex virus infection is a likely explanation. This diagnosis should be made only after other identifiable causes (such as diabetic or traumatic seventh nerve palsies) are excluded. The onset is sudden, with weakness ranging from mild to severe. Patients usually awaken and notice the weakness. There may be pain or numbness in or near the ear or around the angle of the jaw. The upper and lower facial muscles are usually affected equally. The eyebrow droops and wrinkles in the forehead are smoothed. Frowning, raising the eyebrow, and eye closure are difficult or impossible. When the patient attempts to close the eye the globe rolls upwards and slightly inwards—*Bell's phenomenon*. The patient is unable to purse the lips or whistle because of cheek muscle weakness. The cheek blows out in expiration. Food tends to accumulate between the gum and the cheek. When the lesion is at or above the level of the junction of the chorda tympani there will be ipsilateral loss of taste sensation from the anterior two-thirds of the tongue.

Most patients recover completely, although this often takes many months. Aberrant regrowth of facial nerve fibers during recovery can cause abnormal muscle contractions (*synkinesis*) or so-called "crocodile tears," tearing while salivating. Treatment with corticosteroids and the antiviral agent acyclovir probably improves recovery.[11] Other treatment is supportive, especially measures to prevent drying of the eye.

CN VII is tested by examining facial muscles—elevating the eyebrows, closing the eyelids forcefully, smiling, and puffing out the cheeks. Typically, facial nerve abnormalities are apparent during the history taking and only need to be confirmed on examination. Taste sensation is measured by applying solutions of sweet, sour, salty, or bitter substances to the tongue.

5.7 Vestibulocochlear Nerve (CN VIII)

CN VIII contains two sets of fibers, those supplying the cochlea (the organ of hearing), and those supplying the vestibular apparatus (the balance mechanism). These are known as the cochlear and vestibular nerves respectively. The nerve receptors are contained within specialized regions of the *membranous labyrinth*, a fluid-filled set of structures deep within the temporal bone.

Neurologists can differentiate deafness due to middle ear disease from deafness due to involvement of the nerve itself. Two bedside tests are used. In Weber's test a vibrating 512 Hz tuning fork is placed on the patient's forehead at the midline and the patient is asked if the sound is heard in the midline or localized to one ear. In middle ear—*conductive*—disease it is heard best in the affected ear but in nerve—*sensorineural*—disease it is heard best in the normal ear.

In Rinne's test the vibrating tuning fork is applied to the mastoid process and then held near the ear. Normally, the sound is louder when transmitted through the air. With conductive loss the sound may be louder when held on the bone. A variant of the test is to keep the tuning fork on the mastoid until the patient does not hear it and then move it next to the ear. If the patient hears the sound again, air is better than bone *conduction*—a normal response.

Three semicircular canals, the utricle, and the saccule comprise each inner ear's vestibular system. The semicircular canals are arranged approximately at right angles to each other. Head movements produce neural discharges that are proportional to the velocity of movement. When both vestibular systems are not functioning normally the patient experiences vertigo—a false sense of movement. Patients with vertigo have *nystagmus*, abnormal eye movements. The vertigo may be described as the room spinning or that the body itself is either rotating or falling. Patients, however, usually report dizziness, a vague term that the examiner must clarify.

Benign positional vertigo and *viral vestibular neuronitis* are common forms of vestibular dysfunction. Posttraumatic vertigo is seen in patients following minor head trauma or cervical whiplash injuries. Typically, the patient reports a sense of rotation triggered by positional changes—from lying to sitting, sitting to standing, turning over in bed, or rapid head movements. Most have nystagmus when placed in the position that induces their symptoms. Quantitative vestibular function tests define the disturbance more precisely.[12]

Vestibular examination also includes assessment of gait and balance. Bilateral vestibular dysfunction will impair the ability to stand while eyes are closed, the basis of the *Romberg* sign. Normal balance and stance depends on visual, spinal proprioceptive, and vestibular input. At least two of these three systems must be working. In the Romberg test, the patient stands with feet together and then closes his eyes. That eliminates the visual input. If either the vestibular or proprioceptive input is inadequate the patient will lose balance and fall. Clinical examination and history should be adequate to determine whether the deficit is vestibular or proprioceptive.

Hearing and balance problems are quite common. Detailed history and accurate description of the symptoms are critical for diagnosis. Many medications are toxic to the vestibular or auditory structures. Family history is also important because many inherited conditions cause vestibular and auditory dysfunction.

5.8 Glossopharyngeal Nerve (CN IX)

CN IX is a mixed nerve. It carries autonomic fibers that supply the parotid gland, motor input to the stylopharyngeal muscle, taste and general sensory fibers from the posterior third of the tongue, and sensory input from the ear drum and part of the external ear. It is extremely unusual for CN IX to be affected in isolation. Its proximity to CN X, XI, and XII as they run through the jugular foramen means that it is likely to be affected along with one or more of those nerves when there is a lesion in this area.

There is a rare condition known as *glossopharyngeal neuralgia*, similar to trigeminal neuralgia. However, the pain is located in the back of the tongue, throat, side of the neck, or ear. Triggers include swallowing, talking, coughing, and sneezing. The medications useful for trigeminal neuralgia are also helpful for this condition.

Evaluation of CN IX in isolation is difficult because other cranial nerves share many of its functions. For example, the stylopharyngeal muscle elevates the palate along with CN X-innervated muscles. However, sensation in the posterior pharynx and over the posterior third of the tongue can be tested, and dysfunction there localizes to CN IX.

5.9 Vagus Nerve (CN X)

The vagus nerve carries motor fibers to muscles of the pharynx, tongue, larynx, and vocal chords. There is a small sensory supply from around the ear and a portion of the throat. Its autonomic component supplies thoracic and abdominal organs. As with the glossopharyngeal nerve isolated lesions of the vagus nerve are exceptionally rare, although damage to the recurrent laryngeal branch of the vagus nerve is often seen in otolaryngology practice.

Unilateral CN X damage can be identified. The palate will not elevate normally ipsilateral to the lesion. If branches to the larynx are affected the vocal cord will be paralyzed. This can cause hoarseness. There are many tests of vagal autonomic function.[13]

5.10 Spinal Accessory Nerve (CN XI)[14]

This cranial nerve arises partially within the medulla—the cranial or accessory portion—and partially from the upper cervical cord—the spinal portion. The two unite to form an individual nerve trunk. After it exits the skull through the jugular foramen CN XI runs with CN X for a short distance. The cranial portion joins with CN X to form the laryngeal nerve to the larynx. The spinal portion of CN XI passes beneath the sternocleidomastoid muscle, which it innervates, and then crosses the posterior triangle of the neck to supply the trapezius muscle. (Lower portions of the trapezius also have additional cervical nerve root innervation). Long considered a pure motor nerve, there is evidence that CN XI also carries sensory fibers.[15]

The most common area for isolated CN XI nerve injury is the posterior triangle of the neck. Lymph node biopsy and other surgical procedures cause the damage. This portion of the nerve is tested by evaluating the strength of the sternocleidomastoid and trapezius muscles. A unilateral CN XI lesion can weaken the sternocleidomastoid muscle, interfering with head rotation to the opposite side. When the portion of CN XI innervating the trapezius muscle is affected that muscle becomes wasted and the normal curve of the shoulder is affected. The shoulder is lower on the affected side and the scapula rotates downwards and outwards. There may be mild scapula winging. Functionally, the cranial portion of XI is part of CN X and cannot be tested in isolation.

The sternocleidomastoid muscle is unusual in that its cortical supply probably originates mostly in the ipsilateral hemisphere.[16] Thus, a right hemisphere stroke can produce a left hemiparesis plus weakness of the right sternocleidomastoid; the head may be rotated to the right with the left ear tilted down towards the left shoulder, reflecting the unopposed contraction of the normal left sternocleidomastoid.

5.11 Hypoglossal Nerve (CN XII)

This is a pure motor nerve that supplies nearly all the tongue muscles. Damage to CN XII or the nucleus of CN XII in the medulla produces ipsilateral weakness of the tongue with muscle wasting. The tongue deviates towards the paralyzed side. If there is damage above the level of the nucleus, *supranuclear*, the tongue deviates contralateral to the lesion site but there will not be atrophy. Bilateral nerve damage produces bilateral tongue atrophy and interferes with articulation.

CN XII is assessed by asking the patient to protrude the tongue. Prominent tongue fasciculations can indicate motor nerve disease with bulbar involvement, an important clinical finding in amyotrophic lateral sclerosis (see §17.3A). Abnormal involuntary tongue movements occur in *tardive dyskinesia* (see §21.2A) and other movement disorders. Forced tongue deviation can occur during an epileptic seizure.

Endnotes

1. Doty RL. "Cranial nerve I: Olfactory nerve." In: Goetz CG, ed. *Textbook of Clinical Neurology*, 2nd ed. Philadelphia: Saunders; 2003:99-110.

2. *Id.* at 104.

3. Doty RL. *The Smell Identification Test™ Administration Manual*, 3rd ed. Haddon Heights, New Jersey: Sensonics; 1995.

4. Liu GT, Newman NJ. "Cranial nerve II and afferent visual pathways." In: Goetz CG, *supra* note 1, at 111-131.

5. *Id.* at 129.

6. Goodwin J. "Cranial nerves III, IV, and VI: The oculomotor system." In: Goetz CG, *supra* note 1, at 133-164.

7. Olney RK. "AAEM Minimonograph #28: Neuropathies in connective tissue disease." *Muscle Nerve* 1992;15:531-542.

8. Waldman SD. *Atlas of Common Pain Syndromes*. Philadelphia: Saunders; 2002.

9. *Id*. at 36-38.

10. Brackmann DE, Fetterman BL. "Cranial nerve VII: Facial nerve." In: Goetz CG, *supra* note 1, at 181-194.

11. Adour KK, Ruboyianes JM, et al. "Bell's palsy treatment with acyclovir and prednisone compared with prednisone alone: A double-blind, randomized, controlled trial." *Ann Otol Rhinol Laryngol* 1996;105:371-378.

12. Fife TD, Tusa RJ, et al. "Assessment: Vestibular testing techniques in adults and children. Report of the Therapeutics and Technology Assessment Subcommittee of the American Academy of Neurology." *Neurology* 2000; 55:1431-1441.

13. Ravits JM. "AAEM Minimonograph #48: Autonomic nervous system testing." *Muscle Nerve* 1999;20:919-937.

14. Louis ED. "Cranial nerves XI (spinal accessory) and XII (hypoglossal)." In: Goetz CG, *supra* note 1, at 223-233.

15. Bremmer-Smith AT, Unwin AJ, Williams WW. "Sensory pathways in the spinal accessory nerve." J *Bone Joint Surg* 1999;81:226-228.

16. Louis ED, *supra* note 14, at 232.

Additional Reading

Brazis PW, Masdeu JC, Biller H. *Localization in Clinical Neurology*, 2nd ed. Boston: Little, Brown; 1990.

Wilson-Pauwels L, Akeeson EJ, Stewart PA. *Cranial Nerves: Anatomy and Clinical Comments*. Hamilton, Ontario: B.C. Decker; 1998.

Chapter 6

Brain and Higher Cortical Function

6.1 Basic Organization of the Brain

All of our behavior, personality, and interactions with the world at large depend upon the brain. Our memories, hopes, passions, and drives depend upon roughly three pounds of tissue mostly composed of water and fat. The human brain has evolved over eons to sense the world around us, process information, store and recall memories, and produce action. From an evolutionary perspective the brain has three main divisions:[1]

- Protoreptilian—basal ganglia and brainstem
- Paleomammalian—limbic cortex and associated structures
- Neomammalian—neocortex and certain thalamic nuclei

These three systems serve different functions but interact with each other.

A more traditional approach to understanding the brain is to divide it into three major components: brainstem, *diencephalon*, and cerebral hemispheres (*telencephalon*). These three areas are bound together functionally and structurally. The brainstem lies between the diencephalon and the spinal cord. Moving upwards the three parts of the brainstem are the medulla, pons, and midbrain. The cerebellum is tightly interconnected with the brainstem. Most of the cranial nerves arise in the brainstem (Figure 6.1).

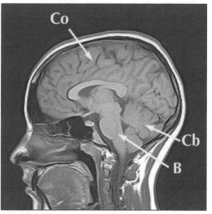

Courtesy of Dr. Roman Klufas.

Figure 6.1 *MRI: Normal Brain. Sagittal image showing cerebral cortex (Co), cerebellum (Cb), brainstem (B).*

The diencephalon lies just above the midbrain. It consists of epithalamus, thalamus, hypothalamus, and subthalamus. With the exception of the pineal gland in the epithalamus these are all paired structures. The thalamus is divided into several groups of cells—*nuclei*—that receive sensory input for processing and transmission to the cortex. Only olfactory input travels to the cortex without passing through the thalamus. Although most of its output is to the cortex the thalamus also plays a role in movement through connections with the extrapyramidal system. The thalamus contains part of the *reticular activating system*, responsible for cortical activation. Thalamic damage can produce contralateral sensory deficits, contralateral spontaneous pain, mild weakness, or abnormal movements.

The hypothalamus is the key brain structure responsible for regulation of autonomic function. It has extensive interconnections with other areas of the brain. It also contains receptors that are sensitive to the internal environment. The hypothalamus regulates body temperature, food intake, and water metabolism, mostly by acting on the pituitary gland. The hypothalamus regulates the manifestations of what is called the "fight or flight" reaction and is involved in emotional behavior through its limbic system connections.

The limbic system is composed of evolutionarily older areas of cortex—hippocampus and cingulate gyrus—and several other structures including the amygdala and mamillary bodies. The limbic system is involved with instinctual behavior, emotional responses, and memory.

The paired cerebral hemispheres make up the telencephalon. The outermost layer of the cerebrum is the cortex. It contains large numbers of nerve cell bodies and is often called the gray matter. Beneath the cortex are the myelinated axons that transmit messages throughout the cortex and to other areas of the brain. The mass of fibers is known as white matter. Deeper in the hemispheres are collections of nerve cells known as the basal ganglia. These are major components of the extrapyramidal system.

The surface of the cortex is folded into convolutions known as gyri. These are separated from each other by spaces known as *sulci*. Each cerebral hemisphere is divided conceptually into four sections, or lobes (Figure 6.2). The occipital lobe is located posteriorly. It contains the primary visual cortex that receives information from the contralateral half of the visual field. That is, input from the right visual field of both eyes goes to the left occipital lobe. The occipital lobe also contains association cortex for more complex processing of visual information.

The parietal lobe extends posteriorly from the large central sulcus. It contains primary somatosensory cortex for processing sensory input from the other side of the body. Much of the inferior parietal lobule, usually the left, is involved in language comprehension. Parietal cortex, particularly the right, is also involved in visuospatial functioning.

The temporal lobes have important roles in learning and memory, and contain much of the limbic cortex. Portions of the temporal lobe also contain primary auditory cortex, the processing region for perception and interpretation of sound.

The frontal lobes are the largest of the four regions. Primary motor cortex is located in the precentral gyrus, immediately in front of the central sulcus. Nearby *premotor cortex* is also involved in movement. The language dominant hemisphere, usually the left, also contains Broca's area. This is involved in production of language. The *prefrontal cortex* is the largest part of the frontal lobe. This region is much more developed in primates than other animals and is particularly large in *Homo sapiens.*

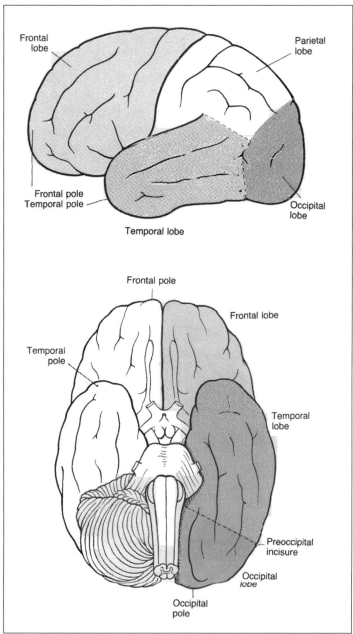

Source: Duus P. Topical Diagnosis in Neurology, 2nd rev. ed. New York: Thieme; 1989:249. Reprinted by permission.

Figure 6.2 Cerebral Lobes. Lateral view of left hemisphere, top, inferior view of brain, below.

Roughly one-third of the entire human brain is prefrontal cortex. Historically, this was known as a silent area of the brain because damage often did not produce any obvious impairment. However, careful analysis of patients with prefrontal damage revealed the importance of this area.

Prefrontal cortex is highly interconnected with other areas, consistent with an integrative role. Prefrontal cortex is responsible for insight, motivation, judgment, planning, and abstraction. These aspects of frontal lobe activity are known as *executive functions*. There is also executive function control over complex cognitive activities served by other regions of the brain. Normal executive functioning requires intact circuits connecting the prefrontal cortex to subcortical areas so it is best to think of this as a *frontal system* and not merely a frontal lobe function.

6.2 Evaluation of Cortical Function

Behavioral or cognitive neurology is the subspecialty of neurology that deals with brain-behavior relationships and higher cortical function. Traditionally, behavioral neurologists have been interested in language, memory, gestural behavior, visuospatial function, and related abilities. More recently, there has been interest in behavioral aspects of epilepsy and the neurologic basis of depression and other "psychiatric" symptoms. Advances in imaging techniques have been a boon to this field. It is now much easier to correlate anatomic disease with clinical symptoms without waiting for autopsy.

The cognitive evaluation performed by behavioral neurologists is known as the *mental status examination*. Some cognitive testing should be part of any patient's evaluation, not just those seeing a neurologist. Dementia, drug intoxication—whether iatrogenic, illicit, or inadvertent—and other causes of cognitive dysfunction are common in general medical practice. Many clinicians will use the mini-mental state examination[2] or similar instruments. However, there are false positive results in depressed patients and false negative results in mildly impaired patients. Furthermore, these are only screening tools and may not be sensitive to particular domains of cognitive function.

Cognitive evaluation begins during the history with observation. The neurologist can obtain a great deal of information about level of consciousness, attention and concentration, comprehension and language output, affect, and general intellectual function simply by watching the patient and engaging in simple conversation. Often, more extensive evaluation is necessary. It is important to use an organized and hierarchical approach.

The examiner first determines level of consciousness, attention, and orientation. Consciousness is described along a spectrum from alert to comatose. *Obtundation* indicates reduced alertness and diminished interaction with the environment. *Stupor* is a state of unresponsiveness from which a patient can be aroused temporarily by vigorous stimulation. *Coma* is a state of unarousable unresponsiveness. Attention is assessed once it is clear that the patient is alert. An *acute confusional state* is characterized by impaired attention and fluctuating alertness—ranging from delirium with agitation to lethargy.

Significant language disturbances are usually obvious early during the history-taking and will require detailed evaluation. This includes assessment of verbal fluency, content of spontaneous output, the ability to name objects presented to the patient, repetition, comprehension, reading, and writing. Acquired language disorders are known as *aphasias*.

Neurologists usually test memory in three parts: digit span for immediate memory, ability to learn and recall three or four words after five or ten minutes for recent memory, and inquiries into general knowledge or personal history for remote memory. There will usually be evaluation of skilled gestural behavior, symbolic recognition, constructional and visuospatial ability, frontal systems motor tasks, and abstraction. Mental status testing can take as little as a few minutes or as long as several hours.

6.3 Coma and Brain Death
A. Coma
Normal alertness and awareness depend upon the cerebral hemispheres and the *ascending reticular activating system* (ARAS). The latter is a network of structures in the brainstem (especially the midbrain) and diencephalon that sends activating impulses to the cortex. Coma can occur with dysfunction in the ARAS or with *bilateral* disturbances of the hemispheres. A unilateral cerebral hemisphere lesion can produce coma only if there is mass effect secondarily compromising the other hemisphere or the reticular structures. Comatose patients do not have a sleep-wake cycle. Their eyes are closed and they do not have any purposeful movements. There are five types of problems causing unresponsiveness:[3]

- Unilateral hemisphere mass lesions
- Bilateral hemisphere mass lesions
- Posterior fossa mass lesions
- Diffuse disturbances of brain function
- Psychiatric unresponsiveness mimicking coma

The neurologist must determine if the unresponsiveness is, in fact, coma. The "locked-in" syndrome caused by pontine lesions can resemble coma. Motor output from the cortex is interrupted; patients have quadriplegia, facial paralysis, and paralysis of horizontal eye movements. However, they are conscious and can communicate through vertical eye movements. Neuromuscular paralysis can produce similar motor findings.

Psychogenic unresponsiveness can be difficult to diagnose. Unlike other psychogenic conditions the physician cannot take a history from the patient or perform mental status testing—essential steps in identifying a psychiatric illness severe enough to explain the symptoms. Conversion reactions and catatonia are likely diagnoses but other conditions can cause psychogenic unresponsiveness. Malingering is also a consideration. Unresponsiveness can be seen in conjunction with psychogenic seizures.

The diagnosis is based on a demonstration that the patient's unresponsiveness is not physiological. This means behaviors inconsistent with true coma such as resisting eye opening, pushing the examiner away, turning away from the examiner, or avoiding injury by having one's raised arm drop to the side instead of onto the face (the so-called drop test). Identification of normal physiologic function in the brainstem and hemispheres is even more important and definitive in diagnosing psychogenic unresponsiveness. For example, the eye movements elicited by *oculocephalic* (head turning) and *oculovestibular* (cold water irrigation of the ear canal) stimulation will be those of an awake person. Also, the EEG will reveal wakefulness.

A detailed neurological examination is performed once the patient is medically stable to determine whether coma is due to brainstem or cerebral hemisphere dysfunction.[4] Pupillary responses, ocular movements, and the respiratory pattern offer localizing clues. The general medical examination often reveals signs indicating the cause of coma. CT or MRI will reveal many structural causes such as tumor and bleeding. However, these may coexist with other conditions that are not apparent with imaging. The differential diagnosis of coma is extensive. It includes: infections, inflammatory diseases, nutritional deficiencies, seizures, thermal injuries, toximetabolic derangements, and trauma.

Coma does not persist indefinitely. If the brainstem is intact patients may survive and enter into a *persistent vegetative state* (PVS). There are as many as 25,000 adults and 10,000 children in the United States with this syndrome.[5] This is a state of unresponsiveness but with alternating periods of sleep and wakefulness. The eyes may be open, and there may be roving eye movements—sometimes mistaken for conscious tracking. The patients are awake but unaware of their environment. Recovery of consciousness is unlikely after twelve months of posttraumatic PVS and rare after three months of nontraumatic (mainly anoxic) PVS; the few who do recover are almost always severely disabled.[6]

PVS should not be confused with a *minimally conscious state*,[7] a condition with some demonstrable conscious response to the surroundings. Courts will usually allow withdrawal of life support in the former but not the latter.[8] It may be difficult to distinguish between the two, leading to controversy.[9]

B. Brain death

Brain death is the irreversible loss of consciousness and brainstem function. The concept of brain death being the death of a person is accepted throughout the world.[10] However, criteria for brain death vary considerably. The diagnosis usually requires:

- A lack of observable function from any brain tissue
- Absent brainstem reflexes—corneal, oculovestibular, pupillary
- Apnea testing—no respiratory movements in response to elevated carbon dioxide levels
- Exclusion of reversible or confounding conditions such as hypothermia, neuromuscular blockade, or sedative overdoses
- Identification of a cause for the destruction of brain tissue
- Repeat examination confirming the lack of function

In neonates and young infants two isoelectric (flatline) EEG studies are also needed for the diagnosis of brain death. In older children and adults confirmatory testing to demonstrate a lack of cerebral blood flow (angiography, transcranial Doppler flow studies) can substitute for a repeat examination.[11]

Beresford[12] identifies three types of errors in determining brain death:

- Judgmental—not accounting for improbable or confounding causes
- Normative—ignoring or rejecting relevant criteria
- Technical—mistakes performing or interpreting the appropriate examinations and tests

6.4 Language Disorders—Aphasias

Language refers to symbolic verbal communication. It should not be necessary to emphasize the critical role language plays in our lives. Many different neuroanatomic syndromes of abnormal language are recognized. Though linguistically more precise, the word "dysphasia" has not gained widespread usage. Aphasia should not be confused with *dysarthria*. The latter is a motor disorder affecting articulation, not language. Aphasia and dysarthria can occur together but need not.

The aphasias are acquired disorders of language. Aphasia is almost always due to left hemisphere damage in the roughly 90 percent of the population that is right-handed. Interestingly, half or more of left-handers also have a language-dominant left hemisphere. Stroke is far and away the most common cause. Aphasias are characterized on the basis of deficits in different language components.

The classic syndromes are due to lesions in frontal, parietal, or temporal cortex around the left Sylvian fissure. However, aphasia may occur with thalamic[13] and subcortical[14] lesions. *Global aphasia* refers to serious impairment of all language abilities and is usually caused by destruction of large parts of the left hemisphere.

A. Broca's aphasia

This is also known as motor, anterior, or expressive aphasia. It is characterized by sparse, effortful, dysarthric, and agrammatic speech. Sentences are short and have a telegraphic style, with preservation of nouns and verbs but loss of short modifiers and connectors. Some patients are mute at onset. Writing is impaired. Naming and repetition are rarely normal but may be better preserved than spontaneous verbal output. The lesion producing Broca's aphasia involves the posterior inferior frontal gyrus and nearby areas of frontal cortex. There is usually a contralateral hemiparesis.

A classic neuroanatomic map refers to a Broca's area in the posterior inferior frontal gyrus. However, lesions restricted to that zone probably do not produce this aphasia syndrome.[15] Instead, they cause a syndrome of mutism that usually improves to dysarthria. This syndrome has been given many names including aphemia, pure motor aphasia, speech apraxia, and cortical dysarthria.

B. Wernicke's aphasia

This disturbance can be viewed as the inverse of Broca's. Other names are sensory, receptive, and posterior aphasia. The key defect is in language comprehension due to a lesion in the posterior superior temporal gyrus. Speech is well articulated, effortless, and fluent. Verbal output is often excessive (*logorrhea*). There are fewer semantically significant words and many *paraphasic* errors (substitution of a wrong word). Sometimes, the verbal output can be virtually unintelligible. Naming and repetition are severely impaired. Wernicke's aphasia may be associated with a hemianopsia but often occurs without paralysis. Some patients are deemed demented or psychotic because of their bizarre language output and placed in psychiatric wards.

C. Conduction aphasia

Another fluent aphasia is conduction aphasia. Unlike Wernicke's aphasia there is good comprehension and meaningful speech output. The striking abnormality is in repetition, out of proportion to any other language deficits. Particularly difficult for patients is repetition of phrases such as "no ifs, ands, or buts." One theory is that conduction aphasia is a *disconnection syndrome* caused by interruption of the *arcuate fasciculus*, the bundle of fibers connecting Broca's and Wernicke's areas.[16]

D. Transcortical aphasia

Transcortical aphasias are produced by lesions in the border zones surrounding the language centers. The striking feature in the transcortical aphasias is preservation of the ability to repeat. The border zones demarcate the boundaries of different cerebral vascular territories. Strokes within these regions are usually the result of diminished perfusion from cardiac arrest or reduced blood volume. There are motor, sensory, and mixed transcortical aphasias. The deficits parallel those in Broca's, Wernicke's, and global aphasia respectively, but with retained repetition.

E. Other syndromes

There is some naming and word-finding difficulty in all aphasias. Often, *anomia* is the residual deficit of an aphasia syndrome. However, a severe *anomic aphasia* can be produced by damage in the posterior inferior temporal lobe or in the *angular gyrus*. The latter is a major connection area between several areas of cortex. The *angular gyrus syndrome* includes fluent aphasia, alexia with agraphia (impaired reading and writing), and *Gerstmann's syndrome* (right-left disorientation, inability to identify fingers, calculation deficits, and poor writing). The wide range of deficits can lead to a mistaken diagnosis of dementia.

Pure word deafness is a rare syndrome characterized by inability to comprehend spoken language despite normal hearing. Nonverbal sounds can be identified and written words can be understood. The presumed cause of pure word deafness is a lesion deep in the temporal lobes disconnecting the primary auditory cortex from Wernicke's area. *Alexia* is an acquired deficit in comprehension of written language. There are several varieties.

6.5 Memory and Amnesias
A. Memory

There is no universally accepted, precise useful definition of "memory." Research psychologists and neurologists use different terminology, often creating confusion. Memory is the process by which the brain stores information and retrieves it at a later time. Implicit in this definition are four elements. First, there must be an input. Second, there must be some change in the brain to acquire the memory, a process often termed *registration*. Next, there are changes in the brain for purposes of information *retention* or *storage*. Finally, there is an output—*retrieval* or *recall*.

Memory begins with reception of some type of sensory input. This is stored for a few hundred milliseconds. Next, there is cognitive processing of the sensory memory to select the items destined for longer-term retention. This is the registration process. Neurologists test this by measuring digit span—the number of digits the patient can repeat either in forward or reverse order. Neurologists refer to this as *immediate* memory while psychologists term this short-term memory. Anatomically, immediate memory relies upon the integrity of the specific sensory modality area being assessed. Thus, there is not just one immediate memory center in the brain.

Retention is the next step in the memory process. Material from immediate memory is encoded and actively selected for transfer to long-term memory. This may occur within seconds of the registration process. Consolidation of memory involves categorization of the information. Neurologists usually divide this long-term memory into *recent* and *remote* memory. The former represents the ability to acquire new memory and is tested by asking the patient to remember three or four unrelated words and then recall them after five or ten minutes. Remote memory is assessed by asking about historical events or personally relevant information.

B. Amnesias

Amnesia is a clinical condition characterized by the inability to learn new material despite adequate immediate memory, normal or near-normal remote recall, and sufficient cognitive ability to cooperate with the evaluation. If there is defective immediate memory function—often the case in acute confusional states, anxiety, and other causes of inattention—further memory assessment is compromised. In such circumstances making an amnesia diagnosis is problematic. Amnesia most often occurs as part of more generalized syndromes, rather than as an isolated disorder. Memory disturbance is frequently the earliest sign of a dementing process.

Amnesic stroke occurs with bilateral medial temporal or posterior thalamic damage, usually due to bilateral posterior cerebral artery occlusion. Critical structures are the hippocampi, fornices, and mamillary bodies. Severe amnesias develop after bilateral temporal lobectomies performed for intractable epilepsy. Unilateral temporal lobectomy can produce amnesia for particular material—left temporal lobectomy impairs verbal memory, right temporal lobectomy impairs nonverbal memory.

Transient global amnesia is a dramatic syndrome of sudden-onset memory loss. Often, this is preceded by some type of emotionally significant event. The amnesia may be accompanied by mild confusion or disorientation, but the memory disturbance is clearly the outstanding feature.

There may be a retrograde amnesia of hours or longer for events prior to the onset of the syndrome. Patients typically engage in repetitive questioning and are usually brought to medical attention by friends or family. In the emergency room the patient might introduce himself each and every time the physician returns to the bedside. Attacks of transient global amnesia usually last for a few hours, occasionally longer. Causes of transient global amnesia include bilateral posterior cerebral artery blockage, temporal lobe seizures, migraine, and medication overdosage.

Korsakoff's syndrome is a syndrome of anterograde amnesia and disorientation, probably secondary to dorsomedial thalamic damage caused by thiamine deficiency. Some patients exhibit *confabulation*—supplying false answers and explanations to questions. Chronic alcoholism is the most frequent underlying disorder. However, this can occur in anyone with chronic inadequate nutrition. It may be caused iatrogenically when thiamine is not given to patients restricted to parenteral nutrition.

Memory disturbances can occur in the absence of any demonstrable brain disease or damage. These are sometimes termed *functional* amnesias. In *psychogenic* amnesia the patient claims an inability to recall personally relevant information—his or her own name, names of family members, place of origin, or job history. However, he or she is able to learn new information, thereby demonstrating the absence of true amnesia.

Some patients will function for long periods of time and then claim no memory for what has transpired. These *fugue* or *dissociative* states usually indicate a psychological disturbance. However, prolonged aimless wandering—*poriomania*—can occur in demented patients. Rarely, poriomania is a postictal automatism followed by retrograde amnesia.[17]

6.6 Apraxia and Agnosia

Apraxias are acquired disorders of the ability to perform skilled, previously learned movements, not due to defects in comprehension or sensorimotor function. The programming—*engrams*—for these gestures are stored in the dominant hemisphere's parietal lobe, usually the left. Damage to that region or its connecting fibers produces the various forms of apraxia.

Ideomotor apraxia refers to impairment in production of simple gestures. Patients may not be able to demonstrate how to comb their hair, swing a baseball bat, or salute. When a left hemisphere stroke damages the engram center, there can be a *sympathetic apraxia* of the left hand along with the expected right hemiparesis. Even though the primary sensorimotor cortex in the right hemisphere is intact, it cannot access the engrams in the left parietal lobe needed for the gestures.

Ideational apraxia is a disturbance in production of sequential acts. The individual steps might be intact but the sequencing is impaired. This form of apraxia usually reflects more diffuse cerebral damage. *Constructional apraxia* refers to impaired drawing. Damage to either parietal lobe causes this though with distinct differences. Right—non-dominant—parietal lesions cause disoriented, scattered, and fragmented drawings, often with extra details. Left parietal lesions lead to more coherent, better oriented drawings but with fewer details. Right parietal lesions may also cause *dressing apraxia*, impairment in the ability to dress. This can be bilateral or only involve the left side of the body.

Agnosias are syndromes of impaired recognition not due to generalized cognitive dysfunction, altered consciousness, or a primary sensory modality deficit. The patient can describe what is perceived but cannot identify or recognize its use. When presented to another sensory modality, the object's nature is readily appreciated. In *visual object agnosia* the patient sees the object, can describe its shape, color, and other attributes, but cannot identify it. There can be agnosia for faces (*prosopagnosia*), sounds (*auditory agnosia*), touch (*tactile agnosia* or *astereognosis*), and localization of objects (*spatial agnosia*).

Nondominant parietal lesions may cause left-sided *asomatognosia*—neglect or lack of recognition of the body's left side. This is usually associated with left spatial neglect, left-sided dressing apraxia, and *anosognosia*—denial of illness or deficit. In its most severe form, the patient might deny that there is anything wrong with the paralyzed left arm and leg. When those limbs are shown to the patient he might even state that they belong to someone else.

Endnotes

1. MacLean PD. *The Triune Brain in Evolution: Role in Paleocerebral Function*. New York: Plenum Publishing; 1990.

2. Folstein MF, Folstein SE, McHugh PR. "'Mini-Mental State.' A practical method for grading the cognitive state of patients for the clinician." *J Psych Research* 1975;12:189-198.

3. Wijdicks EFM. *Neurologic Catastrophes in the Emergency Department*. Boston: Butterworth-Heinemann; 2000.

4. Bleck TP. "Levels of consciousness and attention." In: Goetz CG, ed. *Textbook of Clinical Neurology*, 2nd ed. Philadelphia: Saunders; 2003:3-18.

5. *Id*. at 14.

6. Multi-Society Task Force on PVS. Medical aspects of the persistent vegetative state. *N Engl J Med* 1994;330:1499-1508; 1572-1579.

7. Giacino JT, Ashwal S, et al. "The minimally conscious state. Definition and diagnostic criteria. *Neurology* 2002;58:349-353.

8. Beresford HR. "Irreversible cognitive dysfunction: The legal context." *Continuum* 2003;9(4):101-120.

9. McNeil DG. "In feeding-tube case, many neurologists back courts." *N.Y. Times*, October 26, 2003,£1, at 20.

10. Wijdicks EFM. "Brain death worldwide." *Neurology* 2002;58:20-25.

11. Wijdicks EFM, *supra* note 3, at 11.

12. Beresford HR. "Brain death." *Neurol Clin* 1999;17(2):295-306.

13. Mohr JP, Watters WC, Duncan GW. "Thalamic hemorrhage and aphasia." *Brain Lang* 1975;2:3-17.

14. Naeser MA, Alexander MP, et al. "Aphasia with predominately subcortical lesion sites: description of three capsular/putaminal aphasia syndromes." *Arch Neurol* 1982;39:2-14.

15. Alexander MP, Naeser MA, Palumbo C. "Broca's area aphasias: aphasia after lesions including the frontal operculum." *Neurology* 1990;40:353-362.

16. Geschwind N. "Disconnection syndromes in animals and man, parts I and II." *Brain* 1965;88:237-294, 585-644.

17. Mayeux R, Alexander MP, et al. "Poriomania." *Neurology* 1979;29:1616-1619.

Additional Reading

Cummings JL, Mega MS. *Neuropsychiatry and Clinical Neuroscience.* New York: Oxford University Press; 2003.

Devinsky O, D'Esposito M. *Neurology of Cognitive and Behavioral Disorders.* New York: Oxford University Press; 2003.

Heilman KM, Valenstein E., eds. *Clinical Neuropsychology*, 4th ed. New York: Oxford University Press; 1993.

Mesulam M-M. *Principles of Behavioral and Cognitive Neurology*, 2nd ed. New York: Oxford University Press; 2000.

Plum F, Posner JB. *The Diagnosis of Stupor and Coma*, 3rd ed. Philadelphia: F.A. Davis; 1982.

Strub RL, Black FW. *The Mental Status Examination in Neurology*, 4th ed. Philadelphia: F.A. Davis; 1993.

Chapter 7

Chronic Pain, Somatization, and Symptom Magnification

7.1 Introduction

Pain is a complex, subjective experience that normally occurs in response to a noxious or potentially harmful stimulus. It is more than a mere physiological or sensory phenomenon. There are also important cognitive, emotional, and social components to pain. Sometimes, however, pain does not indicate tissue damage or injury.

Pain is an exceedingly common complaint, suggesting that physicians should be both comfortable and competent treating it. However, there is ample evidence that treatment is often inadequate.[1,2] One major factor is the subjective nature of the complaint—physicians must determine who is truly suffering and who is seeking medication to abuse. This is not a trivial problem. More people abuse prescription pain medications than cocaine, heroin, and hallucinogens combined.[3]

Neurologists have become increasingly active in pain evaluation and management despite a lack of formal training opportunities.[4] The American Academy of Neurology recognizes pain management as a neurological subspecialty, and the American Board of Psychiatry and Neurology now has a certification procedure for the subspecialty of pain medicine.[5] Furthermore, pain control for all inpatients is required by the Joint Commission on Accreditation of Healthcare Organizations.[6]

Neurologists often treat patients with painful conditions such as headache, neuralgia and neuropathy, and radiculopathy. Many manage patients with chronic neck or back pain, though if there is no neurologic cause for the pain it is arguable if this is appropriate or desirable.[7] Some neurologists evaluate pain complaints arising in medicolegal situations such as workers' compensation or personal injury.

Tissue injury triggers mechanical changes and inflammatory processes associated with release of a variety of chemicals including cytokines, histamine, kinins, and prostaglandins. Pain perception begins with activation of specialized pain receptors—*nociceptors*—located at the ends of lightly myelinated A-delta and unmyelinated C sensory fibers. (Nerve fibers are classified according to their diameters and conduction velocities, A fibers being the largest and fastest, C the smallest and slowest.) The A-delta fibers transmit initial pain, a well-localized, sharp sensation lasting as long as the painful stimulus. The C fibers are responsible for a delayed-onset more diffuse, steady, and persistent burning sensation.

The cell bodies of these first-order sensory fibers are located in the spinal dorsal root (for the limbs and trunk) or trigeminal sensory ganglia (for the face and most of the head). The nociceptive fibers connect to second-order sensory neurons in the spinal cord's dorsal gray horn or the brainstem's trigeminal sensory nuclei. These transmit to the contralateral thalamus. Finally, third-order thalamic neurons project to sensory and limbic cortex. Sensory cortex is responsible for localization and discrimination of pain whereas limbic cortex is involved in emotional, memory, and interpretive aspects of pain. The brain also regulates nociception via descending inhibitory circuits, notably from midbrain periaqueductal gray matter.

7.2 Pain Assessment
A. Fundamentals

The physician should perform a thorough and thoughtful evaluation that measures the extent of injury, the nature and severity of pain, the appropriateness of illness behavior, and the significance of any complicating psychosocial factors. This is necessary to identify the specific mechanism causing the pain and to select appropriate treatment. Physicians must be sensitive to variations in pain tolerance and expression due to individual and cultural factors. If the physician detects efforts to exaggerate symptoms treatment is more difficult and usually requires psychologic intervention. Even though pain is a subjective experience it should be possible to:[8]

- Assess the consistency of pain complaints
- Document inconsistencies in the history and examination
- Elicit nonanatomic findings suggestive of symptom magnification
- Identify and measure objective manifestations of disease or injury

All pain is not the same. Therefore, a very detailed pain history is crucial for accurate diagnosis. This should include clear and precise descriptions of the pain's onset and progression, location, quality and nature, severity, variability, and response to treatment. Any exacerbating or alleviating factors and associated symptoms are identified. Information about substance use and abuse, past pain problems, and psychological functioning are all essential parts of the pain history. Finally, the clinician must understand the impact of the pain on the patient's daily life.

The information from the pain history is integrated with the general medical and neurological history and examination to reach a diagnosis. Detailed sensory testing, laborious for both patient and examiner, and a thorough musculoskeletal assessment are especially important parts of the process. The latter might include mechanical tests for nerve root irritation and evaluation of posture, muscle spasm and tenderness, range of motion, and limb size.

B. Pain assessment tools

There are many pain measurement tools used to quantify pain and its impact. Single dimensional tools include the verbal rating scale, visual analog scale, and numeric rating scale. With the last, for example, patients report their pain on a 0 (no pain) to 10 (worst pain imaginable) scale. These tools are simple to use but have limitations. First, a simple pain intensity rating does not explain the broader impact of pain. Second, exaggeration is easy with these scales. Nevertheless, they do provide a useful starting point.

Pain drawings can be very helpful in identifying pain distributions suggestive of a nonanatomic origin, a common sign of dysfunctional illness behavior. A typical pain drawing will have front and rear views of the body with a list of symbols representing different types of pain and other sensations—such as stabbing, burning, and tingling. Using the appropriate symbols the patient indicates the pain's location on the diagram. Possible results include bizarre drawings with anatomically inexplicable pain distributions, unusual combinations of symptoms, drawing outside the borders, emphasis marks, and written commentary to indicate added severity. (See Figure 7.1). There is a scoring system available for pain drawings.[9]

There are also many multidimensional pain and impairment scales. The *McGill Pain Questionnaire* (MPQ)[10] is a well-known instrument that assesses sensory, emotional, and evaluative aspects of pain by having the patient select the best descriptions of pain from twenty sets of adjectives. It also includes a pain drawing, a 0 to 5 visual rating scale for pain intensity, and descriptors about the temporal aspects of pain. A short-form MPQ[11] is also available and widely used. It includes fifteen pain descriptors—eleven reflecting sensory or physical qualities, and four reflecting emotional or affective qualities. The patient rates each on a four-point intensity scale. Scoring determines if pain is expressed predominately with sensory or emotional adjectives, the latter suggesting a strong psychological component to the patient's pain.

There are several functional status inventories in use. The *Oswestry Low Back Pain Disability Questionnaire*[12] uses ten six-point scales to evaluate low-back pain and its impact on a variety of daily activities. The scores are added and expressed as a percentage of the maximum possible score. An overall rating is assigned as follows:

0-20%	Minimal disability
20-40%	Moderate disability

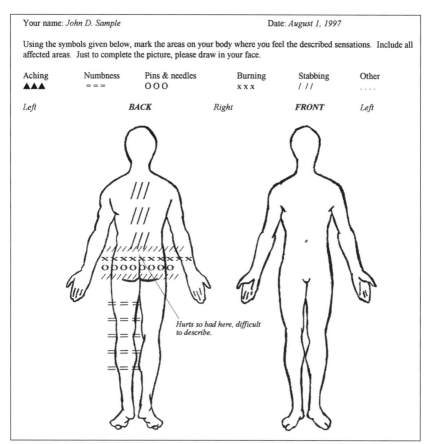

Your name: *John D. Sample*   Date: *August 1, 1997*

Using the symbols given below, mark the areas on your body where you feel the described sensations. Include all affected areas. Just to complete the picture, please draw in your face.

Aching	Numbness	Pins & needles	Burning	Stabbing	Other
▲▲▲	= = =	O O O	x x x	/ / /	. . . .

Left   **BACK**   *Right*   **FRONT**   *Left*

Hurts so bad here, difficult to describe.

Source: Brigham CR. The Comprehensive IME System: Essential Resources for an Efficient and Successful IME Practice. Falmouth, MA: SEAK, Inc; 2000:50. Reprinted by permission.

Figure 7.1 *Pain Drawing. This sample reveals several features suggestive of nonanatomic pain including drawing outside the borders, use of several different pain descriptors, and an "I particularly hurt here" written commentary.*

40-60%	Severe disability
60-80%	Extreme disability, crippled
80-100%	Bedridden or exaggerating

Another widely used index that measures the impact of back pain is the *Roland-Morris*,[13] a twenty-four item questionnaire.

The *Pain Disability Index*[14] allows the patient to rate his or her perceived disability on a 0 to 10 scale in seven different areas of activity:

- Family and home responsibilities
- Life-support activities
- Occupation
- Recreation
- Self-care
- Sexual activity
- Social activity

The perceived disability score is analyzed in light of objective impairments and the overall clinical evaluation to determine if it is disproportionate or inconsistent.

C. Impairment ratings for pain

Physicians may be called on to provide a permanent impairment rating for a patient with a painful condition. This can be a very difficult undertaking. According to the widely used AMA's *Guides to the Evaluation of Permanent Impairment* (hereinafter *Guides*) impairment ratings for most disease states are "based on objective findings,"[15] but when dealing with chronic pain there may be "no demonstrable active disease or unhealed injury."[16] Furthermore, the psychosocial factors that influence pain perception and the subjective nature of pain complaints are not easily integrated into the *Guides'* system.

Conventional disease impairment ratings in the *Guides* already take pain into account. According to chapter eighteen of the *Guides* the physician may give up to a 3 percent quantitative discretionary award for pain, but only if the burden of illness is not adequately accounted for by the conventional impairment rating. However, the *Guides* clearly limit the circumstances when this is appropriate. Most importantly, the pain must be *ratable*:[17]

- a painful, conventionally ratable condition with increased illness burden from pain, or
- a recognized condition without ratable objective findings such as most headaches, or

- a recognized pain syndrome that is part of a ratable disease that does not include pain in its impairment rating—phantom limb pain after amputation, for example.

Other painful conditions are considered *unratable*. Conditions that are controversial or ambiguous, (the best example is fibromyalgia),[18] cannot be rated quantitatively according to the *Guides*. One key point in identifying such syndromes is whether or not there is a widely accepted biological basis for the condition. Even if the pain is unratable the *Guides* recognizes that there may be serious limitations in daily activities from the pain. Chapter eighteen's methodology also includes a qualitative pain rating (the categories are mild, moderate, moderately severe, and severe). If there is a substantial added burden due to unratable pain the physician can perform a formal pain assessment and award a qualitative rating.

There are subsequently published modifications[19] to the pain impairment rating algorithm of the *Guides*. The revised "system is the most current and is the one physicians should use.[20] However, future editions of the *Guides* may include significant changes in the pain rating system.

7.3 Pain Classification

There are many ways to classify pain—by location, cause, duration, or treatment response. Unfortunately, there are limitations with each of these. Furthermore, the terminology used by many physicians when discussing pain—particularly chronic pain—can be confusing. A recent trend is to identify the presumed underlying mechanism that is causing the pain. Thus, clinicians speak of *chronic nociceptive* and *chronic neuropathic* pain, both discussed below. A third type of chronic pain—variously known as psychological, idiopathic, psychogenic, nonanatomic, or nonphysiologic—is discussed at length in §7.4.

Some clinicians label prolonged pain, whether nociceptive or neuropathic, as *persistent pain* and reserve the "chronic pain" label for those individuals whose pain reflects psychological rather than physical factors—*chronic pain syndrome* (see §7.4). However, this is not a common practice so it is always important to clarify what the physician means by chronic pain.

A. Acute and chronic pain

This is probably the most widespread way to classify pain. Acute pain is a temporary result of injury or disease. There is usually a readily identifiable cause. This kind of pain is typically *nociceptive*—due to appropriate activation of peripheral pain receptors by noxious or harmful stimuli. Acute nociceptive pain is protective. Nociceptive pain arising from the internal organs is dull, poorly localized, and often cramping. Nociceptive pain from the skin, musculoskeletal structures, and elsewhere is better localized.

Chronic pain persists even after the pain-producing injury or illness has resolved or for longer than the expected healing time. It is sometimes defined with arbitrary time limits, usually three or six months. Thus, chronic pain is regarded as pathologic, reflecting either nervous system dysfunction or nonphysical factors. Pain arising from a dysfunctional peripheral or central nervous system is termed *neuropathic*.

However, a serious limitation with the acute versus chronic pain scheme is the existence of chronic illnesses that produce ongoing tissue damage or inflammation. Thus, setting up an arbitrary time limit ignores persistent pain-producing diseases. It is important to recognize that nociceptive pain can be both acute and chronic. There is a long list of conditions that can activate pain receptors for longer than three or six months. Some clinicians will distinguish between chronic malignant pain—due to cancer—and chronic benign, or nonmalignant, pain. The latter category includes connective tissue diseases, arthritides and arthropathies, vasculitides, endometriosis and other gynecologic conditions, fibromyalgia, and many diseases of the viscera.

B. Chronic neuropathic pain

When the nervous system's pain mechanisms are injured or function abnormally *pathologic* pain may develop. Unlike "normal" or nociceptive pain, this pain is not protective. The pain is sustained after the inciting injury or illness resolves. It is usually called *neuropathic* pain. The dysfunction can involve either the peripheral or central nervous system, or both. Neuropathic pain occurs after direct injury to neural tissues or indirectly as a result of a non-neural injury that activates the pain system excessively. The result is persistent pain and altered sensory function.

Common causes of neuropathic pain include diabetic and other small-fiber neuropathies, trigeminal neuralgia, postherpetic neuralgia, and radiculopathy. Patients with neuropathic pain usually report constant burning, electric-like, or lancinating pains. Associated sensory symptoms include:

- Allodynia—pain elicited by normally non-painful stimuli; it can be mechanical or thermal, static or dynamic
- Dysesthesia—nonpainful but unpleasant or disturbing sensations, occurring either spontaneously or when evoked by stimulation
- Hyperalgesia—exaggerated pain response to a normally painful stimulus
- Hyperesthesia—increased sensitivity to any stimulus
- Hyperpathia—exaggerated, delayed, and prolonged response to painful stimulus, usually with aftersensation
- Paresthesia—abnormal intermittent painless but annoying sensations, especially tingling or "pins and needles."
- Summation—increasing levels of pain produced by repetitive painful input of constant intensity

There are several putative mechanisms responsible for neuropathic pain, involving both the peripheral and central nervous systems. *Peripheral sensitization* may occur following prolonged activation of nociceptors. The inflammatory chemicals released in response to injury produce changes in the first-order neurons. The activation threshold is lowered and the cells may fire spontaneously, not just in response to noxious stimulation. The latter is called *ectopic discharge*. This is also seen when direct injury to nerve fibers produces aberrant regrowth of axons.

Prolonged abnormal nociceptor activity due to either peripheral nerve injury or tissue damage triggers a second process known as *central sensitization*—"the pivotal physiologic phenomenon underlying the clinical symptoms of neuropathic central pain."[21] Excessive amounts of the neuropeptide substance P and excitatory neurotransmitters, especially glutamate, are released by the nociceptors at synapses in the dorsal horn of the spinal cord and brainstem trigeminal nuclei.[22] The second-order neurons respond with abnormal activation of their N-methyl-D-aspartate (NMDA) receptors, producing hypersensitive CNS neurons. As a result, both spinal cord dorsal root and brainstem trigeminal ganglion cells may generate ectopic discharges.

Another process that contributes to central sensitization is wind-up—persistent activation of C fibers leading to progressively increasing firing rates in second-order neurons. This wind-up phenomenon may explain why constant painful stimulation does not necessarily produce a constant degree of perceived pain. Instead, repetitive stimuli may produce pain only after several seconds. The pain may be explosive when it does occur. Wind-up probably accounts for hyperpathia and summation. However, wind-up is not synonymous with central sensitization. In the acute pain stage wind-up may have a protective role, enhancing pain transmission in order to warn of worsening tissue damage.[23]

Central sensitization affects two kinds of second-order neurons, pain-specific neurons that respond only to nociceptive input and wide-dynamic-range neurons that respond to both painful and nonpainful input. Involvement of the former leads to hyperalgesia, activation of the latter probably explains allodynia.[24] Second-order neurons receive sensory input from different cutaneous locations; sensitization can alter sensory processing of signals coming from outside the original painful zone, leading to a spread of neuropathic pain phenomena. Furthermore, substance P spreads in the dorsal horn and can activate additional second-order neurons remote from the initial receptive zone. This also causes perception of pain beyond the original area of tissue injury or outside of a single nerve or nerve root distribution. Physicians unaware of these neuropathic pain mechanisms might misinterpret such findings as nonanatomic.

Chronic neuropathic pain can also be classified as sympathetically mediated, non-sympathetically mediated, or central.[25] The latter includes post-stroke, spinal cord injury, and phantom limb pain—all believed secondary to altered CNS function. The presumed mechanism for sympathetically mediated pain (SMP) is *alpha-adrenoreceptor excitability*. This occurs with sensitization of wide-dynamic-range neurons that are also connected to cells of the sympathetic division of the autonomic nervous system. This type of pain is severe and burning. There are associated vasomotor and sudomotor changes. SMP can occur in *complex regional pain syndrome I* (formerly known as reflex sympathetic dystrophy), though probably only in a minority of cases.[26] SMP may complicate other painful conditions including neuralgias and neuropathies.[27]

Treatment of chronic neuropathic pain is difficult. Many nonanalgesics can be useful, particularly tricyclic antidepressants and anticonvulsants. The role of opioids is controversial though there is evidence that these are effective and can be used safely.[28]

7.4 Chronic Pain Syndrome (CPS): Nonorganic Pain

Chronic pain syndrome is a commonly used, though unofficial, diagnosis for patients with an array of behavioral problems and chronic pain complaints that occur either without any detectable physical cause or out of proportion to any underlying physical dysfunction. CPS is a complex, destructive condition with physical, functional, social, and psychological causes characterized by abnormal, dysfunctional, learned illness behavior with disability. Usually, this process develops and is reinforced by unconscious mechanisms. However, manifestations of CPS may be produced deliberately, as in *factitious disorder* or *malingering* (see §7.5A). The CPS label should not be used when there are nociceptive or neuropathic mechanisms causing pain unless there is also clear evidence of superimposed exaggeration.

Most CPS patients have additional physical complaints and preexisting psychiatric illness, especially depression, anxiety disorders, personality disorders, and substance abuse.[29] They are preoccupied with their pain, have enhanced pain perception, and exhibit exaggerated pain behaviors. The latter refers to observable verbal and nonverbal manifestations of pain such as complaining, moaning, sighing, grimacing, limping, and grabbing or rubbing the painful area. Pain perception and behaviors are disproportionate to any objective impairment or tissue damage. Often, inaccurate beliefs and fears about the pain and injuries contribute to the perceived disability. Litigation and compensation issues are common. One recent survey of neuropsychologists found probable malingering or exaggeration in 31 percent of chronic pain patients.[30]

Features of CPS can be summarized by the eight Ds:[31]

- Dependence—feelings of helplessness and passivity, demand excessive treatment, cede responsibilities to others
- Depression—unhappiness, despair, impaired coping skills, poor self-esteem

- Diagnostic dilemma—no definite diagnosis despite extensive evaluations
- Disuse—deconditioning due to inactivity, excessive immobilization
- Dramatization—communicate with highly emotional language, histrionic and exaggerated behavior
- Drugs—abuse or misuse of medications, and often alcohol
- Duration—symptoms persisting beyond six months or longer than expected for injury
- Dysfunction—increasing isolation and withdrawal

CPS is a behavioral syndrome affecting only some susceptible individuals. Treatment must address the abnormal illness behavior. Simply prescribing pain medication is ineffective.

7.5 Somatization

There is no single generally accepted definition for *somatization*. This is the process or mechanism—not a final diagnosis—that contributes to the magnification of pain and physical complaints in CPS patients. Somatization refers to conscious or unconscious production of physical symptoms in response to psychological distress. The patient attributes the somatic complaints to injury or illness, often quite vividly, and seeks treatment for them. However, the symptoms are not explained by underlying damage or disease, if any. The presentation typically includes "an inability to discuss nonsomatic issues . . . Another clue is the sense of immediacy in the recounting of the traumatic event, in that a minor remote event is discussed as though it occurred yesterday."[32]

Somatization is very common, accounting for up to 40 percent of all primary care visits, but it is not necessarily indicative of a specific psychiatric disorder nor does it exclude physical illness or injury.[33] Somatization can occur acutely in response to a situational stress, as part of an acute psychiatric illness, or chronically in relation to a life-long psychiatric disorder[34]—particularly the *somatoform disorders* (see §7.5B).

Somatization may occur in the absence of any illness or injury. In such cases the complaints are truly *psychogenic* and indicate psychiatric illness. This is usually a conversion reaction though psychogenic symptoms also develop in the context of other mental disorders including dementia and psychosis. The more difficult diagnostic problem occurs in patients who do have underlying lesions or illnesses but develop dysfunctional illness behavior. Their symptoms—whether pain, other sensory, motor, or autonomic manifestations—may seem quite plausible for their injury, at least superficially. There are different types of such patients.

Some have *psychogenic modification* of what otherwise would be a nondisabling problem.[35] These patients have an unconscious psychological reaction that magnifies the seriousness of the underlying injury or illness, even to the point of total disability; they are emotionally ill and typically present with evidence of psychological distress. This is different than a *litigation (compensation) reaction*—an exaggerated concern for health by someone who is not physically or emotionally ill that "manifests itself in . . . continuing neck or back pain coupled with a concern that, upon formal severance from her claim to compensation, deterioration in health may occur."[36] Unlike malingerers these patients are not trying to mimic or create physical impairment.

A. Factitious disorders and malingering

Deliberate and conscious production of signs and symptoms of illness characterizes *factitious disorders*. These are psychiatric illnesses. The patient's unconscious motivation is to maintain the patient role; unlike malingering there are no external incentives such as financial gain.[37] Diagnosis is very challenging because these patients are generally uncooperative with efforts to detect their deception. Some go to extreme lengths in their illness: injecting foreign substances, enduring multiple invasive tests and surgeries, and traveling endlessly to new physicians, healthcare facilities, and locations to continue their deceptions. The general public might know this as *Munchausen's syndrome*. When the patient produces the symptoms in a third person, usually a child, this is known as Munchausen's by proxy.

Malingering is the deliberate and conscious attempt to feign or exaggerate illness for external gain. It is not a psychiatric or medical disorder. Possible goals of the deception are avoiding work, evading criminal sanctions, obtaining drugs, or receiving undeserved financial benefits. There is not an extensive literature about the frequency of malingering in CPS patients. Thus, though "some pain physicians believe that malingering is not rare within pain facilities, there is no reliable evidence to support this belief."[38] On the other hand, malingering "is thought to be uncommon, based on little data."[39]

Malingering is a medicolegal concept that requires the examiner to identify both conscious efforts to create or magnify symptoms and improper external motives. A physician should be able to identify symptom magnification but is on shakier grounds when it comes to determining motivation and deciding if efforts are conscious or unconscious. Incorrect labeling of someone as a malingerer could expose the physician to liability for defamation. Therefore, some physicians will use unclear language in an attempt to suggest malingering without explicitly stating so. A more straightforward approach is simply to document any inconsistencies and explain why the complaints do not relate to the injury in question.

According to DSM-IV warning signs for malingering include:[40]

- Antisocial Personality Disorder
- Lack of cooperation during diagnostic evaluation and in complying with the prescribed treatment regimen
- Marked discrepancy between the person's claimed stress or disability and the objective findings
- Medicolegal context of presentation

There are different ways to malinger. Patients might *fabricate* their complaints in the absence of any illness, *exaggerate* the effects of an injury, *misattribute* legitimate signs and symptoms to a false cause, or *perseverate* in their complaints even after healing.[41] Among the clinical features suggestive of malingering are frequent missed appointments or lateness, a lack of response to treatment or inability to tolerate any treatment, never seeking treatment, and hostile or suspicious behavior during evaluation.[42]

B. Somatoform disorders

Somatization is characteristic of a group of chronic, primary somatizing psychiatric illnesses described in DSM-IV, the *somatoform disorders*.[43] These include: somatization disorder, undifferentiated somatoform disorder, conversion disorder, hypochondriasis, and pain disorder. These have "physical symptoms that suggest a general medical condition . . . and are not fully explained by a general medical condition, by the direct effects of a substance, or by another mental disorder.[44]

Needless to say, diagnosis requires accurate evaluation to exclude any medical conditions that could be producing the symptoms. This raises an interesting issue. Many, perhaps even most, neurologists and other nonpsychiatrists do not utilize DSM-IV routinely for diagnostic purposes; these physicians may lack the necessary education and training to do so. Conversely, few psychiatrists undertake the extensive physical examination necessary to identify physical impairment, somatization, and symptom magnification. These factors may limit accurate application of the somatoform diagnoses in the chronic pain syndrome population.

Pain disorder is diagnosed when pain "is the predominant focus of the clinical presentation . . . causes significant distress or impairment . . . Psychological factors are judged to play a significant role in the onset, severity, exacerbation, or maintenance of the pain."[45] If there are no associated medical conditions the diagnosis is pain disorder associated with psychological factors, previously known as *psychogenic pain*. If there is also a medical condition the subtype is pain disorder with both psychological factors and a general medical condition. If there is an associated medical condition but no significant psychological factors the pain disorder subtype is not considered a mental disorder. There are several problems with the validity and reliability of these diagnoses:[46]

- No guidelines are provided for assessing the role of the psychological factors
- Overinclusive criteria—almost all chronic pain patients have pain as the predominant focus of the presentation and significant impairment, easily meeting the first two criteria
- Underinclusive criteria—"specific pain" caused by identifiable medical conditions may be common in chronic pain patients but precludes a psychiatric pain disorder diagnosis

7.6 Assessing Symptom Magnification

Identifying exaggeration is often thought of as something done by independent medical examiners on behalf of employers and insurers defending against claims. Certainly, this is a major part of such evaluations. However, there is no reason why treating physicians should be any less vigilant when it comes to their patients who present with pain and related complaints. If there are significant psychological factors underlying the symptoms narcotic analgesics or anesthetic injections are not the proper therapies.

The evaluation requires a thorough examination and a careful analysis of whatever additional information is available. Certain pieces of background information should raise suspicions including:

- Past injuries with prolonged recovery times
- Recent unemployment or impending job loss
- Symptoms worsen or recur just before a scheduled return to work, or soon thereafter
- Workplace disputes or disciplinary problems

The physician must be very observant. Does the patient use or move body parts while in the waiting area or when undressing and dressing but not during direct examination? Are there pain behaviors only in the presence of the physician? Are the assistive devices brought to the medical visit actually being used?

Symptom magnification is likely when there are:[47]

- Excessive healthcare utilization or extensive testing without abnormality
- High levels of reported pain and impairment that are inconsistent with objective findings
- Inconsistencies among the medical records or between the patient's history and the medical records
- Nonphysiologic examination findings
- Pain behaviors

Nonphysiologic (or nonanatomic) signs are not explained by any identifiable illness or tissue damage; there may be pain, sensory, and motor manifestations.[48] There are dozens of maneuvers and techniques to identify and elicit such evidence of magnification.[49]

The *Waddell* signs are perhaps the best known and most widely used collection of physical findings that suggest a nonorganic origin. They were developed to identify low-back pain patients whose symptoms suggest the existence of psychological factors that should be addressed along with the physical complaints. Such patients do not have a simple medical problem that responds to back surgery. The presence of Waddell signs does not mean the patient is faking or that there is no low back pathology. Furthermore, at least three of the eight signs should be present; some physicians, however, use the occurrence of only one or two signs to make a "nonorganic" diagnosis. This is particularly problematic in older patients who often have multiple positive signs. Waddell signs are intended only for low back pain; similar signs for cervical pain are available.[50]

There are eight Waddell signs in five categories:[51]

- Tenderness: superficial (1) and nonanatomic (2) pain produced by palpation
- Simulation: pain produced by seemingly painful, but actually nonpainful, maneuvers—*axial loading* (3) and *truncal rotation* (4)
- Distraction: performing a painful maneuver when the patient is distracted—usually seated versus supine straight leg raising (5)—produces inconsistent responses
- Regional disturbance: nonanatomic distribution of motor (6) or sensory (7) findings
- Overreaction: dramatic, disproportionate, excessive, and inconsistent behaviors (8)

The physician must be careful to exclude physical problems that could explain the apparently nonorganic findings. Fibromyalgia is one condition often mentioned as a cause of widespread nonanatomic pain and tenderness. However, many physicians question the reality of fibromyalgia as a legitimate diagnosis, and would not consider it a "ratable" condition for impairment purposes.[52]

There are other problems with the Waddell signs. Overreaction, in particular, requires a subjective judgment that is "open to considerable observer bias."[53] Furthermore, a recent review of studies of the validity and reliability of the Waddell signs found correlations with decreased function and greater pain, but not with psychological distress or abnormal illness behavior; data in the reviewed studies show the signs themselves are organic and do not distinguish between organic and nonorganic findings.[54]

Nondermatomal somatosensory deficits (NDSD), one of the Waddell signs, are not restricted to low back pain patients. They are often used to support a diagnosis of symptom magnification. As noted in §7.3B, neuropathic pain is associated with some nondermatomal spread of symptoms. Additionally, a recent study found abnormal cortical responses underlying some NDSD. Functional MRI in four chronic pain patients demonstrated "diminished perception is associated with altered processing within the somatosensory system."[55] In other words, the brain changes in response to pain and a "nonorganic" finding may, in fact, have a psychophysiologic basis. "NDSD constitute an unsuccessful attempt of the CNS to shut down or inhibit all peripheral inputs . . . in an effort to control pain."[56] Why this occurs in some individuals is unclear, but "there may be an interaction between peripherally generated nociceptive or neuropathic pain and psychological vulnerability factors.[57]

There is controversy is this area. One pain researcher recently stated "nonorganic findings, including NDSD, do not discriminate between organic and nonorganic problems and are not associated with secondary gain . . . NDSD are not psychological phenomena."[58] However, most neurologists probably would agree with the view that "personality and psychological factors are indeed associated with the onset, maintenance, severity, or exacerbation of chronic pain *and* with the presence of NDSD.[59]

It is important that the physician not over interpret any seemingly nonorganic findings in isolation. These should be analyzed along with the medical records, patient's history, test results, and other physical findings.

7.7 Legal and Regulatory Aspects of Pain Management

Although physicians fear sanctions the likelihood of investigation or criminal prosecution for overprescribing pain medication is quite low,[60] even though state medical disciplinary boards do discipline more physicians for overtreatment than undertreatment of pain.[61] The impact of an investigation with its negative publicity can be devastating. Physicians see that news of an investigation receives more publicity than notice of being cleared of wrongdoing. Since undertreatment is so common physicians may avoid treating pain aggressively so as not to violate community standards—even if those standards are inadequate.

Nevertheless, the risks to physicians for undertreating pain are increasing. California recently became the second state (Oregon was first in 1999) to discipline a physician for undertreating pain.[62] There is also potential liability from private civil litigation. A nurse and her nursing home employer suffered a $15 million verdict (half compensatory, half punitive damages) in an action arising from her refusal to follow a physician's order to give morphine to a dying patient.[63] The advocacy group *Compassion in Dying* successfully brought an action for undertreatment against one California physician under an elder abuse statute and has reached settlements in a second case.[64]

Finally, undertreatment of pain might lead to criminal charges. In Michigan, a surgeon was indicted under a vulnerable adult abuse statute for two counts of allegedly failing to provide adequate pain control in patients being treated for chronic wounds.[65]

Hopefully, improvements in physician education and awareness of these negative consequences will lead to better care of people in pain.

Endnotes

1. Parrott T. "Pain management in primary-care medical practice." In: Tollison CD, Satterthwaite JR, Tollison JW, eds. *Practical Pain Management*, 3rd ed. Philadelphia: Lippincott Williams & Wilkins; 2002:729-759.

2. Weinman BP. "A constitutional right to pain relief." *J Legal Med.* 2003;24:495-539.

3. Substance Abuse and Mental Health Services Administration. "2002 National Survey on Drug Use and Health." Available at www.samsha.gov, accessed March 13, 2004.

4. Jacobson PL, Mann JD. "Evolving role of the neurologist in the diagnosis and treatment of chronic noncancer pain." *Mayo Clin Proc* 2003;78:80-84.

5. Details at www.abpn.com, accessed December 24, 2004.

6. Joint Commission on Accreditation of Healthcare Organizations. *2001 Hospital Accreditation Standards.* Oakbrook Terrace, IL: JCAHO Publications, Inc; 2001. Relevant portions available at www.jcrinc.com (*Pain Assessment and Management Standards—Hospitals*), accessed December 24, 2004.

7. Benbadis SR, Herrera M, Orazi U. "Does the neurologist contribute to the care of patients with chronic back pain?" *Eur Neurol* 2002;48:61-64.

8. Brigham CR. *The Comprehensive IME System: Essential Resources for an Efficient and Successful IME Practice*. Falmouth, MA: SEAK, Inc; 2000.

9. Ransford AO, Cairns D, Mooney V. "The pain drawing as an aid to the psychologic evaluation of patients with low back pain." *Spine* 1976;1:127-134.

10. Melzack R. "The McGill Pain Questionnaire: major properties and scoring methods." *Pain* 1975;1:277-299.

11. Melzack R. "The Short-form McGill Pain Questionnaire." *Pain* 1987;30:191-197.

12. Fairbank JCT, Couper J, et al. "The Oswestry Low Back Pain Questionnaire." *Physiotherapy* 1980;66:271-273.

13. Roland M, Morris R. "A study of the natural history of back pain. I. Development of a reliable and sensitive measure of disability in low-back pain." *Spine* 1983;8:141-144.

14. Tait RC, Chibnall JT, Krause S. "The Pain Disability Index: Psychometric properties." *Pain* 1990;40:171-182.

15. Cocchiarella L, Andersson GBJ, eds. *Guides to the Evaluation of Permanent Impairment, Fifth Edition*. Chicago: AMA Press; 2001, at 569.

16. *Id*. at 566.

17. *Id*. at 570-571.

18. Cocchiarella L, Lord SJ. *Master the Guides Fifth: A Medical and Legal Transition to the Guides to the Evaluation of Permanent Impairment, Fifth Edition*. Chicago: AMA Press; 2001, at 288.

19. *Id*. at 292.

20. Robinson J, Turk DC, Loeser JD. "Pain evaluation: Fifth edition approaches." *The Guides Newsletter* 2002;January/February:1-5, 9-11.

21. Schwartzman RJ, Grothusen J, et al. "Neuropathic central pain." *Arch Neurol* 2001;58:1547-1550.

22. Urban MO, Gebhart GF. "Central mechanisms in pain." *Med Clin N Amer* 1999;83(3):585-596.

23. Stong C. "Pathologic pain and central neuroplasticity - new implications for pain research." *Neurology Reviews* 2002;10(11):35-38.

24. Bennett RM. "Emerging concepts in the neurobiology of chronic pain: Evidence of abnormal sensory processing in fibromyalgia." *Mayo Clin Proc* 1999;74:385-398.

25. Bajwa ZH. "Neuropathic pain." *Practical Neurology* 2002;1(7):18-22.

26. Pappagallo M. "Neuropathic pain in peripheral neuropathies." In: Tollison CD, Satterthwaite JR, Tollison JW, eds., *supra* note 1, at 431-448.

27. *Id.* at 441.

28. Rowbotham MC, Twilling L, et al. "Oral opioid therapy for chronic peripheral and central neuropathic pain." *N Engl J Med* 2003;348:1223-1232.

29. Covington EC. "Treatment of chronic neck and back pain." In: Evans RW, ed. *Saunders Manual of Neurologic Practice*. Philadelphia: Saunders; 2003:772-778.

30. Mittenberg W, Patton C, et al. "Base rates of malingering and symptom exaggeration." *J Clin Exp Neuropsychol* 2002;24:1094-1102.

31. American Medical Association. *Guides to the Evaluation of Permanent Impairment*, 4th ed. Chicago: AMA Press; 1995:308-309.

32. Covington, EC. "Pain medicine approach to chronic low back pain." *Continuum* 2001;7(1):112-140.

33. Fishbain DA. "The somatizing disorders: Diagnostic and treatment approaches for pain medicine." In: Tollison CD, Satterthwaite JR, Tollison JW, eds., *supra* note 1, at 580-594.

34. *Id.* at 581.

35. McCulloch JA, Snook D, Weiner BK. "Differential diagnosis of low back pain." In: Tollison CD, Satterthwaite JR, Tollison JW, eds., *supra* note 1, at 389-410.

36. *Id.* at 390.

37. American Psychiatric Association. *Diagnostic and Statistical Manual of Mental Disorders*, 4th ed. Washington, DC: American Psychiatric Association; 1994:471-475.

38. Fishbain DA, *supra* note 33, at 589.

39. Covington, EC, *supra* note 29, at 773.

40. American Psychiatric Association, *supra* note 37, at 683.

41. McCulloch JA, Snook D, Weiner BK, *supra* note 35, at 391.

42. *Id*. at 393.

43. American Psychiatric Association, *supra* note 37, at 445-469.

44. *Id*. at 445.

45. *Id*. at 458.

46. Fishbain DA, *supra* note 33, at 587-589.

47. Brigham CR, *supra* note 8, at 62-63.

48. *Id*. at 63-65.

49. Brigham CR, Ensalada LH. "Nonorganic findings." *The Guides Newsletter* 2000;July/August:4-8.

50. Sobel JB, Sollenberger PT, et al. "Cervical nonorganic signs: a new clinical tool to assess abnormal illness behavior in neck pain patients: A pilot study." *Arch Phys Med Rehabil* 2000;81:170-175.

51. Waddell G, McCulloch JA, et al. "Nonorganic physical signs on low-back pain. *Spine* 1980;5:117-125.

52. Robinson J, Turk DC, Loeser JD, *supra* note 20, at 2.

53. Waddell G, Turk DC. "Clinical assessment of low back pain." In: Turk DC, Melzack R, eds. *Handbook of Pain Assessment*. New York: Guilford Press; 1992:15-36.

54. Fishbain DA, Cole B, et al. "A structured evidence-based review on the meaning of nonorganic physical signs: Waddell signs." *Pain Med* 2003;4:141-181.

55. Mailis-Gagnon A, Giannoylis I, et al. "Altered central somatosensory processing in chronic pain patients with 'hysterical' anesthesia." *Neurology* 2003;60:1501-1507.

56. *Id.* at 1506.

57. *Id.*

58. Fishbain DA. "Chronic nonmalignant pain." Letter to the editor. *J Rheumatol* 2002;29:2243.

59. Mailis A, Nicholson K. "Reply." Letter to the editor. *J Rheumatol* 2002; 29:2243-2244.

60. Ziegler SJ, Lovich NP. "Pain relief, prescription drugs, and prosecution: A four-state survey of chief prosecutors." *J Law Med. & Ethics* 2003;31:75-100.

61. Hoffman DE, Tarzian AJ. "Achieving the right balance in oversight of physician opioid prescribing for pain: The role of state medical boards." *J Law Med. & Ethics* 2003;31:21-40.

62. Division of Medical Quality of the Medical Board of California. *In the Matter of the Accusation filed Against Eugene B. Whitney, M.D.*, No: 12-2002-133376, December 15, 2003.

63. *Estate of Henry James v. Hillhaven Corp.*, No. 89CVS64 (Super. Ct. Div., Hertford County, NC, Nov. 20, 1990).

64. Compassion in Dying, www.compassionindying.org, accessed December 24, 2004.

65. Dr. Frank Paul Bongiorno was acquitted of additional fraud charges but as of late 2004 was still facing criminal charges under the vulnerable adult abuse statute. E-mail from Donald L. Allen, Jr., Michigan Assistant Attorney General, Health Care Fraud Division, October 26, 2004.

Additional Reading

Ballantyne J, Fishman SM, Abdi S, eds. *The Massachusetts General Hospital Handbook of Pain Management*, 2nd ed. Philadelphia: Lippincott Williams & Wilkins; 2002.

Iyer, Patncia. Medical-Legal Aspects of Pain and Suffering. Tucson: Lawyers & Judges Publishing Company, Inc., 2003.

Melzack R, Wall PD, eds. *Handbook of Pain Management: A Clinical Companion to Textbook Of Pain.* New York: Churchill Livingstone; 2003.

Turk DC, Melzack R, eds. *Handbook of Pain Assessment,* 2nd ed. New York: Guilford; 2001.

American Pain Society: www.ampainsoc.org, accessed December 24, 2004.

American Academy of Pain Management: www.aapainmanage.org, accessed December 24, 2004.

American Academy of Pain Medicine: www.painmed.org, accessed December 24, 2004.

Federation of State Medical Boards of the United States, Inc. "Model guidelines for the use of controlled substances in the treatment of pain." May 1998. Available at www.fsmb.org, accessed December 24, 2004.

International Association for the Treatment of Pain: www.iasp-pain.org, accessed December 24, 2004.

Chapter 8

Traumatic Brain Injury

8.1 Introduction

Head and brain injuries are exceedingly common. Many victims suffer significant damage and have persistent disabling problems. Others have complaints that seem disproportionate to an apparently trivial trauma. Head and brain injuries often occur in association with musculoskeletal damage as well as other systemic trauma. Motor vehicle accidents, falls, occupational accidents, and recreational mishaps cause most blunt head injuries. Spontaneous intracranial bleeding, alcohol and drug intoxication, and metabolic disturbances are among conditions that may be confused with brain injury or contribute to it.

The terms "head injury" and "brain injury" are not synonymous though they are often used interchangeably. Head injury includes damage to the skull, scalp, and face, as well as the brain. Not all head injuries cause brain damage. In fact, most skull fractures are not associated with brain damage. There are many causes of brain injury besides head trauma—stroke and infection for example. This chapter focuses mainly

133

on *traumatic brain injury* (TBI) due to blunt trauma—also known as closed head injury (CHI). Penetrating brain injury will be discussed briefly.

"Concussion" is often used in discussions of brain injury. Unfortunately, different neurologists mean different things when they use this word. Some use concussion as a synonym for mild brain injury; others intend concussion to mean head injury with headache and dizziness, but without any cognitive impairment. This leads to considerable confusion, particularly when physicians diagnose *postconcussion syndrome* (PCS) in patients with a wide range of different persisting complaints. In this volume, concussion refers to "a trauma-induced alteration in mental status that may or may not involve loss of consciousness. Confusion and amnesia are the hallmarks of concussion."[1]

The precise incidence of head and brain injuries is unknown. Epidemiological data is derived from emergency room and hospital discharge records. The mildest head and brain injuries may not be listed if patients were treated for other more severe injuries. Furthermore, most individuals with very mild TBI do not receive emergency treatment. There are probably several million head and brain injuries annually in the United States. Perhaps two million such patients are seen in emergency rooms, with one-quarter of these admitted to hospitals. Head injuries are most common in teenagers and young adults. There is a clear male predominance.

Mild TBI may be overlooked in the emergency room when a patient presents with other serious injuries. The clinicians are unlikely to take the time to assess cognitive function in a conscious and coherent patient with broken bones, internal injuries, or serious bleeding. Later, other medical or surgical specialists may not recognize even prominent neurological sequelae of TBI. Fortunately, most mild TBI patients recovery completely (see §8.5).

Severe TBI has devastating consequences to patients and their families. Improvements in diagnosis and management of acute TBI have led to a significant reduction in mortality. However, this means there are more survivors with serious impairments who require intensive care and support. Only about one-third of severe TBI patients are able to return to their previous work within two years of the injury.[2] Since it is young adults who are the typical victims there is a chance of life-long impairment and disability. The presence of the ∈4 allele of the apolipoprotein E gene (also a risk factor for Alzheimer's disease) is associated with poorer outcome after brain injury.[3]

8.2 Assessment of Severity

TBI patients often have serious systemic injuries that require assessment and stabilization before neurological evaluation is possible. Once this is accomplished the neurologist evaluates the patient's level of consciousness. Often, this is done with descriptive terminology—the patient is described as awake, drowsy, alert, attentive, distractible, or delirious. However, these words are subject to differing interpretations. Therefore, it is preferable to use one of the many standardized tools available for this purpose.

The Glasgow Coma Scale[4] (GCS) is probably the best known instrument for measuring coma severity. This quick and reliable test requires assessment of eye opening, verbal response, and motor response. The scoring is standardized and easily replicated. Scores range from 3 to 15; 3 to 8 indicates severe, 9 to 12 moderate and 13 to 15 mild coma. The GCS score also provides important prognostic information.

However, most TBI patients are not unconscious when they are evaluated in a neurologist's office or, for that matter, even when they are examined in the emergency room. Most of these patients suffered mild brain injury and have a GCS score of 15. Nevertheless, they can have various neurobehavioral deficits due to damage not severe enough to produce unconsciousness. Also, some patients can have a serious focal brain injury without loss of consciousness. The GCS may not be sensitive to these injuries.

Another way to assess the extent of brain damage is to determine the duration of *posttraumatic amnesia* (PTA). This refers to the time when a patient is seemingly alert yet confused or disoriented and unable to form new memories. Once recovered, the patient is unable to recall what happened during the amnesic period. Often, patients express this by describing what they first remember after "waking up" or "coming to." It is quite unlikely that a patient will awaken from a coma and have normal memory function without an intervening period of PTA. The duration of PTA following a coma is a useful measure of outcome.[5] The duration of coma can also be used to evaluate the severity of brain damage, but only if there is reliable information about the duration of unconsciousness.

Retrograde amnesia refers to loss of memory for events preceding the injury. As the patient recovers the retrograde amnesia shrinks closer and closer to the moment of injury. Most patients are left with no more than seconds or a few minutes of retrograde amnesia. There are rare instances of more prolonged permanent retrograde amnesia occurring without other signs of serious injury. However, in the absence of substantial brain damage loss of personal identity and other similar information (birthplace, job, name of spouse or children) suggests a dissociative or other psychiatric disturbance, or even deliberate production of symptoms.

TBI severity can be classified as follows:

- Very mild—less than five minutes PTA, no loss of consciousness
- Mild—five to sixty minutes PTA, less than twenty to thirty minutes of unconsciousness
- Moderate—one to twenty-four hours PTA, greater than twenty to thirty minutes of unconsciousness
- Severe—greater than one day PTA
- Very severe—greater than one week PTA

Routine head CT scans are not needed for mild TBI patients without skull fractures, focal neurologic deficits, persistent headache, seizures, or risk factors for bleeding—though the lack of this test is a focus of complaint for some patients if they do not recover quickly.

8.3 Injury Mechanisms

The pathophysiology of brain injury may be categorized according to whether the damage is primary or secondary, direct or indirect, blunt or penetrating, intracerebral or extracerebral, early or late, and focal or diffuse. The clinical manifestations of TBI reflect the mechanisms of injury. The different kinds of damage produce fairly predictable results. Not all damage is obvious at the time of injury. Secondary processes evolve over hours, days, or even weeks. Posttraumatic epileptic seizures may not occur for years. Cognitive deficits may be noticed only after the patient stops taking analgesic medications, gets out of bed, and attempts to return to normal activities.

Primary damage occurs at the time of injury. *Direct* (or contact) injury refers to an actual impact to the head. Thus, a primary direct injury refers to an object striking the head (a baseball bat, falling brick) or the head hitting an unyielding surface such as a windshield. Typical results of primary direct injury include scalp lacerations, skull fractures, superficial brain bruises (*contusions*), and bleeding deeper in the brain (*intracerebral hemorrhage*). Contusions at or beneath the point of impact are known as *coup* injuries; those occurring at the opposite end of the brain are called *contrecoup* lesions. Contusions also develop at the site of depressed skull fractures.

The typical automobile collision involves rapid acceleration and deceleration of the head and neck. This produces powerful horizontal and rotational inertial forces. In addition to any direct impact injury there is other damage. The brain moves within the confines of the skull. Regardless of the external impact site there are certain areas of the brain where injury is expected. These are adjacent to the irregular bones at the base of the skull, particularly the tips and undersurfaces of the frontal and temporal lobes.

Inertial movements also produce *diffuse axonal injury* (DAI), a specific type of damage to nerve fibers that is probably the cause of concussions, whether mild or severe. The long axons that connect the brainstem to the cortex and the axons traversing the *corpus callosum* connecting the cerebral hemispheres are the most prone to stretching and tearing due to the mechanical forces unleashed by the trauma (Figure 8.1). Less severe forces temporarily disrupt axonal function but more severe injury pro-

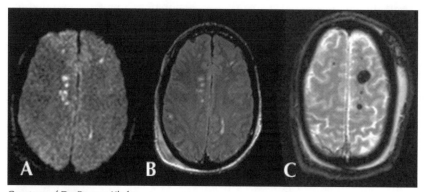

Courtesy of Dr. Roman Klufas.

Figure 8.1 Shear Injury. *Scattered small brain hemorrhages due to shearing seen in diffusion-weighted (A), FLAIR (B), and gradient-echo (C) MRI images.*

duces irreversible axonal destruction. This process develops over hours or days, one explanation for progression of symptoms after the injury.

The severity of DAI varies and accounts for the range of clinical manifestations from trivial concussion to persistent coma. In other words, the amount of axonal damage determines clinical severity. The mildest DAI does not produce abnormalities on MRI scanning. It is visible under the microscope but, unless the patient dies from other causes, brain tissue is not routinely available for evaluation in such cases. Thus, the existence of DAI in mild TBI is inferred from the clinical picture. More severe DAI produces small hemorrhages in the corpus callosum that are visible with MRI; the severest DAI also causes brainstem hemorrhages.

Secondary brain damage can be produced by both intracerebral and extracerebral causes. The more severe the head injury, the more likely are multiple systemic injuries. Blood loss, chest wall injuries, and airway obstruction are all common extracerebral complications. They can produce both respiratory and circulatory insufficiency, leading to inadequate blood flow (ischemia) and insufficient oxygenation (hypoxemia). A healthy brain is able to compensate and regulate its blood supply in order to maintain its supply of oxygen and nutrients; brain injury impairs these mechanisms. Thus, the injured brain is more prone to *hypoxic-ischemic injury* (HII).

HII produces stereotypical patterns of damage occurring in conjunction with DAI. These include diffuse neuronal loss, focal brain damage in susceptible regions, and strokes in the "watersheds" between vascular territories. Neuroimaging procedures can reveal the larger areas of destruction typical of HII. However, it is difficult to distinguish clinically between damage from DAI and the diffuse neuronal loss of HII. The latter is suggested by a slower or poorer recovery than expected.

Intracerebral processes can also produce secondary damage. Increased intracranial pressure is the main factor. Traumatic brain injury leads to *edema*—fluid leaking from damaged blood vessels and nerve cells—and increased cerebral blood volume. There may also be large blood clots. The added fluid within the confines of the bony skull produces increased pressure. Brain structures can be pushed out of their usual positions, a potentially fatal problem known as *herniation*. A fixed and dilated pupil is a sign of one common form of herniation.

8.4 Consequences of TBI

The clinical manifestations of traumatic brain injury are fairly predictable. Variations from patient to patient reflect the distribution and relative proportion of diffuse and focal injuries, as well as the severity of the injuries. TBI can produce many types of psychopathology and neurobehavioral syndromes. Anxiety and mood disorders are common. There are several other factors that contribute to the outcome including:

- Alcohol and substance abuse
- Family and social support network, before and after TBI
- Litigation
- Pre-existing impulse control disorders
- Premorbid personality
- Previous brain injury or dysfunction

A. DAI and coma

Altered consciousness or coma after TBI is almost always the result of DAI. The more severe the axonal injury, the more prolonged the coma. There is a rather predictable pattern of recovery. The stages of recovery are more prolonged following severe injury and there is always the possibility that the victim will not reach full recovery. Recovery may take years after very severe DAI. Inattention, poor concentration, and slowed information processing are common sequelae of DAI. These are best documented with formal neuropsychological testing.

The sequence of recovery from coma begins when the patient enters a vegetative state. There is wakefulness and unresponsive vigilance. Next, some cognitive activity returns and the patient responds inconsistently to commands but is often mute. The next stage is a confusional amnesic state characterized by agitation, poor attention, and impaired learning. As the posttraumatic amnesia resolves there is a stage of emerging independence with some ongoing significant deficits. Finally, the patient reaches a level of intellectual and social competence. There may be deficits that do not resolve.[6]

B. Focal brain damage

The location of focal lesions predicts the clinical outcome. Any part of the brain can be damaged but the anterior and inferior frontal and temporal lobes are particularly prone to injury. These areas are important cortical centers of the *limbic system*. This is a complex interconnected group of structures involved in regulation of emotion, behavior, and personality. Damage in these regions often leads to impulsive, explosive, and disinhibited behavior. Anterior temporal lobe injury frequently impairs memory function.

The *dorsofrontal* section of the frontal lobes is the seat of many higher cortical functions such as abstraction, insight, judgment, foresight, planning, and motivation. Dorsofrontal damage can produce apathetic and unmotivated behavior. Patients will make poor decisions, have difficulty with problem-solving, and be unable to function independently in society. Often, the behavioral and personality changes are not accompanied by obvious physical deficits. A standard neurological examination and even routine psychometric tests may not reveal the problems. Specialized neuropsychological tests are needed to measure these problems.

C. Epilepsy

Epileptic attacks can occur at the moment of brain trauma. These *impact* or *immediate* seizures are a nonspecific response to the trauma or irritation from bleeding. They are significant because they complicate the management of severely injured patients. Interestingly, impact seizures do not increase the risk of permanent epilepsy.

Early *posttraumatic epilepsy* (PTE) refers to seizures occurring within one week of a TBI, but excluding impact seizures. These are most common in young children in whom even mild injury may cause early seizures. In adults, early PTE usually occurs only with more severe injuries, particularly if there are depressed skull fractures, prolonged unconsciousness or PTA, or intracerebral bleeding. While early PTE is a risk factor for persistent seizures, most early PTE patients do not develop permanent epilepsy.

Late posttraumatic epilepsy is the term for recurrent seizures that develop more than one week after the TBI. The overall risk is approximately 5 percent but that is a misleading figure because it includes patients with the mildest injuries who have little or no increased risk as well as the severely injured whose risk is quite high. Individual patients should be assessed according to the particular features of their injuries. The first posttraumatic seizure can occur years or even decades after the injury. However, roughly a quarter of these patients experience the initial seizure within three months of the injury, half within one year.[7] The main risk factors (with rates expressed as percent) for developing late PTE are:[8]

- Depressed skull fracture (3–70)
- Early posttraumatic epilepsy (25)
- Intracranial blood clots (25–30)
- Penetrating head injury (33–50)
- Prolonged coma or posttraumatic amnesia (35)

The wide range in risk with skull fracture depends on whether one or more of the following factors are present:[9]

- Early posttraumatic epilepsy
- Focal neurologic abnormalities caused by the fracture
- Penetration of the dura (the thick membrane surrounding the brain)
- Posttraumatic amnesia longer than twenty-four hours

The risk of developing seizures after TBI also varies with the time since injury. In a study of more than 4,000 TBI patients classified as mild (LOC or amnesia less than thirty minutes), moderate (skull fracture, or LOC or amnesia up to twenty-four hours), and severe (brain contusion, subdural hematoma, or LOC or amnesia greater than twenty-four hours) the incidence ratio of seizures compared to the control population varied considerably with time:[10]

- Mild: 1.5 overall—3.1 in year one; 2.1 in years one to four; no increased risk thereafter
- Moderate: 2.9 overall—6.7 in year one; 3.1 in years one to four; 3.0 in years five to nine
- Severe: overall 17.0—95.0 in year one; 16.7 in years one to four; 12.0 in years five to nine; 4.0 after ten years

These data indicate the risk of new seizures following severe TBI persists even beyond ten years. However, after five years there is no increased risk from a mild TBI; after ten years there is no increased risk following moderate TBI. More importantly, the results reinforce the importance of characterizing a patient's TBI accurately in order to assess seizure risk.

Prophylactic use of anticonvulsant medication does not appear to prevent development of late PTE. However, medication effectively controls seizures in most patients with late PTE. If the seizures are uncontrolled the patient may have serious social, vocational, and recreational limitations.

D. Hydrocephalus

Cerebrospinal fluid is produced in the ventricles. After moderate to severe TBI the ventricles may enlarge, a condition known as *hydrocephalus*. This occurs in two ways. If there is a loss of brain tissue—*atrophy*—the ventricles enlarge to fill the space. If the normal flow of spinal fluid is blocked, the ventricles also will enlarge. A gradual onset of hydrocephalus from this blockage can produce an abnormal gait, loss of urinary control, and dementia. An abrupt blockage produces headache, optic nerve swelling and visual changes, nausea and vomiting, alterations in consciousness, and brain herniation. Neurosurgical intervention is needed to shunt the fluid and bypass the blockage. There is no treatment for ventricular enlargement due to atrophy.

E. Hematomas

TBI can produce bleeding. *Subdural hematomas* are blood clots in the space between the brain and its membranous covering, the dura (Figure 8.2). This blood comes from leaking veins. Acute subdural hematomas are very common in severe head injury patients. Patients will present with signs suggesting a mass in the brain. This is diagnosed readily by CT or MRI scanning. Large clots are drained through burr holes in the skull.

Chronic subdural hematomas develop weeks or even months after TBI. The blood accumulates very slowly, eventually causing symptoms when the compressed brain tissue can no longer compensate for the distortion. Symptoms include changes in personality, headache, unilateral weakness, impaired thought processes, and coma. Patients with pre-existing brain atrophy, bleeding tendencies, and the elderly in general are at higher risk of chronic subdural hematomas.

Epidural (or *extradural*) *hematomas* occur outside the dura but beneath the inner skull surface. These are usually due to arterial bleeding,

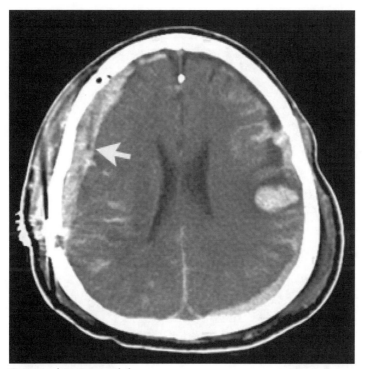

Courtesy of Dr. Roman Klufas.

Figure 8.2 *Subdural Hematoma. There is a subdural bleed at the arrowhead. There are contusions in the other hemisphere and subarachnoid blood is seen diffusely.*

especially from a torn middle meningeal artery. The blood is under higher pressure than the venous bleeding that causes most subdural blood clots and, therefore, can expand quite rapidly. A rapidly expanding epidural bleed usually requires neurosurgical intervention to avoid brain damage and death. A minority of patients will present with a lucid interval after their concussions only to succumb hours or a few days later from the epidural bleeding (Figure 8.3).

F. Cranial nerve lesions

Several cranial nerves are especially subject to traumatic injury. The olfactory and facial nerves are the most frequently damaged. Even mild TBI can injure the receptive fibers of the olfactory nerve. *Anosmia*—loss of smell—is a common result of head injury. The facial nerve has a long

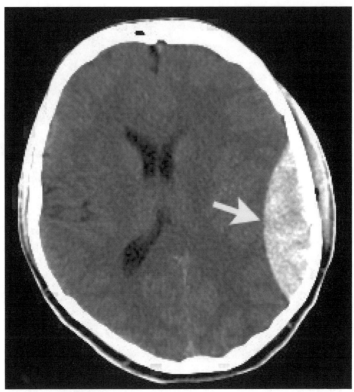

Courtesy of Dr. Roman Klufas.

Figure 8.3 *Epidural Hematoma. Blood clot at arrowhead has a typical lens-like shape in this CT image. Note also the mass effect, pushing the brain to the other side and partially obliterating the lateral ventricle.*

course through the temporal bone. Fractures there can sever the nerve and produce facial paralysis. The eighth cranial nerve can also be injured by a temporal bone fracture though direct trauma to the middle and inner ears is a more likely cause of damage to that nerve.

The optic and oculomotor nerves are the next most susceptible, though more severe trauma is usually required to damage these nerves. Traumatic injury to the trigeminal and lower cranial nerves is less common.

8.5 Mild Head Injury and Postconcussion Syndrome

Perhaps no issue related to TBI generates more controversy and confusion than the topic of mild head injury. Severe TBI produces obvious abnormalities. Mild TBI, however, often produces complaints that appear to have no physical basis. Brain damage is difficult to document or even infer after transient alteration of consciousness. The patient's complaints seem unconvincing given the lack of evidence of brain injury. Furthermore, the reality of mild TBI is quite different from the fictionalized portrayal typical of television and cinema. Most people have seen hundreds or thousands of depictions of concussion followed by almost immediate recovery—usually the hero being knocked out only to be up chasing the villain after the commercial break.

Very rarely, mild TBI causes delayed, catastrophic diffuse cerebral swelling and death. These cases occur mostly in male teenagers injured in athletic contests. Risk factors are poorly understood. Some clinicians postulate that repeated concussions lead to the swelling—the so-called *second impact syndrome*,[11] but a recent analysis does not support this contention.[12] However, the AAN has released cautious guidelines about concussion and return to athletic contests.[13]

Though most mild TBI patients are not hospitalized there are so many of these injuries that the bulk of TBI hospitalizations are for mild injury. Most patients recover within weeks or months but a small group does not. Since mild head injury is so common, even a 15 percent rate of prolonged symptoms generates a disease incidence equal to that of Parkinson's disease, multiple sclerosis, Guillain-Barré syndrome, motor neuron disease, and myasthenia gravis combined.[14]

The clinical features of mild TBI reflect the underlying pathology—diffuse axonal injury.[15] As the patient recovers from the posttraumatic confusion and amnesia particular cognitive deficits related to diffuse axonal injury become apparent. These include reduced speed of information processing, reduced processing capacity, impaired attention and concentration, and deficits in learning and memory. If there are also frontal and temporal bruises—and these are common—there may be additional difficulties with attention and memory as well as problems with behavioral control and executive functions. Patients may present with disturbing complaints related to their memory and other cognitive deficits though routine office-based testing by the neurologist is unrevealing. Many phy-

sicians will suspect symptom magnification or exaggeration. Formal neuropsychological testing is especially important in such circumstances.

Most patients have several other complaints after mild closed head
injury. This is not surprising since other structures of the head are injured.
The combination of behavioral, emotional, cognitive, and somatic complaints comprises the *postconcussion syndrome*. The most common complaints include:

- Behavioral and emotional—anxiety, depression, impulsivity, irritability, personality changes, reduced libido
- Cognitive—forgetfulness, inattention and impaired concentration,
  reduced information processing speed, slow reaction time
- Somatic—dizziness, double vision, fatigue, headaches, hearing loss,
  hypersensitivity to light and sound, insomnia, lightheadedness, loss
  of smell and taste, tinnitus, weakness

PCS improves slowly but steadily. The attention and memory deficits
usually resolve within several weeks to a few months. Young concussion
patients who do not experience frank unconsciousness may recover
within days. Older patients are slower to recover. A very mild uncomplicated TBI patient (GCS of fifteen, brief unconsciousness, PTA less than
one hour) heals within six to twelve weeks but those with more severe
mild TBI (GCS of thirteen or fourteen, longer coma or PTA) may not heal
for months or even years. Probably 85 to 90 percent recover within one
year of the injury.[16]

It is not clear why the remainder develop persistent or chronic PCS.
Age over forty years, alcohol abuse, prior TBI, lower educational and socioeconomic status, and female sex are risk factors. Premorbid psychiatric
illness or stress does not account entirely for the ongoing symptoms.
These patients typically were more likely to be suffering significant stress
at the time of injury. They are more likely to experience greater disruption
in their lives after the incident, and are more likely to develop mood or
anxiety disorders. Appropriate diagnostic testing can exclude undiag-
nosed or unrecognized injuries.

Many symptoms of chronic PCS are common in the population at
large. Thus, there is considerable skepticism within the medical community about these complaints. Some physicians believe that complaints

lasting more than a few months indicate malingering. These physicians will point to the normal examination and diagnostic testing as proof of the absence of brain injury. However, this point of view tends to ignore the extensive scientific evidence from neuroimaging, neuropathology, neurophysiology, and neuropsychology studies regarding the presence of abnormalities in mild TBI patients.

Posttraumatic headache typifies the kind of disagreements in this area. Some clinicians regard this as a neurobehavioral disorder with several possible causative mechanisms.[17] Others point to the lack of correlation between the injury severity and the headache severity or duration. Instead, they consider these *rebound* headaches due to analgesic overuse (see §15.4).[18]

It is inappropriate to assume that all patients with prolonged PCS are faking or merely suffering from a psychogenic or somatization disorder. Certainly, litigation increases stress and raises the specter of secondary gain, but persistent PCS also occurs in patients who are not involved in legal battles. Resolution of a lawsuit does not always lead to resolution of symptoms. Therefore, these patients warrant a thorough evaluation including a detailed medical and psychiatric history, analysis of the injury mechanisms, identification of any factors that may be contributing to the complaints, and a clear understanding of the symptoms themselves. Such an approach is more likely to lead to successful treatment than relying on a particular theoretical bias about whether the complaints have a physical basis or not.

At the other extreme are those physicians who uncritically accept each and every patient complaint, and find all causally connected to the injury. Depression, anxiety, chronic pain, and other conditions can interfere with attention and memory. Therefore, it is not always appropriate to conclude that the patient's forgetfulness and inattentiveness are due to a mild TBI months or years earlier. Neuropsychological evaluation can detect memory and attention problems but not necessarily determine the cause. There should be an effort to identify other factors that better explain a given patient's symptoms "because everyone with a TBI from closed head injury has impaired concentration, it does not mean that in everyone with impaired concentration after closed head injury the cause is neurologic."[19]

Endnotes

1. American Academy of Neurology Quality Standards Subcommittee. "Practice parameter: The management of concussion in sports (summary statement)." *Neurology* 1997;48:581-585.

2. Dikmen SS, Temkin NR, et al. "Employment following traumatic head injuries." *Arch Neurol* 1994;51:177-186.

3. Friedman G, Froom P, et al. "Apolipoprotein E-e4 genotype predicts a poorer outcome in survivors of traumatic brain injury." *Neurology* 1999;52:244-248.

4. Teasdale G, Jennet B. "Assessment of coma and impaired consciousness: A practical scale." *Lancet* 1974;2:81-84.

5. Ellenberg JH, Levin HS, Saydjari C. "Posttraumatic amnesia as a predictor of outcome after severe closed head injury." *Arch Neurol* 1996;53:782-791.

6. Katz DI, Black SE. "Neurological and neuroradiological evaluation." In: Rosenthal M, Griffith ER, et al. *Rehabilitation of the Adult and Child with Traumatic Brain Injury*, 3rd ed. Philadelphia: F.A. Davis; 1999:89-116.

7. Bachmann DL. "The diagnosis and management of common neurologic sequelae of closed head injury." *J Head Trauma Rehabilitation* 1992;7:50-59.

8. Hammond FM, McDeavitt JT. "Medical and orthopedic complications." In: Rosenthal M, Griffith ER, et al., *supra* note 6, at 53-73.

9. Bachmann DL, *supra* note 7, at 51.

10. Annegers JF, Hauser WA, et al. "A population-based study of seizures after traumatic brain injuries." *N Engl J Med* 1998;338:20-24.

11. Saunders RL, Harbaugh RE. "The second impact in catastrophic contact sports head trauma." *JAMA* 1984;252:538-539.

12. McCrory PR, Berkovic SF. "Second impact syndrome." *Neurology* 1998;50:677-683.

13. American Academy of Neurology Quality Standards Subcommittee, *supra* note 1.

14. Alexander MP. "Mild traumatic brain injury: Pathophysiology, natural history and clinical management." *Neurology* 1995;45:1253-1260.

15. *Id*. at 1254.

16. *Id*. at 1255.

17. Saper JR. "Posttraumatic headache: A neurobehavioral disorder." *Arch Neurol* 2000;57:1776-1778.

18. Warner JS. "Posttraumatic headache - a myth?" *Arch Neurol* 2000;57:1778-1780.

19. Alexander MP, *supra* note 14, at 1257.

Additional Reading

Cooper PR, Golfinos JG, eds. *Head Injury*, 4th ed. New York: McGraw-Hill; 2000.

Dobkin BH, ed. *The Clinical Science of Neurologic Rehabilitation*, 2nd ed. New York: Oxford University Press; 2003.

Evans RW, ed. *Neurology and Trauma*. Philadelphia: Saunders; 1996.

Brain Injury Association of America: www.biausa.org, accessed December 24, 2004.

Chapter 9

Spine and Nerve Root Disorders

9.1 Introduction

To understand spinal disorders it is essential to distinguish between the *spinal* (or *vertebral*) *column* and the *spinal cord*. It does no good to refer to a second lumbar lesion, for example, without specifying whether it is the second lumbar vertebra or the second lumbar segment of the spinal cord. The distinction is important because spinal cord segments are not necessarily contiguous with their corresponding vertebrae (Figure 9.1). Unfortunately, clinicians are not always clear about this in their reports.

Most vertebrae are composed of a body, pedicles, facet joints, and lamina. A *spinal canal* is formed by these bony elements and the various ligaments that run the length of the column. The spinal canal contains the spinal cord. The paired spinal nerve roots exit the canal through openings, *foramina*, formed by pairs of vertebrae. The diameter of the canal varies along its length. Developmental abnormalities and degenerative diseases can narrow the canal, *stenosis*, thereby compressing the spinal cord. The symptoms and signs produced by this narrowing are known as *myelopathy*. The foraminal openings are also subject to these pathologic processes.

151

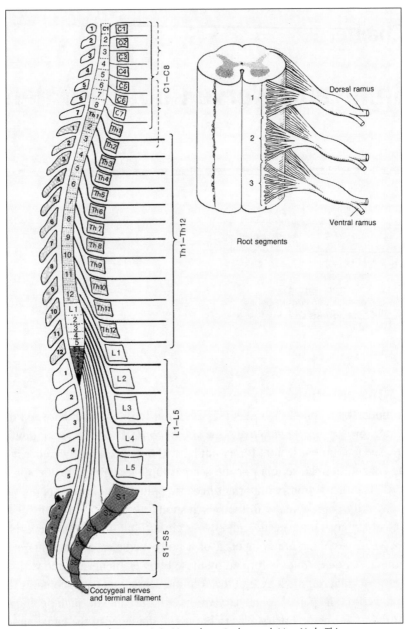

Source: Duus P. Topical Diagnosis in Neurology, 2nd rev. ed. New York: Thieme; 1989:22. Reprinted by permission.

Figure 9.1 *Spinal Cord and Column. Note that the cord ends between the first and second lumbar vertebrae but the nerve roots descend to their exit levels.*

Narrowing can be sufficient to compress an exiting nerve root, causing *radiculopathy*.

The bony spinal column is composed of four sections—cervical, thoracic, lumbar, and sacral. There are seven cervical vertebrae, twelve thoracic vertebrae, and five lumbar vertebrae. The five sacral vertebrae fuse together into a single bony mass. At the lower end of the sacrum are the five coccygeal bones. Occasionally, there are variations in components of the spinal column, especially in the lower lumbar or upper sacral area. The vertebral bodies increase in size from the cervical to the lumbar region. The lumbar vertebrae are specialized for weight bearing, whereas the cervical vertebrae are the most mobile of the vertebral column.

The intervertebral discs lie between vertebral bodies. Their function is to maintain the interspace width while binding together the opposing vertebral surfaces in a way that permits small degrees of painless motion. The discs consist of an elastic ring, the *annulus fibrosis*, surrounding a gelatinous core, the *nucleus pulposus*. With aging these components become fibrotic and less flexible. The intervertebral space narrows and the foramina become smaller. The spine is less mobile and nerve roots are more easily compressed. Extrusion of the nucleus pulposus through the annulus fibrosis, *disc herniation*, is a common cause of radiculopathy.

The spinal cord and spinal column are roughly the same length at birth. Therefore, pairs of segmental spinal nerve roots are at the same level as their corresponding vertebrae. The roots travel horizontally as they pass out of the column. However, the bony spinal column grows more than the spinal cord. In adults the cord terminates at a level between the first and second lumbar vertebrae. The nerve roots still exit the canal through their original foramina. To accomplish this, the roots lengthen and take a more vertical course caudally. Below the lower tip of the spinal cord, the *conus medullaris* (or *terminalis*), the spinal canal contains the nerve roots traveling to the lower lumbar and sacral foramina. The collection of fibers resembles coarse hair in a horse's mane, accounting for the name given to this bundle—the *cauda equina*.

9.2 Low-Back and Neck Pain

Low-back and neck pain are among the most common complaints leading to physician visits. Millions of people present for treatment annually, with costs well into the tens of billions of dollars.[1] Few individuals are fortunate enough to avoid at least one episode of significant neck or low-back pain. Low-back pain is a very common and costly chronic illness in young and middle-aged adults, and a leading source of disability; neck pain is nearly as widespread and important. Risk factors for low-back and neck pain include depression, heavy labor, increasing age, job stress and dissatisfaction, obesity, and substance abuse.

A. Acute neck and low-back pain

Most patients with these complaints seek initial care from primary care physicians, chiropractors, or orthopedists.[2] Neurologists are rarely involved in management of uncomplicated acute neck or low-back pain. Instead, patients are referred for neurological consultation if they have signs of nerve root or spinal cord involvement, or their symptoms become chronic without obvious explanation. Most acute neck and low-back pain is of musculoskeletal origin and improves significantly within days or weeks; however, relapses and some persistent pain is common.

The challenge facing caregivers is to identify patients with neurologic involvement or whose pain indicates more serious diseases. Metastatic disease spreading to the vertebrae, referred pain from diseased abdominal or thoracic organs, and spinal column infections are among the ominous possibilities. The history is of paramount importance in evaluating neck and low-back pain patients. The pain characteristics must be defined in detail. This includes onset, quality, location, spread, duration, exacerbating and alleviating factors, time of day, and associated symptoms. There are different kinds of pain, each with different diagnostic significance:

- Local pain—deep, achy, nonradiating: from periosteum, ligaments, joints
- Radicular pain—sharp, stabbing, shooting: radiates in a dermatomal distribution, indicating nerve root compression or inflammation
- Referred pain—dull, diffuse, deep: not dermatomal, poor localizing value, possibly due to cervical or lumbar spondylosis, or facet joint pathology

Pain that is unrelieved or worsened by lying supine, or that awakens the patient at night, is suspicious for a spinal malignancy. Leg pain that worsens when standing or walking may indicate diminished blood flow to the spine, *vascular claudication*, or spinal narrowing, *neurogenic claudication*. The physician must be alert to other warning signs or "red flags" that suggest serious problems. These include recent trauma, risk factors for infection, impaired bowel, bladder, or sexual function, unexplained weight loss, and fever.

Examination focuses on neurological and musculoskeletal evaluation. Detailed sensory, motor, and reflex testing should localize any radicular deficits due to nerve root entrapment. Spastic gait or unexpectedly brisk reflexes suggest spinal cord dysfunction—*myelopathy*. Provocative maneuvers such as straight-leg raising may elicit signs of nerve root involvement. Hip and other joint disease can produce referred pain that is confused with radiculopathy; various maneuvers are performed to reproduce the patient's symptoms and localize the problem.

Diagnostic testing, especially MRI and EMG, are rarely needed for uncomplicated neck and low-back pain.[3] In fact, an abnormal MRI can be misleading because disc abnormalities are common even in asymptomatic persons—one study revealed disc bulges in 52 percent of subjects and protrusions in 27 percent.[4] EMG and MRI are complementary studies[5] that should be reserved for patients with clear evidence of nerve root or spinal cord abnormality. As noted earlier (see §3.3B), a normal EMG does not exclude nerve root involvement.

Nonspecific neck and low-back pain account for most of these cases. The source of the pain (muscle, tendon, ligament, facet joint) is usually unclear. Patients are given diagnoses such as sprain, strain, spasm, or myofascial syndrome. Most respond to simple analgesics or nonsteroidal anti-inflammatory agents. Muscle relaxants may also be helpful. Reduced activity to avoid eliciting more pain is a common-sense recommendation but prolonged bed rest is not helpful and may even be counter-productive. Patients become deconditioned quickly and they make an association between "many days in bed and severe illness."[6] Therefore, bed rest should be avoided or limited to a day or two.[7] There is little evidence to support use of the many other treatments offered to these patients.[8]

Early mobilization and resumption of normal activities with modifications to avoid eliciting pain is probably the more reasonable and effective approach. This recommendation does run counter to what many patients involved in workers' compensation or personal injury cases feel they need to do—stay inactive and in bed to prove how severely injured they are. Despite the evidence against it, prolonged bed rest is still recommended by many physicians treating these patients.

B. Chronic neck and low-back pain

Some patients do not recover from an episode of acute mechanical neck or low-back pain. Chronic neck or low-back pain is often defined by arbitrary time limits—pain persisting for more than three to six months is a typical criterion. Physicians must be certain that such patients are not suffering from unrecognized chronic diseases such as inflammatory arthropathies (ankylosing spondylitis, for example), spinal instability, post-surgical arachnoiditis, metastatic cancer, or other conditions that are known causes of pain. These account for some of the chronic cases and must be excluded by appropriate diagnostic means.

However, many other patients have chronic neck or low-back pain in the absence of identifiable tissue damage or, seemingly out of proportion to any measurable impairment. These patients pose difficult diagnostic and therapeutic dilemmas. Most exhibit maladaptive learned illness behaviors that create barriers to recovery. Symptom magnification, depression, anxiety, and analgesic overuse are common. Chronic pain and related issues are discussed in Chapter 7.

Many patients have already seen several physicians and other caregivers. They have undergone extensive testing and failed to respond to many different treatments. Unfortunately, this serves to reinforce the belief that there is a serious medical problem responsible for the pain. No simple treatment plan is likely to alter the situation. These patients have a combination of physical and psychological problems that create and maintain their pain. Therapy must address each component. These cognitive, behavioral, and psychologic issues usually require a combination of counseling and medication. Deconditioning and fears of re-injury require an exercise program and work hardening.

There are many kinds of programs that integrate several treatment modalities. *Functional restoration* is one form of multidisciplinary chronic pain treatment that "utilizes physical/functional capacity and psychosocial assessments to organize a physician-directed, interdisciplinary team treatment approach to restore patients to productivity."[9] The assessments are detailed and quantified. There is a progressive exercise program with an emphasis on increasing function rather than reducing pain per se.

Participants usually do improve; they are more likely to return to work and less likely to overutilize the healthcare system.

A few patients do not respond to any reasonable therapy. Some have psychiatric or psychosocial problems that prevent improvement. Progressively more invasive interventions should be avoided. Narcotic analgesics provide relief but there may be little else to recommend.

9.3 Spinal Cord Injury
A. Background
Trauma is the most common cause of spinal cord injury. Infection, vascular disease, tumors, and degenerative conditions also cause many spinal cord injuries. Like head injury, spinal cord injury is more likely to affect males than females and is most frequent in teenagers and young adults. Motor vehicle accidents are the leading cause of spinal injuries. Accidental falls, recreational incidents, and violence are also leading causes.

The features depend on the location and severity of the damage. Complete injuries are those without any sensory or motor function below the level of injury (Figure 9.2). If there is some preservation of neurologic function the injury is termed incomplete. Rarely, there is spinal cord dysfunction above the injury level. Detailed sensory and motor examination will determine the distribution and severity of neurologic involvement. Sensory testing should include modalities from both the lateral and posterior columns. A rectal examination is essential to identify *sacral sparing*, the preservation of function in sacral nerve roots. That is suggestive of a central cord syndrome. Plain radiographic examination indicates the level of the bony abnormality and MRI can delineate the level and severity of damage to the spinal cord and surrounding tissues.

There are several varieties of incomplete spinal injuries. A *central cord syndrome* occurs when the cervical spinal cord is compressed both anteriorly and posteriorly. Middle-aged and older individuals with degenerative disease of the spine are predisposed to this. There is bilateral moderate to severe arm weakness and, possibly, a lesser degree of leg weakness. There are usually sensory abnormalities in the arms. There may be abnormalities in bowel, bladder, and sexual function.

The *anterior cord syndrome* occurs when there is compression of the anterior aspect of the spinal cord, usually from a herniated disc, vertebral dislocation, or fracture. There is weakness or paralysis below the level of

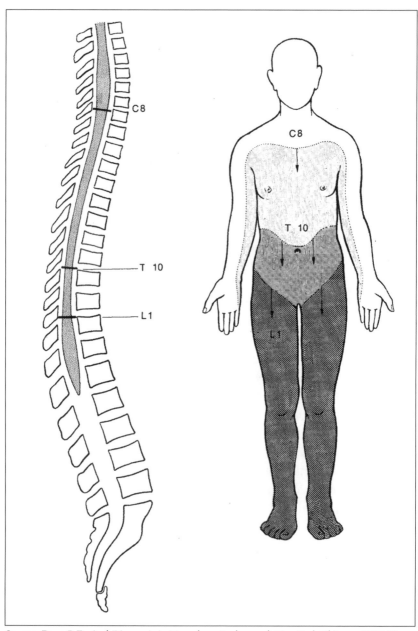

Source: Duus P. Topical Diagnosis in Neurology, 2nd rev. ed. New York: Thieme; 1989:57.
Reprinted by permission.

Figure 9.2 *Paralysis. Distribution of weakness from three different lesion levels.*

compression. Pain and temperature sensation are lost but there is preservation of posterior column sensory functions (fine touch and proprioception).

The *Brown-Séquard* or *hemisection syndrome* occurs when one side of the spinal cord is injured. Stab wounds or projectile injuries can cause this. Below the level of damage there is ipsilateral paralysis and loss of posterior column sensory function. There is contralateral loss of pain and temperature sensation, beginning a couple of spinal segment levels more inferiorly (Figure 9.3).

B. Acute management

Spinal injury patients must have their spines immobilized. Any life-threatening medical or surgical problems must be addressed and the patient stabilized. Neurological evaluation should be performed as soon as possible. Most spinal injury patients are given high dose intravenous methylprednisolone within eight hours of the injury. This appears to improve the outcome. If the infusion is started within three hours of injury it should be continued for twenty-four hours; if the infusion was started between

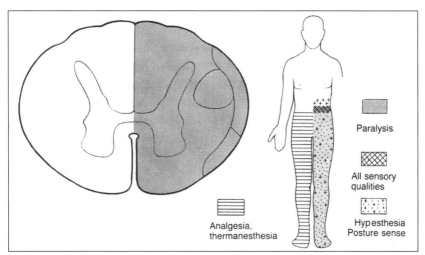

Source: Duus P. Topical Diagnosis in Neurology, 2nd rev. ed. New York: Thieme; 1989:56. Reprinted by permission.

Figure 9.3 Brown-Séquard Syndrome. A left thoracic hemisection of the spinal cord produces ipsilateral weakness and loss of posterior column function and contralateral loss of pain and temperature sensation.

three and eight hours after injury, administration is continued for forty-eight hours.[10]

Surgical intervention is often necessary but there is controversy regarding the timing of surgery. Spinal column instability may require surgical fusion or specialized bracing. Surgical decompression and spinal realignment are often needed, particularly for thoracic and lumbar lesions. Traction may be sufficient for realignment and decompression in the cervical region.

The prognosis for recovery is best in those who have an incomplete spinal lesion and in those with signs of some recovery of motor or sensory function within forty-eight hours of the injury. The higher the lesion is located in the spinal column, the greater the degree of neurological dysfunction. If no function has returned within three months of the injury, the prognosis is poor. Some recovery can continue for up to two years. In the case of the late Christopher Reeve, there was recovery even more remote in time. Beginning more than two years after injury he had a degree of recovery never before documented.[11]

C. Rehabilitation considerations

Spinal cord injury rehabilitation requires a multidisciplinary approach. The usual team includes physicians, nurses, rehabilitation specialists, vocational counselors, social workers, physical therapists, occupational therapists, nutritionists, and others. The goal of rehabilitation is to maximize the patient's residual abilities and facilitate the highest possible level of independence and functioning. Among the most common problems requiring management are:

- Bladder dysfunction
- Muscle spasms and spasticity
- Posttraumatic syringomyelia
- Pressure sores
- Respiratory insufficiency
- Sexual dysfunction

In lesions below the L2 vertebra the cauda equina nerve roots are involved, but the spinal cord itself is spared. The predominant problem is a disrupted nerve supply to the bowel and to the bladder. Sexual function may also be affected. With lesions at or below the L2 vertebra, the distribution and degree of weakness depends upon the level of the lesion. Involvement of the lower nerve roots causes weakness of the foot; at higher levels there is weakness of the knee; and at the highest level, weakness of the hip. *Cauda equina syndrome* is most often caused by a large disc herniation at the L4-5 or L5-S1 level.[12] This is a neurosurgical emergency because neurologic deficits present at diagnosis often do not improve.[13] Patients typically report severe back pain, recent trauma, bilateral leg complaints, and bowel and urinary dysfunction. MRI or CT myelography is needed on an emergency basis to confirm the diagnosis.

Injury at the level of the twelfth thoracic or first lumbar vertebra can damage the end of the spinal cord, producing a *conus medullaris syndrome*. There is usually flaccid paralysis of bowel and bladder, loss of sexual function, and anesthesia in a "saddle" distribution. Management of bladder problems is critically important. Urinary tract infections and other urologic complications are still frequent causes of mortality in these patients. Sexual dysfunction also requires a variety of interventions as well as counseling.

Injury in the lower thoracic spinal column will usually damage the spinal cord itself, making it probable that the patient will require a wheelchair for mobility. Normally, activities of daily life including personal hygiene are easily achieved. Damage to the upper lumbar region of the spinal cord will usually produce spastic weakness of bladder and bowel muscles. Spinal reflexes will produce automatic voiding and a drainage device is usually not needed. At upper thoracic spinal cord levels a wheelchair will probably be needed; transfers, dressing, and attention to personal hygiene will require great training and persistence.

Damage to the spinal cord at the C7 and C8 levels involves innervation to the hands, significantly limiting the patient's dexterity. There will usually be limited grip strength, although shoulder and upper arm movement is preserved. Wheelchair modifications are often required because of the impaired grip. Dressing and personal hygiene may require help, and adaptations for bathroom systems are required.

At the C6 cord level considerably more upper limb function is lost. Using the arms for eating requires adaptations. It is still possible to use a manually operated wheelchair, but most patients prefer electrically operated wheelchairs. Dressing and personal hygiene usually require assistance, as do transfers. With damage at the C5 level the patient has shoulder and elbow function but no wrist or hand function. Eating becomes increasingly difficult, and transfers, dressing, and personal hygiene are almost impossible without assistance.

Patients with upper cervical cord lesions and some with a C4 level, require artificial ventilation with a portable respirator attached to the wheelchair. Most patients require permanent tracheostomy, and clearly require full-time care. Due to the involvement of respiratory muscles chest infections are a recurrent problem.

9.4 Spinal Spondylosis and Disk Disease

Spondylosis is a degenerative process affecting the intervertebral discs, facet joints, spinal ligaments, and other elements of the vertebral bones. It is a natural part of aging, found in most adults by middle age. *Radiculopathy* refers to dysfunction or irritation to a spinal nerve root. The nerve roots contain both a motor and a sensory component. Either or both can be involved in a radiculopathy. The structural abnormalities of spondylosis can produce radiculopathy and even dysfunction of the spinal cord, *myelopathy*. A sudden herniation of the intervertebral disc is one form of *spondylotic* radiculopathy. Non-spondylotic nerve root irritation can be caused by infections, tumors, blood clots, inflammatory disorders, trauma (Figure 9.4), and other conditions.

The main risk factors for spondylotic radiculopathy are aging, heavy manual labor and lifting, operating vibrating equipment, and coughing. Disc herniation is the commonest cause of spondylotic radiculopathy. Clinical symptoms vary according to the size, location (central, paracentral, or lateral), and spinal level. Cervical disc herniations occur less frequently than lumbosacral herniations.

The most common cervical herniation occurs between the C6 and C7 vertebrae, compressing the C7 nerve root. C6 compression due to herniation between the C5 and C6 vertebrae is the next most common, followed by C8 and C5 radiculopathies. A typical radiculopathy presents with neck pain and stiffness. This is followed by pain radiating into the dermatome supplied by the involved nerve root. There may be weakness in muscles supplied by that nerve root and paresthesia. However, the weakness is often not noted by the patient but found only on examination. Most acute attacks of cervical radiculopathy resolve with time, particularly when

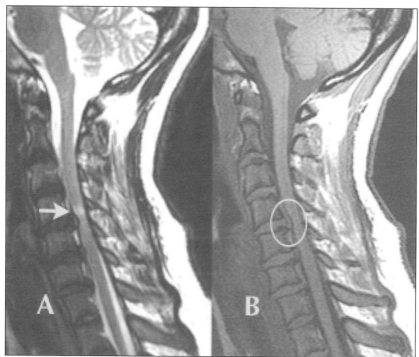

Courtesy of Dr. Roman Klufas.

Figure 9.4 *Cervical Spine Trauma. A cervical spine contusion, arrowhead, is seen in the T2-weighted image (A) but not in the T1-weighted image (B). However, the encircled disc herniation is better seen in B.*

aided by appropriate physical therapy techniques. Those patients who do not improve may develop a chronic syndrome, with intermittent dull, aching discomfort and clear-cut signs of dermatomal sensory abnormality, reflex changes, and muscle wasting. Their symptoms may respond to surgery.

Cervical spondylosis usually involves two adjacent levels with most cases occurring at C5 and C6. Radiculopathy due to degenerative changes usually occurs at an older age than disc herniations. The typical presenting symptom is neck pain with restriction of neck movement and referred pain to the shoulder. Pain is often exacerbated by carrying with the affected arm. There is pain at the back of the neck extending to the head. Patients are typically more symptomatic first thing in the morning, with a recurrence of their symptoms towards the end of the day.

Cervical spondylotic myelopathy develops when the diameter of the spinal canal narrows to a point where the spinal cord is compressed. Flexion and extension of the neck reduces the cervical canal's volume. If a large portion of the canal is already occupied by spondylotic disease or disc protrusion that reduction may be significant in a narrow diameter canal, but of less significance in a wide diameter canal. Symptoms of spondylotic myelopathy develop over years, but can be precipitated by injury or trauma to an underlying abnormal canal. Initial complaints include difficulty in walking, with aching pain in the lower limbs that is worsened by exercise and relieved by rest. Burning paresthesia can also occur in the legs. Bladder dysfunction is a late occurrence. Progression of this syndrome leads to additional impairments in gait.

Lumbar disc herniations are even more common than the cervical variety. They occur mostly in young to early middle-aged individuals. The most common level is between the L4 and L5 vertebrae, compressing the L5 nerve root (Figure 9.5A). S1 radiculopathy due to compression between the L5 and S1 levels is almost as frequent (Figure 9.6). The usual initial complaint is back pain; radicular pain and paresthesia in the lower limb follow. *Sciatica* refers to pain radiating from the back into the leg below the knee. Leg weakness is less common. Infrequently, a large mid-

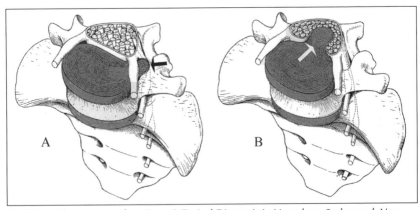

Modified with permission from Duus P. Topical Diagnosis in Neurology, 2nd rev. ed. New York: Thieme; 1989:63.

Figure 9.5 *Lumbar Herniations. Posterolateral protrusion of the L4-L5 disc compressing the L5 nerve root (A), central posterior protrusion compressing the cauda equina (B). Arrowheads indicate protrusions.*

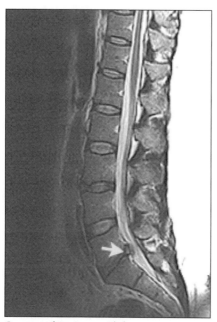

Courtesy of Dr. Roman Klufas.

Figure 9.6 *Lumbosacral Disc Herniation. MRI image reveals disc material at the L5-S1 level extending into the spinal canal, indicated by arrowhead.*

line herniation can compress multiple nerve roots in the cauda equina, causing bowel or bladder dysfunction (see Figure 9.5B).

Although typical herniation patients complain of sensory disturbances actual sensory loss is often not detected on examination. Most patients with lumbar herniations recover with conservative treatment. However, if symptoms are intractable or neurologic impairments such as bowel and bladder dysfunction occur, surgical intervention is recommended.

Lumbar spondylosis is the most common cause of lumbar spinal stenosis. Symptoms may be progressive or can occur suddenly. Patients may have *neurogenic claudication* in the legs. Symptoms include leg pain when standing that is worse with hyperextension and better with flexion at the waist. Walking becomes more and more difficult. This condition must be distinguished from *vascular claudication* due to impaired circulation. Surgical decompression is often necessary.

9.5 Whiplash

Whiplash refers to the cervical sprain and strain injury caused by sudden hyperextension and flexion movements, usually due to a rear-end motor vehicle collision. There are a few million such accidents annually, many producing whiplash. Roughly 80 percent of whiplash patients recover within six months.[14] Whiplash should not be diagnosed when there are other specific structural injuries such as fractures, herniated discs, nerve root or plexus damage, or spinal cord injury. Patients with these problems should not be placed in the "uncomplicated" whiplash category. If there

are symptoms indicating neurological involvement (radicular pain, paresthesia, weakness, myelopathy), investigation is indicated prior to beginning treatment.

There are four phases in a hyperextension-flexion injury.[15] Immediately following a rear-end impact the torso is forced backwards into the
seat while the head and neck initially remain fixed and the vehicle contin-
ues moving forward. Next, the head and neck begin to extend. In the second phase, the forces in the seat begin to return to normal, pushing the
torso forward while the head and neck are still moving backwards. In the
third phase, the torso has stopped moving forward and the head and neck
start their acceleration forward. In the fourth phase, the head and neck
have stopped moving forward and then the head snaps back, causing further extension.

It is highly improbable that an individual will be sitting in a perfectly
vertically aligned position. Therefore, there is also an element of rotation;
this may contribute to the neurologic injury in whiplash.

Neck pain develops in 65 percent of patients within six hours, in an
additional 28 percent within twenty-four hours, and within seventy-two
hours in the others.[16] The pain is usually associated with reduced neck
movement, stiffness, and tenderness. Initial treatment includes application of ice, nonsteroidal anti-inflammatory agents, muscle relaxants, and
pain medication. Prolonged use of soft cervical collars should be avoided.
Some patients respond to trigger point injections and myofascial release
techniques (stretch and spray).

Other common complaints following a whiplash injury are headache,
dizziness, paresthesia in the upper extremities, and arm weakness. Headaches occur in the great majority of whiplash patients and are usually occipital or generalized. They can last from minutes or hours to days. The
headaches usually have characteristics of muscle-contraction headache—
dull, aching, or squeezing—but can have migrainous qualities. However,
cervicogenic headache (see §15.5) is also common after whiplash. Headache pain may originate in the occipital nerves or the upper cervical spine.
Nonsteroidal anti-inflammatory medications, muscle relaxants, and tricyclic antidepressants are often effective treatments for these headaches.
Anesthetic nerve block injections may be useful for cases caused by occipital neuralgia.

MRI and x-ray studies of the cervical spines of asymptomatic individuals reveal a high rate of cervical spondylosis and disc abnormalities, including herniation and cord compression. In one study,[17] 20 percent of subjects forty-five to fifty-four years old and 57 percent over sixty-four years had disc protrusions; 16 and 26 percent respectively of these groups had spinal compression. In such patients a whiplash injury may convert a pre-existing asymptomatic radiculopathy or myelopathy into a symptomatic condition.

Several lines of evidence from imaging studies support the notion that whiplash can hasten development of cervical spondylosis and disc disease:[18]

- Higher rate of degenerative disc disease in whiplash victims compared to controls, 39 versus 6 percent
- Long-term follow-up of patients with pre-existing degenerative changes at the time of the whiplash revealed new degenerative changes at another spine level in 55 percent
- Ten-year follow-up demonstrated that degenerative spondylosis was more common following whiplash injury, occurring in 33 percent of thirty to forty-year-old patients, compared to 10 percent of controls

Few topics generate more controversy than the question of whether or not there is a physical basis for symptoms lasting longer than several months. The incidence of symptoms is higher for those involved in rear-end, as opposed to front or side impact, collision. Associated neurologic complaints are correlated with pain intensity, probably related to both specific injury-related factors and nonspecific posttraumatic factors.[19]

Somatization and malingering have to be considered in all patients with a whiplash injury but there is evidence that most patients who are still symptomatic at the end of litigation are not cured by the verdict, and that response to treatment and recovery rates are similar in those suing and those not.[20] The exception is the distinct minority who consciously exaggerate or malinger. However, there is also contrary evidence that eliminating compensation for pain and suffering improves the prognosis and decreases the incidence of whiplash complaints.[21]

Each case must be examined closely. It is clear that pain can trigger anxiety and depression. Cognitive complaints are well-known complications of these psychologic problems. Therefore, it is incorrect to assume automatically that an underlying brain injury is responsible.[22] In the context of whiplash clinicians and attorneys need to understand that "cognitive symptoms do not mean brain damage. Psychological symptoms do not mean malingering."[23]

Endnotes

1. Malanga GA, Nadler SF. "Nonoperative treatment of low back pain." *Mayo Clin Proc* 1999; 74:1135-1148.

2. Deyo RA, Tsui-Wu Y-J. "Descriptive epidemiology of low back pain and its related medical care in the United States." *Spine* 1987;12:264-268.

3. Atlas SJ, Nardin RA. "Evaluation and treatment of low back pain: An evidence-based approach to clinical care." *Muscle Nerve* 2003;27:265-284.

4. Jensen M, Brant-Zawadzki M, et al. "Magnetic resonance imaging of the lumbar spine in people without back pain." *N Engl J Med* 1994;331:69-73.

5. Nardin RA, Patel MR, et al. "Electromyography and magnetic resonance imaging in the evaluation of radiculopathy." *Muscle Nerve* 1999;22:151-155.

6. Byrne TN, Benzel EC, Waxman SG. *Diseases of the Spine and Spinal Cord.* New York: Oxford University Press; 2000: at 114.

7. Malanga GA, Nadler SF, *supra* note 1, at 1139.

8. Atlas SJ, Nardin RA, *supra* note 3, at 274-278.

9. Levin KH, Covington EC, et al. "Functional restoration of the patient with chronic spine pain." *Continuum* 2001;7(1):152-178.

10. Bracken MB, Shepard MJ, et al. "Administration of methylprednisolone for 24 or 48 hours or tirilazad mesylate for 48 hours in the treatment of acute spinal cord injury: Results of the third National Acute Spinal Cord Injury Randomized Controlled Trial." *JAMA* 1997;227:1597-1604.

11. McDonald JW, Becker D, et al. "Late recovery following spinal cord injury: Case report and review of the literature." *J Neurosurg (Spine 2)* 2002;97:252-265.

12. Goldsmith ME, Weisel SW. "Clinical evaluation of low back pain." *Comp Ther* 1998; 24:370-377.

13. Della-Guistina DA. "Emergency department evaluation and treatment of back pain." *Emergency Med Clin N Amer* 1999;17(4):877-897.

14. Radanov BP, Sturznegger M, DiStefano G. "Long-term outcome after whiplash injury: A 2-year follow-up considering features of injury mechanism and somatic, radiologic, and psychosocial findings." *Medicine* 1995;74:281-297.

15. Foreman SM, Croft AC. *Whiplash Injuries - The Cervical Acceleration/Deceleration Syndrome.* Baltimore: Williams & Wilkins; 1995.

16. Evans RW. "Whiplash injuries." In: Evans RW, ed. *Saunders Manual of Neurologic Practice.* Philadelphia: Saunders; 2003:526-529.

17. Teresi LM, Lufkin RB, et al. "Asymptomatic degenerative disc disease and spondylosis of the cervical spine: MR imaging. *Radiology* 1987;164:83-88.

18. Evans RW. "Whiplash injuries." In: Evans RW, Baskin DS, Yatsu FM, eds. *Prognosis of Neurologic Disorders*, 2nd ed. New York: Oxford University Press; 2000:152-167.

19. Kasch H, Bach FW, et al. "Development in pain and neurologic complaints after whiplash: A 1-year prospective study." *Neurology* 2003;60:743-761.

20. Evans RW, *supra* note 16, at 528.

21. Cassidy JD, Carroll LJ, et al. "Effect of eliminating compensation for pain and suffering on the outcome of insurance claims for whiplash injury." *N Engl J Med* 2000;342:1179-1186.

22. Alexander MP. "In the pursuit of proof of brain damage after whiplash injury." *Neurology* 1998;51:336-340.

23. Alexander MP. "Whiplash: Chronic pain and cognitive symptoms." *Neurology* 2003;60:733.

Additional Reading

Dobkin BH, ed. *The Clinical Science of Neurologic Rehabilitation*, 2nd ed. New York: Oxford University Press; 2003.

Evans RW, ed. *Neurology and Trauma*. Philadelphia: Saunders; 1996.

Narayan RK, Wilberger JE, Povlishock JT, eds. *Neurotrauma*. New York: McGraw-Hill; 1996.

The National Spinal Cord Injury Association: www.spinalcord.org, accessed December 24, 2004.

Chapter 10

Peripheral Neuropathy

10.1 Introduction

Peripheral neuropathies—disorders of the peripheral nerves—are common in general neurologic practice. Many neuropathies have medicolegal significance because they are the result of trauma or arise in the workplace. Neuropathies can be a significant source of pain, impairment, and disability. Unfortunately, many neuropathies cannot be cured or even treated effectively.

Symptoms reflect the extent of damage, the type of nerve fibers affected, and the location or distribution of dysfunction. Weakness is the most common motor symptom. It may be associated with some muscle wasting, indicative of a long-standing neuropathy. Guillain-Barré syndrome, lead neuropathy, multifocal motor neuropathy with conduction block, and tick paralysis are some examples of predominantly motor neuropathies.

Typical sensory neuropathy symptoms include burning, pain, pins and needles, and tingling. The most common sensory symptom, however, is loss of sensation—numbness. In most generalized neuropathies this begins in the toes and slowly ascends the legs. Eventually, deficits appear in the fingers and spread up the arms. The result is a classic "stocking and glove" distribution. A less common presentation is loss of proprioception, causing unsteady gait and clumsy hand movements. The incoordination is termed *sensory ataxia*. Predominantly sensory manifestations are seen with acute idiopathic or paraneoplastic sensory neuronopathy, carcinoma, diabetes mellitus, inherited sensory neuropathies, leprosy, paraproteinemias, vitamin B6 toxicity, and many other conditions.

Autonomic neuropathy can cause loss of sweating, postural hypotension (fall in blood pressure upon standing), impaired lacrimation and salivation, gastrointestinal dysfunction, and impotence. Autonomic dysfunction can predominate in neuropathies due to amyloidosis, diabetes mellitus, Guillain-Barré syndrome, idiopathic pandysautonomic neuropathy, porphyria, and vincristine toxicity.

Selected peripheral neuropathies are discussed below.

A. Classification of neuropathies

There are many ways to classify peripheral neuropathies. Neurologists rely on several schemes in order to narrow the field of diagnostic possibilities. First, neuropathies are either acquired or inherited. Acquired neuropathies are further categorized by cause. Common etiologies include:

- Connective tissue (collagen vascular) diseases—lupus, rheumatoid arthritis, and others
- Diabetes—the most common cause of neuropathy
- Infection—Hansen's disease (leprosy), HIV, Lyme disease
- Inflammatory processes—demyelinating polyradiculoneuropathies, vasculitis
- Medications—chemotherapy agents, isoniazid
- Nutritional deficiencies—vitamins B1, B12, E

- Systemic diseases—kidney, liver, lung failure
- Toxins—arsenic, lead, organophosphates
- Trauma—crush, stretch, and laceration
- Tumor—direct invasion of nerve fibers, remote effects (paraneoplastic syndromes)

However, unless the relationship between a specific cause and the neuropathy is unmistakably clear an etiologic classification is not the most useful for diagnostic purposes. More helpful is classifying neuropathies according to their anatomic distribution. Involvement of a single nerve is *mononeuropathy*. There may be *multiple mononeuropathy*—mononeuropathy multiplex in older literature—two or more nerves individually affected. Generalized involvement of peripheral nerves is *polyneuropathy*. A functional classification is also used—motor, sensory, autonomic, or mixed neuropathy—because the different types of nerve fibers are susceptible to different pathologic processes.

The type of onset is also helpful to classify neuropathies:

- Acute—hours or days: Guillain-Barré syndrome, infection, thallium poisoning
- Subacute—weeks or months: most toxic exposures, nutritional deficiencies
- Chronic—months or years: inherited neuropathies, paraneoplastic syndromes

The pace of onset has prognostic significance. Patients with an acute-onset neuropathy usually seek medical attention quickly, possibly before permanent and irreversible nerve damage. In contrast, patients with chronic neuropathies may not recognize a problem until the damage is beyond any hope of treatment or recovery. Neuropathies are also subdivided on the basis of biopsy and electrodiagnostic studies into those mainly affecting myelin—*demyelinating neuropathies*—and those mainly affecting axons—*axonal neuropathies*—again because these categories suggest different causes.

B. Evaluation

Diagnosis of neuropathies can be haphazard. Some clinicians use a costly "shotgun" approach, ordering a broad range of laboratory tests without first categorizing the neuropathy. Others rely on their knowledge of neuropathies to recognize a pattern with diagnostic significance. The cause may never be determined. Using an orderly, methodical approach is likely to increase the diagnostic yield while limiting unnecessary testing.[1]

The process should begin by confirming the presence of a peripheral neuropathy and determining its anatomic or functional distribution. The history and examination may provide enough information to determine an obvious etiology. If not, the neurologist should establish the underlying pathology—whether axonal or demyelinating, and whether affecting small or large nerve fibers. Other clinical features of the illness are explored and associations with systemic diseases are considered. EMG and NCS "are the most cost-effective and useful initial screening test for evaluation of peripheral neuropathy."[2]

If the cause is still unclear routine testing should include:[3] blood count, chemistries, sedimentation rate, serum B12 level, serum protein electrophoresis, and immunoelectrophoresis. Additional studies are selected based on the initial results or specific clinical suspicions.

10.2 Peripheral Nerve Trauma
A. Mechanisms of damage

Any nerve can be injured by compression, sharp or blunt trauma, or traction. Peripheral nerve injuries occur as a result of falls, motor vehicle accidents, penetrating trauma such as lacerations, and work-related incidents. Upper limb nerve injuries are more common than lower. The radial, ulnar, and median are the most frequently damaged arm nerves; the sciatic and peroneal the most commonly injured leg nerves.[4]

Nerve fibers have only a few possible pathologic responses to traumatic injury. The most widely used classification scheme is Seddon's:[5]

- *Neurapraxia*—mildest degree of injury: probably due to disruption of the myelin without axonal damage; nerve conduction may be blocked or slowed but the muscle is not disconnected, or *denervated*; recovery is typical but occasionally takes weeks or longer; the unpleasant tingling and pain caused by hitting the ulnar nerve ("funny bone") at the elbow is a common neurapraxia injury

- *Axonotmesis*—more severe injury: usually due to crush or stretch; axons and myelin affected, supportive tissue intact to variable degree; axon regrowth and recovery possible
- *Neurotmesis*—most severe injury: nerve completely severed or severe disruption of axons, myelin, and supportive tissues; no spontaneous recovery

The axonal wasting beyond the site of damage in axonotmesis and neurotmesis injuries is called *Wallerian degeneration*. Nerve conduction fails. The muscle supplied by the nerve may atrophy and weaken. If the site of injury is very close to the cell body degeneration and destruction may also move proximally. Axonal regrowth after Wallerian degeneration is possible only if the three layers of surrounding supportive tissue are not disrupted. Sunderland's nerve injury classification scheme[6] divides axonotmesis into three categories based on the degree of damage to the supportive tissue. Surgical reconstruction of the nerve may improve the chances of axonal regrowth after axonotmesis and is the only hope in neurotmesis. The timing of surgery depends on the type of trauma.[7]

B. Double crush syndrome

This refers to simultaneous compression of a single nerve at more than one location. The term was coined in 1973, in a study of one hundred fifteen patients with ulnar neuropathy at the elbow or carpal tunnel syndrome.[8] According to the authors most also had cervical nerve root abnormalities. The hypothesis is that proximal compression, not necessarily severe, predisposes the nerve to a second distal compression. The concept has been extended to include metabolic processes such as diabetes as the predisposing lesion. Also, a reverse double crush syndrome is described where a preexisting distal compression predisposes to proximal symptoms.[9]

The double crush concept is quite appealing and widely accepted. However, the original study did not use electrodiagnostic testing to confirm cervical root involvement in all cases. It is probable that many did not have cervical radiculopathy.[10] Furthermore, a very detailed analysis of double crush did not find experimental support for the notion that the portion of a nerve distal to a focal lesion is more susceptible to injury.[11]

Also, an intraspinal canal sensory nerve root lesion cannot be the predisposing site for a distal lesion producing sensory complaints, the most common clinical situation where double crush is invoked. The simple anatomic reason for this is the lack of continuity of the nerve fibers between the two locations.[12] Sensory neuron cell bodies lie outside the spinal canal in groupings known as ganglia. There are separate fibers transmitting from the periphery to the cell bodies and from the cell bodies to the spinal cord. A typical herniated disc might affect the latter but not the former.

Therefore, double crush syndrome is an overused label that deserves skepticism.

10.3 Carpal Tunnel Syndrome

The *median nerve* is formed by the union of portions of the lateral and medial cords of the brachial plexus. It supplies the forearm flexor muscles of the wrist and fingers. Median injury creates grip weakness and sensory loss in the first through third digits and radial half of the fourth digit. The median nerve may be compressed near the elbow by the pronator teres muscle. It is also vulnerable to diagnostic or therapeutic needle punctures in the antecubital fossa.

Entrapment at the wrist is due to the *carpal tunnel syndrome* (CTS). This is the most common entrapment neuropathy and is often bilateral. Typical symptoms include:

- Improvement with shaking the hands
- Nocturnal exacerbations
- Numbness, burning, tingling, and pain in the hand and median-innervated digits
- Pain radiating up the arm, sometimes into the shoulder
- Wrist and palm pain

CTS is more common in women, with a prevalence of 3 percent compared to 2 percent in men.[13] Spontaneous cases are associated with acromegaly (gigantism), diabetes, pregnancy, rheumatoid arthritis, and thyroid disease. Acute wrist trauma can also cause CTS. Work-related CTS probably accounts for at least half of all cases.

The diagnosis of work-related CTS often has medicolegal ramifications. The neurologist's role is to make an accurate diagnosis and to analyze issues of causation carefully. Most workers with hand and arm complaints do not have CTS. Tendonitis and other musculoskeletal injuries are much more common than CTS. Also, median nerve conduction slowing occurs naturally with age and is not necessarily symptomatic.[14]

A reliable CTS diagnosis requires the presence of typical symptoms in conjunction with definite nerve conduction abnormalities. Special techniques and additional measurements are necessary to evaluate possible CTS in patients with polyneuropathy.[15] A small portion of patients with typical clinical symptoms of CTS will have normal electrodiagnostic studies. There are several newer more sensitive nerve conduction techniques that increase diagnostic accuracy but false negative results are still possible.[16] There are also false positive results because some asymptomatic workers have mild nerve conduction abnormalities. Therefore, although nerve conduction studies have an essential role in the diagnostic process, they should not be relied upon to the exclusion of clinical symptoms.

Causation questions in work-related cases require the neurologist to document:[17]

- Clear evidence of the diagnosis
- History of both work and nonwork factors that could contribute to CTS
- Whether it is more probable or not that the CTS is work-related

The neurologist must be aware of the worker's job duties in order to address causation. High risk activities involve repetitive movements with high force and awkward positions, strong vibrations, or pressure on the wrist.[18]

10.4 Other Mononeuropathies
A. Upper limb
The *radial nerve* is a continuation of the posterior cord of the brachial plexus. It innervates the triceps and extensor muscles of the wrist and fin-

gers. It also carries sensory information from the lower half of the radial aspect of the arm and part of the back of the hand. Damage to the radial nerve above the elbow produces wrist and finger drop, as well as sensory loss. The nerve is most vulnerable to damage in the spiral groove of the humerus, and is often injured there by a fracture. Compression of the radial nerve is the classic cause of *Saturday night palsy*. This occurs when the nerve is compressed when an intoxicated individual falls asleep with the arm draped over the arm of a chair. Less common causes are misplaced injections and improper positioning of a patient during surgery.

The *ulnar nerve* is derived from the eighth cervical and first thoracic spinal nerves. It lies behind the medial condyle of the humerus at the elbow. It supplies the muscles that flex the wrist on the ulnar side and most of the intrinsic hand muscles. Damage to the nerve at the elbow causes weakness of grip in the ulnar side of the hand and wasting of the interosseus muscles. Sensory loss is in the fifth finger, the ulnar side of the fourth finger, and the ulnar edge of the hand extending to the wrist. Ulnar neuropathy may occur after minor trauma, for example, in someone who drives with the left elbow resting on the window or who sits for long periods with elbows propped on a table. It is also common in diabetics.

Ulnar neuropathies occur peri-operatively, and can be bilateral. They occur more frequently in men and in thin or obese individuals rather than average-sized individuals. Most are attributed to arm positioning during surgery. However, recent more detailed analysis indicates that operative positioning is probably not the cause of these neuropathies. Rather, they develop post-operatively, due to pressure on the nerve while the patient is recumbent during the recuperative period.[19] Lacerations may injure the ulnar nerve at the wrist. A pressure neuropathy of the deep palmar branch of the ulnar nerve can occur in individuals who have prolonged or recurrent pressure on the outer part of the palm.

The *long thoracic nerve* is derived from the 5th, 6th, and 7th cervical roots. It supplies the serratus anterior, a muscle that fixes the scapula to the chest wall. Weakness causes a form of winged scapula. A typical cause is pressure on the nerve at the shoulder from backpacks, book bags, or other heavy objects.

B. Lower limb

The *femoral nerve* is derived from the lumbar plexus. It forms in the psoas muscle, passes through the pelvis, and enters the thigh beneath the inguinal ligament lateral to the femoral sheath and femoral vessels. In the abdomen it sends branches to the iliacus muscle. In the femoral triangle, it divides into terminal branches supplying the sartorius and quadriceps muscles. The sensory branches of the nerve supply the anterior and medial aspects of the lower two-thirds of the thigh. The terminal saphenous branch supplies sensation to the inner aspect of the leg and the foot.

The major clinical finding in femoral nerve palsy is weak knee extension due to paralysis of the quadriceps. The leg gives way when walking, climbing stairs, or attempting to stand. There is loss of sensation in the cutaneous distribution of the nerve. Femoral neuropathies can be caused by abscess in the psoas muscle, blood clot in the iliacus muscle, pelvic tumors, pelvic fractures, hip dislocation, or hip replacement surgery. Most of the surgical injuries are caused by stretching of the nerve, particularly by abdominal retractors, though excessive hip flexion or extension can also damage this nerve.[20]

The *sciatic nerve* is derived from the lumbosacral plexus. It runs through the pelvis, out into the buttock through the sciatic notch, and then descends in the posterior thigh. Close to the popliteal fossa, it divides into the common peroneal and tibial nerves. In the thigh, the sciatic supplies the hamstring muscles. The common peroneal and tibial nerve branches of the sciatic supply all of the muscles below the knee. A complete sciatic nerve lesion produces weakness in the knee flexors and all leg and foot muscles. Foot drop occurs as a result of paralysis of the anterior tibial and peroneal muscles; patients drag the toes of the affected foot and are unable to stand on their heels. Sensory loss is over the outer and lower aspect of the lower leg and across the dorsum of the foot. The sciatic nerve may be damaged as a result of fractures of the pelvis or femur; the commonest cause, however, is a misplaced injection in the buttock.

The *common peroneal* (or lateral popliteal) nerve runs around the head of the fibula and is most likely to be damaged at that site, usually by external compression. This can occur with knee or upper tibia trauma. The nerve can also be damaged in patients in the lithotomy position if the straps are incorrectly placed. Most common peroneal palsies resolve over a period of several months. They can be confused with L5 radiculopathy.

10.5 Brachial Plexus Abnormalities
A. Anatomy (Figure 10.1)

The brachial plexus is formed by the fifth through eighth cervical and the first thoracic spinal nerves, with some variations. If there is a contribution from the fourth cervical nerve, the plexus is said to be "prefixed". In a "postfixed" plexus, there is no contribution from the fourth cervical root, but a major contribution from the second thoracic root.

Above the clavicle the spinal nerve roots form three *trunks*—C5 and C6 the upper, C7 the middle, and C8 and T1 the lower. Behind the clavicle each trunk divides into anterior and posterior divisions. Finally, the divisions unite below the clavicle to form three cords—the three posterior divisions forming the posterior, the two upper anterior divisions the lateral, and the lower anterior division the medial. Thus, the lateral cord contains nerve fibers from the fifth through the seventh spinal roots. The medial cord contains fibers from the eighth cervical and first thoracic nerve. The posterior cord contains fibers from the fifth through eighth cervical nerves. The radial and axillary nerves are the main terminal branches of the posterior cord. The musculocutaneous nerve and lateral head of the median nerve are the terminal branches of the lateral cord. The medial cord terminates as the ulnar nerve and medial head of the median nerve.

B. Brachial plexopathies

The brachial plexus lies in the neck. Brachial plexus disorders due to lesions above the clavicle are *supraclavicular*. Lesions below the clavicle produce the more common *infraclavicular* plexopathies. The supraclavicular region contains nerve roots and trunks; the infraclavicular area includes the cords and terminal peripheral nerves. Electrodiagnosis requires a clear understanding of the anatomy and nerve innervation of the arm muscles. Brachial plexopathies usually produce axonal damage. Needle EMG may reveal signs of denervation. Nerve conduction studies may show reduced amplitude responses. The sensory studies are especially important in differentiating plexus from nerve root lesions; amplitudes are not reduced by nerve root lesions.

Upper plexus lesions (C5 and 6 roots, trunks) mainly affect the shoulder girdle muscles. A severe upper plexus lesion causes the upper arm to hang uselessly, rotated so that the palm of the hand is visible from the rear (waiter's tip position). With infraclavicular plexus lesions, there is in-

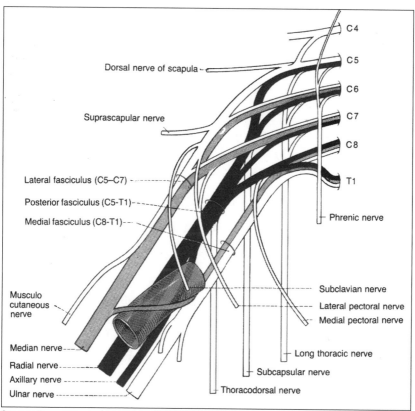

Source: Duus P. Topical Diagnosis in Neurology, 2nd rev. ed. New York: Thieme; 1989:24.
Reprinted by permission.

Figure 10.1 Brachial Plexus. The nerve roots forming this plexus first combine to form three trunks-upper, middle, and lower. These divide into anterior and posterior divisions that, in turn, form the three fasciculi, or cords. For simplicity the trunks and divisions are not labeled.

volvement mainly of the proximal portions of the median, radial, and ulnar nerves. The weakness is in forearm or hand muscles.

The brachial plexus is prone to traction injury, primarily because of the distance between the fixation points (the vertebral column and the axillary sheath). The plexus is at risk of open injury from gun shot wounds and other penetrating trauma. Closed injuries occur with birth trauma, falls, shoulder dislocations, improper positioning on operating tables, and sports and traffic accidents. Surgical procedures in the supraclavicular fossa may damage the plexus. Radiation therapy is a well-known cause of brachial plexopathy; another is neoplastic infiltration, particularly from lung tumors (*pancoast syndrome*).

An idiopathic form of brachial plexopathy—*neuralgic amyotrophy* (Parsonage-Turner syndrome)—is characterized by an abrupt onset of severe shoulder and upper arm pain. As the pain subsides over the next week or so, weakness becomes apparent. Recovery takes place over weeks or months, and is usually good. Precipitating factors include viral infections, vaccinations, childbirth, and surgical procedures. Neuralgic amyotrophy is probably an autoimmune disorder. There is also a rare inherited form of the condition.

A recent detailed review of brachial plexopathies, including anatomic and electrodiagnostic considerations, is available.[21]

C. Thoracic outlet syndrome

Classic or undisputed neurogenic thoracic outlet syndrome (TOS) is a rare non-traumatic brachial plexopathy caused by compression of the medial cord or lower trunk of the plexus by a cervical rib or fibrous band. Electrodiagnostic and clinical testing reveals abnormalities in the affected nerves and their muscles. Reduced ulnar sensory amplitudes and denervation in median thenar muscles are the most common findings. The medial antebrachial cutaneous sensory response is an especially sensitive test.[22] Classic neurogenic TOS produces dull intermittent pain radiating into the medial aspect of the hand and forearm. There may be atrophy of the *thenar* hand muscles. This condition mostly affects young adult women. Surgical treatment is recommended, but only if the diagnosis is clearly established.

Disputed or *nonspecific* neurogenic TOS refers to a syndrome of pain and sensory changes in a similar distribution to true TOS, but without electrodiagnostic or objective clinical findings. Several compression sites might exist, reflected in different labels used for these symptoms—*scalenus anticus*, *costoclavicular*, and *hyperabduction syndromes*.[23] There is considerable controversy about this diagnosis. A leading proponent claims this is an underdiagnosed, legitimate diagnosis whose symptoms reflect brachial plexus involvement too mild to produce the definitive findings of classic TOS.[24] However, one skeptic points out that the proposed mechanisms offered to explain disputed neurogenic TOS are unproven.[25] Needless to say, the role of surgery in disputed neurogenic TOS is also disputed.

10.6 Other Acquired Neuropathies
A. Acute acquired neuropathies

The most common cause of acute generalized neuropathic weakness is Guillain-Barré syndrome[26] (GBS), also known as *acute inflammatory demyelinating polyradiculoneuropathy*. There are a few thousand cases annually. GBS usually follows infections, especially viral gastroenteritis and upper respiratory infections, but is not itself an infectious disease. It can occur after vaccinations and has been reported in association with pregnancy, surgical procedures, and a variety of systemic diseases. In about one-third of cases, no antecedent cause is identified.

Typical patients present with weakness in the feet that then ascends, eventually involving the muscles of respiration and the upper limbs in many cases. Maximal weakness occurs within a few weeks, rarely in days. Approximately one-quarter of patients require ventilator support.[27] Patients often complain of sensory disturbances or low-back pain, but objective abnormality of sensation is unusual except in the very rare *pure sensory* variant. Muscle stretch reflexes are diminished or lost. Cranial nerves are usually spared, with the notable exception of the less common *Miller-Fisher* GBS variant characterized by ophthalmoplegia (paralysis of eye movement), lost reflexes, and incoordination.

Nerve conduction studies reveal significant conduction slowing or conduction block, indicating a demyelinating process. Sometimes, the only abnormality is prolongation of the F wave, an electrical measure sensitive to dysfunction in the proximal portions of the nerve. Almost all patients will have abnormal cerebrospinal fluid, with an elevated protein level but no abnormal increase in cells. This so-called *albuminocytologic dissociation* distinguishes GBS from most infectious processes. However, repeat lumbar punctures may be needed to capture this finding.

Standard treatments that reduce recovery time are intravenous immunoglobulin therapy and plasmapheresis; corticosteroids are not effective.[28] Patients also require supportive care and appropriate interventions to manage common complications such as autonomic dysfunction, respiratory insufficiency, and infections. Most patients recover but some are left with significant permanent impairment.

The differential diagnosis for GBS includes other causes of acute neuropathy and weakness—tick paralysis, diphtheria, botulism, heavy metal

poisoning, and several varieties of porphyria, especially the acute intermittent form.

B. Subacute acquired neuropathies

In these patients the neuropathy develops over weeks or months. Most are
due to deficiency states, toximetabolic disturbances, or inflammatory
conditions. The patient usually complains of unpleasant sensations, particularly in the feet, that gradually spread proximally. Eventually, there is
involvement of the fingers and hands. Weakness is usually less prominent
than the sensory abnormality and tends to develop later.

Causes of subacute acquired neuropathies include alcohol, arsenic,
lead, industrial solvents (particularly *n*-hexane), and medications (certain
antibiotics, anticonvulsants, cytotoxics, cardiovascular drugs, and many
others).

C. Chronic acquired neuropathies

In these patients the symptoms develop over months or years. Chronic
neuropathies are associated with carcinomas, paraproteinemias, connective tissue disorders, and amyloidosis. Diabetes mellitus is the most common cause of chronic polyneuropathy. Most diabetics will develop nerve
conduction abnormalities indicative of a distal, symmetric sensorimotor
neuropathy. This neuropathy is length-dependent; the longest nerves are
affected first. Patients will lose sensation and may develop paresthesia in
the feet. The changes ascend over months or years. At some point the upper extremities are affected.

Small-fiber neuropathy is the most common form of painful sensory
neuropathy in people over fifty.[29] The pain is caused by damage to small
myelinated (A-delta) and unmyelinated (C) fibers. Patients may have autonomic dysfunction and some large-fiber involvement. Causes include
diabetes, toxins, amyloidosis, and inherited neuropathies.[30] The pain has
neuropathic qualities (see §7.3B) and is often worse at night. There is diminished pinprick and touch sensation, relative or total sparing of position
and vibration sense, and normal muscle stretch reflexes. Antiepileptics
and tricyclic antidepressants may be helpful for the pain.

Chronic inflammatory demyelinating polyradiculoneuropathy is an
autoimmune condition that resembles GBS. However, the symptoms
progress for at least two months and autonomic dysfunction is unusual.

Corticosteroids, intravenous immunoglobulin, plasma exchange, and immunosuppressants are effective but there is a high relapse rate.

10.7 Inherited Neuropathies

DNA and biochemical analysis have changed our understanding of this diverse group. The main category is the *hereditary motor and sensory neuropathies* (*HMSN*). Types I (demyelinating) and II (axonal)—formerly known as Charcot-Marie-Tooth disease or peroneal muscular atrophy—are by far the most common. Severity of nerve dysfunction and clinical deficits vary considerably among the numerous HMSN subtypes and also within afflicted kinships. Motor involvement is usually greater than sensory. There is no effective treatment for these slowly progressive diseases.

One HMSN subtype deserves special mention. *Hereditary neuropathy with liability to pressure palsies* (HNPP) produces recurrent painless sensory or motor neuropathies. Symptoms are triggered by mild trauma or compression that would not cause difficulty in normal individuals (leaning on an elbow, crossing legs).[31] HNPP must be considered in any worker with multiple neuropathies in a limb because occupational multiple mononeuropathies in one limb are rare.[32]

There are five subtypes of *hereditary sensory and autonomic neuropathy*. The loss of sensory function can be severe enough to produce indifference to pain and associated mutilating deformities. There are several varieties of *familial amyloid polyneuropathy*. These are characterized by sensory and autonomic dysfunction and failure of other organs due to the abnormal deposition of the amyloid protein. Liver transplantation may stop the progression of symptoms. Many rare metabolic diseases also cause neuropathies—Refsum's disease, Fabry's disease, and Tangier disease, to name but a few.

Endnotes

1. Dyck PJ, Dyck JB, et al. "Ten steps in characterizing and diagnosing patients with peripheral neuropathy." *Neurology* 1996;47:10-17.

2. Pourmand R. "Evaluating patients with suspected peripheral neuropathy: Do the right thing, not everything." *Muscle Nerve* 2002;26:288-290.

3. *Id.* at 289.

4. Robinson LR. "AAEM Minimonograph #28: Traumatic injury to peripheral nerves." *Muscle Nerve* 2000;23:863-873.

5. Seddon HJ. *Surgical Disorders of the Peripheral Nerve*, 2nd ed. New York: Churchill Livingstone; 1975.

6. Sunderland S. *Nerves and Nerve Injuries*, 2nd ed. New York: Churchill Livingstone; 1978.

7. Robinson LR, *supra* note 4, at 10.

8. Upton RM, McComas AJ. "The double crush in nerve entrapment syndromes." *Lancet* 1973;2 (7825):359-362.

9. Dahlin LB, Lundborg G. "The neurone and its response to peripheral nerve compression." *J Hand Surg Br* 1990;15:5-10.

10. Swensen RS. "The double crush syndrome." *Neurology Chronicle* 1994; 4(2):1-6.

11. Wilbourn AJ, Gilliatt RW. "Double-crush syndrome: A critical analysis." *Neurology* 1997;49:21-29.

12. *Id.* at 26-27.

13. Katz JN, Simmons BP. "Carpal tunnel syndrome." *N Engl J Med* 2002; 346:1807-1812.

14. Nathan PA, Keniston RC, et al. "Natural history of median nerve sensory conduction in industry: Relationship to symptoms and carpal tunnel syndrome in 558 hands over 11 years." *Muscle Nerve* 1998;21:711-721.

15. Vogt T, Mika A, et al. "Evaluation of carpal tunnel syndrome in patients with polyneuropathy." *Muscle Nerve* 1997;20:153-157.

16. Stevens JC. "AAEM minimonograph #26: The electrodiagnosis of carpal tunnel syndrome." *Muscle Nerve* 1997;20:1477-1486.

17. Rosenbaum RB, Franklin GM, et al. "Carpal tunnel syndrome." *Continuum* 2001; 7(5):12-31.

18. *Id.* at 20.

19. Stewart JD, Shantz SH. "Perioperative ulnar neuropathies: a medicolegal review." *Can J Neurol Sci* 2003;30:15-19.

20. Warner MA. "Perioperative neuropathies." *Mayo Clin Proc* 1998;73:567-574.

21. Ferrante MA. "Brachial plexopathies: Classification, causes, and consequences." *Muscle Nerve* 2004;30:547-568.

22. Katirji B. "Neurogenic thoracic outlet syndrome." In: Evans RW, ed. *Saunders Manual of Neurologic Practice*. Philadelphia: Saunders; 2003: at 611-614.

23. *Id*. at 611.

24. Roos DB. "Thoracic outlet syndrome is underdiagnosed." *Muscle Nerve* 1999;22:126-129.

25. Wilbourn AJ. "Thoracic outlet syndrome is overdiagnosed." *Muscle Nerve* 1999;22:130-136.

26. Weinberg DH. "AAEM case report 4: Guillain-Barré syndrome." *Muscle Nerve* 1999;22:271-281.

27. Hughes RAC, Wijdicks EFM, et al. "Practice parameter: Immunotherapy for Guillain-Barré syndrome: Report of the Quality Standards Subcommittee of the American Academy of Neurology. *Neurology* 2003;61:736-740.

28. *Id*. at 737-738.

29. Mendell JR, Zarife S. "Painful sensory neuropathy." *N Engl J Med* 2003; 348:1243-1255.

30. Lacomis D. "Small-fiber neuropathy." *Muscle Nerve* 2002;26:173-188.

31. Machkhas H, Harati Y. "Genetically determined peripheral neuropathies." In: Evans RW, *supra* note 22, at 593-603.

32. Rosenbaum RB, Franklin GM, et al., *supra* note 17, at 17.

Additional Reading

Dyck PJ, Thomas PK, et al., eds. *Peripheral Neuropathy*, 4th ed. Philadelphia: Saunders; 2005.

Mendell JR, Kissel JT, Cornblath DR, eds. *Diagnosis and Management of Peripheral Nerve Disorders*. New York: Oxford University Press; 2001.

Stewart JD. *Focal Peripheral Neuropathies*, 3rd ed. New York: Elsevier; 2001.

The Neuropathy Association: www.neuropathy.org, accessed December 24, 2004.

Chapter 11

Seizures and Epilepsy

11.1 Background

Seizures are sudden, excessive, abnormal electrical discharges in the cerebral cortex. Some seizures produce dramatic clinical manifestations but others produce few or no overt signs. Epileptic seizures can produce changes in behavior, emotion, level of consciousness, motor function, or sensation—or any combination thereof. *Nonepileptic seizures* (see §11.3) are paroxysmal spells occurring without abnormal electrical discharges. These can be very difficult to distinguish from epileptic seizures.

Epilepsy is a chronic condition characterized by recurrent unprovoked seizures arising in an individual with a brain dysfunction. Individu-

189

als who have had a single epileptic seizure do not necessarily have epilepsy and may not require treatment. *Epileptic syndromes*—or *epilepsies*—have characteristic manifestations; some are discussed below in §11.5. There are approximately two million persons in the United States with epilepsy and 100,000 new cases annually.[1] The incidence is highest in neonates and the elderly.

A seizure is a symptom of cerebral dysfunction, not a final diagnosis. A first seizure should trigger a search for a cause. Epileptic seizures are classified broadly into two types: partial and generalized (see §11.4). Seizures are considered *idiopathic* or *primary* if they have a genetic basis or no identifiable cause. These account for more than half of all seizures.

Symptomatic or *secondary* seizures have an underlying, identifiable cause. The frequency of specific etiologies varies according to the patient's age. In the first month of life seizures commonly occur because of prenatal or perinatal injuries, inborn metabolic abnormalities, congenital malformations, or CNS infections. Developmental disorders, infections, metabolic abnormalities, and trauma are the main identifiable causes of seizures in older infants and young children. In teenagers and young adults head trauma, illicit drug use, alcohol withdrawal, and brain tumors become more common causes. In elderly patients, cerebrovascular disease is the likeliest cause of secondary seizures. Brain tumors, toximetabolic derangements, trauma, and degenerative disorders are also frequent causes of seizures in adults.

Symptomatic seizures can be classified as acute or remote, according to whether the seizure occurs in the presence of the noxious influence or only after exposure. These are not mutually exclusive categories. Traumatic brain injury can produce acute impact seizures as well as remote late-onset seizures; cerebral hemorrhage can provoke acute seizures due to irritation from the blood and remote seizures from the resulting scar tissue.

Acute symptomatic seizures are usually associated with a disturbance in cerebral electrical function—*encephalopathy*—caused by electrolyte imbalance, a metabolic disorder, or a drug effect. They may occur in drug withdrawal states, particularly from alcohol, barbiturates, and benzodiazepines. Remote symptomatic causes of epilepsy include hypoxic-ischemic cerebral insults—when the brain is starved of oxygen or blood—

and hippocampal sclerosis, a type of scarring within a region of the temporal lobe.

Cognitive and other neuropsychiatric problems are common in people with epilepsy.[2] More than half of all children with epilepsy have IQ scores below 90, more than a quarter below 70.[3] These impairments may reflect seizure discharges, psychological issues triggered by the functional limitations of the epilepsy, or medication side effects. Depression and memory complaints are particularly common.

Underemployment and unemployment in adults with epilepsy contribute to the huge economic burden of the disease. In one survey of people with epilepsy, 25 percent were unemployed—and most of them blamed their epilepsy.[4] Employment rights for these individuals are expanding slowly.[5]

11.2 Diagnosis

The diagnosis of epilepsy rests firmly on the clinical history. The first step is to determine if, in fact, the patient has had epileptic seizures. This may require interviews with friends or family members who witnessed the episodes in question. The history should include information about the onset of the episode and any associated features. A past history of similar episodes as well as a history of head trauma and other potential causes of seizures is important.

A detailed neurological examination is the most important investigation in a new seizure patient. Any abnormality, particularly if asymmetric, increases the likelihood of an intracranial cause for the seizure. The general medical examination may reveal signs of infection, congenital or developmental abnormalities, alcohol or illicit drug use, or cancer. Blood count, chemistries, and urinalysis are performed to identify evidence of infection, toximetabolic disturbances, and other disorders.

MRI is the imaging procedure of choice to detect tumors, vascular malformations, abscesses, and other epileptogenic intracranial abnormalities. MRI shows greater structural detail than CT. Special imaging techniques should be used to identify hippocampal sclerosis and other lesions that cause partial-onset seizures. Standard MRI scans interpreted by nonexpert readers are significantly less sensitive than specialized epilepsy protocol scans interpreted by experts, and may fail to identify more than half the potentially treatable structural lesions.[6] If MRI is unavailable or cannot be used, CT should be performed. In either case, contrast enhancement is recommended to increase the diagnostic yield. Functional imaging—PET, SPECT, and magnetic resonance spectroscopy—may add important information in evaluation of epilepsy surgery candidates.[7]

Electroencephalography (EEG) is surrounded by mystique. The EEG can detect abnormal electrical activity. However, this information must be correlated with the clinical picture. A small number of normal individuals have so-called *epileptiform discharges* but no clinical evidence of seizures. Even more important, the initial routine EEG may be normal in roughly half the patients with clear-cut clinical evidence of seizures.[8] Thus, a normal EEG does not exclude a diagnosis of epilepsy. Hyperventilation, photic stimulation, and sleep deprivation are *activation techniques* used to provoke epileptiform abnormalities during recording of the routine EEG. Doubts have been raised about the epileptogenic effect of sleep deprivation.[9]

Miniaturized EEG recording equipment is available. This allows prolonged *ambulatory* EEG monitoring, as noted earlier (see §3.3A). Prolonged monitoring with simultaneous video recording is done mostly in specialized inpatient epilepsy centers in cases where the diagnosis is uncertain.

11.3 Nonepileptic Seizures

There are many paroxysmal events that can be confused with seizures.[10] These occur in medical, neurologic, and psychiatric disorders. Nonepileptic spells are classified as either *physiologic* or *psychogenic*. The key to determining the nature of a particular episode is a thorough understanding of the manifestations of both epileptic seizures and the nonepileptic conditions that mimic epilepsy. Diagnosis may be complicated by the coexistence of both epileptic and nonepileptic episodes in the same patient.

Stress may trigger epileptic seizures, but is more likely to produce panic attacks or syncope. Epileptic auras rarely last more than seconds, whereas longer-lasting symptoms often precede nonepileptic spells. Epileptic seizures are stereotyped in most patients and rarely last more than a few minutes; nonepileptic spells are more variable and tend to last longer. Nonepileptic seizures can mimic almost any seizure type.[11]

A. Physiologic nonepileptic paroxysmal disorders

Physiologic nonepileptic seizures can be caused by syncope, migraine, night terrors and other sleep disorders, toximetabolic disturbances, transient ischemic attacks, vertigo, and movement disorders.

Probably the most common is syncope, or fainting. This is caused by reduced blood flow to the brain. Convulsive movements can occur during fainting spells, causing more diagnostic confusion. However, unconsciousness precedes the convulsive muscle stiffening in syncope whereas the contractions occur simultaneously with loss of consciousness in most seizures. There are several other differentiating features.[12]

A detailed history and physical examination should lead to the correct diagnosis. EEG can be very helpful but is often normal in epileptic patients. Electrocardiogram and prolonged cardiac monitoring are needed when there is suspicion of cardiac arrhythmia. The physical examination is especially important in patients with suspected cardiovascular causes for their spells. They may have signs of peripheral vascular disease or murmurs from abnormal cardiac valves.

The diagnosis of migraine is also largely based on history. Migrainous auras have a more gradual onset and tend to last longer than epileptic auras. The characteristic headache after the aura and a family history of migraine are other helpful distinguishing features. However, migrainous auras can occur without a subsequent headache.

Dyskinesias—abnormal movements—are generally more persistent than seizures. Most dyskinesias disappear during sleep whereas many seizures are triggered by sleep. There are several rare paroxysmal movement disorders that are difficult to distinguish from seizures. These are more likely to involve different body parts randomly, rather than occur in a stereotyped fashion as with most motor seizures.

B. Psychogenic nonepileptic paroxysmal disorders

Panic attacks, dissociative episodes, and rage attacks can all be confused with epileptic seizures. However, when patients themselves believe that they are having seizures and attempt to convince others of this, terms such as *pseudoseizures*, *nonepileptic psychogenic spells*, or *psychogenic seizures* are used. Some clinicians argue against use of the word "pseudoseizure" because of its connotation of deliberate falsification of symptoms. Indeed, psychogenic spells often elicit very negative, and even hostile, reactions from medical personnel.

Psychogenic spells are the most common nonepileptic events, occurring in up to 40 percent of patients with intractable spells evaluated in epilepsy centers.[13] Misdiagnosis can occur if clinicians rely on clinical signs only; urinary incontinence and tongue biting are common in nonepileptic psychogenic spells. Accurate diagnosis is exceedingly difficult without video EEG monitoring. Patients are hospitalized unnecessarily for seizures and subjected to the potential side effects of anticonvulsant medication.

Even after making the diagnosis of psychogenic spells the outcome is not good. In a study of 164 psychogenic seizure patients (none of whom had coexisting epileptic seizures) 71.2 percent continued to have spells after a mean of four years following diagnosis and more than half were unable to work because of the spells.[14] Part of the blame for the poor outcome may relate to the underlying psychopathology seen in many of these patients. A lack of communication with other clinicians on the part of the diagnosing neurologist is another factor. Indeed, less than one-fifth of psychiatrists trust a psychogenic diagnosis made by video EEG.[15]

Psychogenic spells usually indicate a conversion reaction. They may be a manifestation of *somatization disorder* or other *somatoform* conditions (see §7.5B). Psychogenic spells can occur in *factitious disorder* (Munchausen's syndrome), where symptoms are produced in order to maintain the patient role (see §7.5A). Malingering—the conscious and deliberate feigning of illness for improper gain—is another possible cause of psychogenic spells. Malingering is a medicolegal concept, not a formal psychiatric diagnosis (see §7.5A). It is probably much less common than other causes of psychogenic episodes.

Psychiatric illness is the rule in patients with psychogenic nonepileptic episodes.[16] Many patients will have more than one psychiatric diagnosis. Depression, anxiety disorders (especially post-traumatic stress disorder), conversion and other somatoform disorders, dissociative disorders, and personality disorders are all common. A trauma or abuse history is more common in these patients than in epilepsy sufferers without psychogenic spells.[17]

11.4 Seizure Types

Appropriate treatment requires proper classification of seizure types and epileptic syndromes. Most seizures can be classified as either partial or generalized based on clinical and EEG findings. Manifestations of a seizure—the *ictus*—are known as *ictal* events.

A. Partial seizures

These seizures begin in one area of the brain and are also known as focal-onset seizures. *Simple partial seizures* occur without alteration or loss of consciousness. Many patients refer to these as "small" or "minor" seizures. The manifestations reflect the site of the abnormal electrical discharges. Motor and sensory phenomena are common. Discharges in motor cortex can produce tonic-clonic movements. If the electrical abnormality spreads the movements also spread, something known as a *Jacksonian* seizure. Abnormal sensations include visual, olfactory, and gustatory (taste) hallucinations. More complex cognitive phenomena are also common (e.g., *déjà vu*).

In *complex partial seizures*, normal awareness of the environment is lost and there may be complete loss of consciousness. These usually arise in the temporal lobe. This is the most common seizure type in adults. Patients seem to stare vacantly into space and do not respond appropriately, or at all, to questions. They may have repetitive, seemingly purposeless movements—*automatisms*—such as lip smacking, chewing, grimacing, or hand wringing. The combination of automatisms and altered consciousness is also called a *psychomotor* seizure.

A simple partial seizure may progress either to a complex partial or a secondarily generalized seizure, or first to a complex partial and then a generalized seizure. Complex partial seizures can also become secondarily generalized. Sometimes, patients may not realize they are having partial seizures. Only after a generalized convulsive seizure do they come to medical attention.

Most partial seizures last less than three minutes. Patients then enter into a *postictal* phase characterized by drowsiness, confusion, and headache. This can last anywhere from minutes to several hours. In the case of focal motor seizures there may be a postictal paralysis in the involved muscles. This is known as *Todd's paralysis*. After a generalized convulsion, the presence of such weakness suggests that the seizure had a focal rather than a generalized onset.

The temporal lobes and related limbic structures are the most common sites of origin for partial seizures. Temporal lobe seizures are often associated with complex memory and cognitive manifestations. These include episodes of déjà vu or jamais vu and related cognitive phenomena. Temporal lobe uncus seizures produce hallucinations of smell and taste.

Complex visual hallucinations include alterations in size, shape, and form of objects. A common visceral manifestation of temporal lobe epilepsy is a warm sensation that seems to rise from the abdomen. Fear or panic is common and many patients receive psychiatric treatment for an anxiety disorder. Depersonalization and derealization can also occur with temporal lobe seizures. It is not uncommon for patients to have more than one symptom occurring at the time of their partial seizures. If a partial seizure does secondarily generalize patients usually refer to the cognitive and sensory experiences as their *aura*. It is worth emphasizing that the aura is a seizure.

B. Generalized seizures

These begin throughout the cortex, more or less simultaneously. Primary generalized seizures are much more likely to have a genetic basis than partial seizures. These seizures usually occur for the first time in children or teenagers. There are several types of generalized seizures.

Absence seizures—petit mal seizures—consist of brief staring spells. These seizures occur in children, rarely in adults. There may be hundreds per day. Sometimes, a teacher detects these in a child who seems inattentive. Eye blinking and lip smacking can occur. Absence seizures are distinguished from complex partial seizures by their shorter duration, higher frequency, and lack of postictal confusion. The EEG reveals a characteristic three per second spike and slow wave discharge. *Atypical absence seizures* last longer, are associated with mental retardation and other neurologic abnormalities, and have a slower abnormal EEG discharge.

Generalized tonic-clonic seizures—grand mal or major motor seizures—begin with abrupt loss of consciousness. There may be a forced expiration that sounds like a muffled scream. The body stiffens and then muscles begin to jerk. The seizure usually lasts three minutes or less. Patients may bite their tongues or lose control of bowel and bladder function, but the absence of such manifestations does not prove there was no seizure. It is important to recognize that consciousness is lost because the epileptic discharges impair function in both cerebral hemispheres. Therefore, a patient who claims to be aware of bilateral, generalized convulsive movements is probably not describing an epileptic seizure.

Myoclonic seizures are usually quite brief. These consist of sudden, symmetric jerking movements of the extremities or trunk or both. They may occur without loss of consciousness. *Atonic seizures*—epileptic drop attacks—consist of sudden loss of muscle tone. The head may drop forward; in more severe episodes the legs give way and the patient falls.

11.5 Epilepsy Syndromes

The epilepsies are classified according to the seizure type—partial or generalized—and whether or not there is an identified cause. Thus, there are:

- Idiopathic localization-related (partial) epilepsies
- Symptomatic localization-related (partial) epilepsies
- Idiopathic generalized epilepsies
- Symptomatic generalized epilepsies

A. Localization-related epilepsies

These focal or partial epilepsies are classified according to where in the cortex they arise. Temporal lobe epilepsy is the most common. Many of these focal epilepsies are symptomatic.

Benign childhood epilepsy with central temporal spikes (benign rolandic epilepsy) is an idiopathic localization-related epilepsy and a fairly common cause of seizures in children under age fifteen. Seizures occur mostly at night and begin with twitching of the mouth and excessive salivation. There may be secondary generalization. This form of epilepsy is inherited and usually resolves before adulthood.

B. Generalized epilepsies

There are several idiopathic generalized epilepsy syndromes. *Childhood absence epilepsy* is also known as petit mal epilepsy. Some of the children also develop generalized tonic-clonic seizures. The absence seizures usually disappear by adulthood. Correct identification of this seizure type is important because certain anticonvulsant medications used for partial seizures can exacerbate absence seizures.

Juvenile myoclonic epilepsy usually begins in teenagers. There are myoclonic jerks as well as absence and generalized tonic-clonic seizures, all most likely to occur just after awakening. Valproate and some of the newer antiepileptic drugs are very effective for these seizures, but some of the older antiepileptic drugs can cause exacerbations. Juvenile myoclonic epilepsy, unlike several of the other inherited syndromes, is unlikely to remit.

West syndrome begins before age one year. It is characterized by spasms of the head, trunk, and limbs—*infantile spasms*. Cerebral malformations, infections, and hypoxic-ischemic damage are common causes of West syndrome. It is associated with *hypsarrhythmia*, a severely abnormal EEG pattern. The spasms are very difficult to treat. Most patients are mentally retarded and have chronic seizures.

Multiple seizure types that are difficult to control characterize *Lennox-Gastaut* syndrome. The seizures begin within the first few years of life and rarely remit. Most patients have mental retardation and other neurologic abnormalities. Felbamate appeared to be a very promising treatment for this syndrome but use of that drug is now restricted because of fatal side effects.[18]

11.6 Epilepsy Treatment
A. General considerations

Patients suffering from epilepsy and society in general continue to have major misconceptions and fears regarding the disease. It is important, therefore, that a detailed explanation of the reasons for therapy and the limitations the disease places upon the individual accompany initiation of drug therapy. This is also the opportunity for the physician to dispel the many myths surrounding epilepsy.

Antiepileptic medication is prescribed to prevent seizures in patients who are likely to have recurrent seizures. Knowledge of the seizure type or epilepsy syndrome helps to determine the risk of recurrent attacks. If a patient presents with a series of seizures in a short time there is little controversy regarding the need for anticonvulsant medication. Difficulties arise with the patient who presents after a single seizure or with the patient who has long gaps between seizures. Side effects from anticonvulsants, especially the older agents, are common. Therefore, the decision to treat is a complex one.

Most neurologists would withhold drug therapy after a single seizure unless there is a clear-cut EEG abnormality, evidence of a structural abnormality known to provoke seizure activity, or if the patient has an epilepsy syndrome with a high risk of seizure recurrence. The risk of recurrence after a first idiopathic seizure in a patient with a normal EEG is only 24 percent, but with a remote symptomatic seizure and an abnormal EEG the risk is 65 percent.[19] However, some patients may insist on treatment because any risk of seizure recurrence is unacceptable to them. If medication, drug abuse, or metabolic disturbances provoked the single seizure then treatment is designed to eliminate the causative factor. Sleep deprivation is a common cause of provoked seizures, especially in college students preparing for examinations and shift workers.

More than half of all patients will achieve complete seizure control with a single anticonvulsant drug—*monotherapy*. The choice of drug depends upon the seizure type and individual patient considerations. For example, agents that induce hepatic enzymes should be avoided in women taking oral contraceptives because such anticonvulsants can interfere with the contraceptive. If it is clear that the chosen anticonvulsant is ineffective or not tolerated, a second drug is added. The dose is increased to an effective range and the first medication gradually withdrawn. Most neurologists will try two or three different agents as monotherapy before using combination treatment—*polytherapy*.

Noncompliance is common and may explain recurrent seizures despite treatment. However, if noncompliance seems unlikely and the neurologist has chosen an appropriate anticonvulsant medication, the patient should be re-evaluated. Polytherapy may be necessary but is avoided whenever possible because of a higher incidence of adverse reactions, toxicity, and noncompliance.

There are two groups of antiepileptic agents, the traditional agents (carbamazepine, ethosuximide, phenobarbital, phenytoin, primidone, and valproate) and the "new" medications approved in the past decade (felbamate, gabapentin, lamotrigine, levetiracetam, oxcarbazepine, tiagabine, topiramate, and zonisamide). All the traditional agents save ethosuximide are effective for partial and secondarily generalized seizures. Ethosuximide and valproate are first-line choices for absence seizures; valproate is also a first choice for other primary generalized seizures. Some of the new agents are approved only for adjunctive use, particularly for partial seizures. However, many neurologists prescribe these new agents as monotherapy for both partial-onset and primary generalized seizures.

This type of *off-label* prescribing is not unusual or forbidden by the Food and Drug Administration. Indeed, it "has become an important part of mainstream, legitimate medical practice,"[20] accounting for about half of all prescriptions written in the United States.[21]

Antiepileptic medications produce a variety of side effects. These can be dose-related, independent of dosage (idiosyncratic), acute, or chronic. Dose-related side effects common to many antiepileptics include incoordination, sedation, dizziness, and gastrointestinal distress. Idiosyncratic reactions include rash, behavior changes, and weight gain. Several antiepileptics interfere with bone metabolism, causing osteopenia and osteoporosis. The risk is not restricted to women. Vitamin D and calcium supplementation may prevent this complication. Cognitive impairment—including poor memory and concentration, as well as general slowing of thinking—is probably the most disturbing chronic side effect from the patient's perspective.

Most patients who are seizure-free for more than two years with antiepileptics can remain seizure-free after withdrawal of the medication.[22] The decision to stop medication is a difficult one that requires an individualized analysis of the potential benefits and risks.[23] Almost all seizure recurrences occur in the first year after discontinuation.[24] There is no definitive way to predict who will remain seizure-free. Factors favoring a lower risk of recurrence are:[25]

- Fewer seizures before and during treatment
- Normal brain imaging studies
- Normal neurologic examination
- Patient seizure-free for several years with treatment
- Single drug controls the epilepsy

B. Pregnancy and epilepsy

Several antiepileptic medications interfere with the efficacy of oral contraceptives, increasing the risk of pregnancy. If the antiepileptic cannot be changed the woman should be using a contraceptive with a higher estrogen dose or alternate methods of birth control. Anticonvulsant drugs have the potential to cause fetal malformations.[26] This risk must be discussed in detail with women of childbearing years. Most malformations are minor but major defects are not rare. Fortunately, at least 90 percent of babies born to women with epilepsy are normal. Major congenital defects occur in approximately 4 to 6 percent of these babies, double the risk of the general population.[27]

Ideally, preventive efforts should begin many months before conception. Birth defects are most common in women receiving polytherapy at high doses. If possible, doses should be lowered and the patient converted to monotherapy. Folic acid may help to prevent birth defects. Valproate is associated with a 1-2 percent risk of neural tube defects;[28] carbamazepine has a slightly lower risk of this grave abnormality. If the seizures can be controlled with alternative agents treatment should be changed. However, seizures themselves can harm the mother and fetus. Therefore, except in the case of simple partial seizures (where there is no alteration of consciousness) treatment usually should not be withdrawn in women who are, or intend to become, pregnant. The best antiepileptic medication is the one that controls the patient's seizures without producing side effects.

During pregnancy seizure frequency changes in some women though most remain seizure-free.[29] More intensive monitoring is needed during pregnancy, with particular attention to appropriate dosing and serum levels of medication.

C. Surgical treatment

Surgical intervention is increasingly common for patients with uncontrolled seizures—*refractory epilepsy*. The threshold for referral varies according to the impact of seizures on the patient's life. Epilepsy surgery is an underutilized option in patients who have failed medication treatment (at least three monotherapy and two polytherapy trials with adequate dosing and good compliance) and have an operable brain lesion responsible for the seizures. Although there are 100,000 to 200,000 potential surgical candidates only a few thousand procedures are performed annually.[30]

Prospective patients undergo a very detailed assessment to confirm the diagnosis and localize the lesion. This can include invasive EEG monitoring, with electrodes on the surface of the brain or in deeper brain structures. Functional neuroimaging with PET scans may also be needed. Specialized testing is performed to determine the location of language and other critical cognitive functions. The procedure is contraindicated if significant impairment of these is likely. The success rate for epilepsy surgery is highest in cases where a single lesion is identified and can be removed.

Another option for intractable seizures is vagus nerve stimulation by means of an implanted device that generates small electric shocks. The device is programmed externally with radiofrequency signals. The patient controls the unit with a hand-held magnet.

11.7 Sudden Unexpected Death in Epilepsy Patients (SUDEP)

Mortality for epilepsy patients is some two to three times higher than an age-matched control population.[31] In part, this is due to the etiology of epilepsy in some patients (brain tumors, for example) as well as the risk of injury during a seizure (head trauma, suffocation, drowning).

However, epilepsy patients are at risk of sudden unexplained death. Despite careful investigation and autopsy, no identifiable cause for the death can be found. Features of SUDEP include:

- Death occurred during normal activities and in benign circumstances
- Death occurred suddenly
- No obvious cause of death was found
- Patient died unexpectedly while in a reasonable state of health
- Patient suffered from epilepsy
- Seizure was not the direct cause of death

SUDEP accounts for almost one-fifth of deaths in epileptics, with an incidence of approximately one in 1,000.[32] For the subgroup with severe and longstanding disease the incidence is higher. The main risk factor for SUDEP appears to be seizure severity. This means uncontrolled seizures or needing multiple medications for seizure control. The risk appears higher for acquired epilepsy—particularly due to traumatic brain injury or encephalitis—than for idiopathic epilepsy. Other risk factors for SUDEP include early age of onset, underlying brain lesions, and tonic-clonic seizures.

Neurologists differ in their approach to counseling patients about SUDEP. Some mention this to all patients at the time of diagnosis, others wait until asked.[33]

11.8 Epilepsy and the Law
The epilepsy diagnosis carries serious social consequences, often more disabling than the disease itself.

A. Driving
Each state regulates licensing of drivers. There is a hodgepodge of statutes, rules, and regulations regarding seizures and other causes of unconsciousness. Many states require or recommend a seizure-free interval—most in the three to twelve months range—before allowing a patient to drive again but others have no set interval. Some states have medical panels making these decisions, some rely on the treating neurologist's input, and some a combination of both. Most of these states provide immunity to the physicians for their recommendations or decisions.

Six states (California, Delaware, Nevada, New Jersey, Oregon, and Pennsylvania) require physicians to report their seizure patients.[34] Mandatory reporting violates confidentiality and interferes with the physician-patient relationship. Furthermore, these laws may not be effective; patients may withhold information about their seizures from physicians if they know they will be reported and thereby lose their licenses.

In states without mandatory reporting physicians face a dilemma if a patient drives after being warned not to. There is a conflict in roles: as a patient advocate who honors confidentiality versus a less well defined duty to protect the public at large. Rhode Island, for example, immunizes physicians from liability for decisions either to breach or to maintain confidentiality in such circumstances.[35] However, not all states provide this immunity. Physicians must document in the medical record their discussions with patients regarding driving restrictions. Inability to prove a patient was told not to drive could open the door to third-party liability in those states that extend a physician's legal duty to foreseeable third parties.

Driving decisions can be nerve-racking for the physician. There is a lack of driving evaluation training and little published research. Recently, a study found that reducing the seizure-free interval from twelve to three months did not lead to a significant increase in seizure-related accidents.[36] Perhaps this data will change recommendations and policies about driving restrictions.

B. Aggression, criminal acts, and the epilepsy defense

Neurologists may be asked whether a particular criminal act, violent or otherwise, could be the result of an epileptic seizure. This is a controversial subject that has been reviewed quite extensively.[37,38] The neurologist must determine whether or not a seizure occurred, the relationship between the alleged criminal act and the seizure, and whether there was evidence of conscious decision-making. Potential confounding factors are the presence of underlying brain damage and medication side effects. Both can impair impulse control and predispose to violent outbursts, independently of any seizure.

Violence occurring during a seizure itself is known as *ictal violence*. This is likely to be random rather than a directed, organized attack. During complex partial seizures with some retained awareness of the surroundings there may be directed aggression but this will not be the only manifestation of the seizure.[39] Violent behavior is more likely to occur during the period immediately following a seizure. This *postictal* violence may be triggered by attempts to restrain the patient, *resistive violence*. Patients are confused and the movements are "unorganized and simple."[40]

Postictal psychosis is a well-known but uncommon condition associated with violent outbursts. In these cases, there are "well-directed, well-organized attacks against human beings because of irrational behavior."[41] Episodes of postictal psychosis usually follow complex partial seizures. The presence of delusions, paranoia, and hallucinations, and the lack of amnesia for the acts, distinguishes postictal from resistive violence.[42] The vast majority of seizure patients do not develop postictal psychosis.

More controversial is the topic of *interictal* (between seizures) *violence*. Some researchers have identified a spectrum of baseline personality traits—including irritability and poor impulse control—in temporal lobe epileptics, though others dispute this relationship.[43] Aggressive acts during the interictal period are not a direct result of seizure activity. Brain injury, impaired cognitive function, and unfavorable socioeconomic factors may be to blame.[44]

There are guidelines for examining violent acts in relation to epilepsy. The criteria are:[45]

- Documentation of epileptic automatisms by history and video monitoring
- Epilepsy diagnosis made by an epileptologist (a neurologist with expertise in epilepsy)
- Neurologist's judgment that act was part of a seizure, and not too complex to have been part of an epileptic automatism
- Simultaneous ictal EEG abnormalities and video-recorded aggressive acts
- Violent act is typical of patient's usual seizures and associated with other manifestations

Endnotes

1. Browne TR, Holmes GL. "Epilepsy." *N Engl J Med* 2001;344:1145-1151.

2. Bortz JJ. "Neuropsychiatric and memory issues in epilepsy." *Mayo Clin Proc* 2003;78:781-787.

3. Leonard EL, George MRM. "Psychosocial and neuropsychological function in children with epilepsy." *Pediatr Rehabil* 1999;3(3):73-80.

4. Fisher RS, Vickrey BG, et al. "The impact of epilepsy from the patient's perspective: I. Descriptions and subjective perceptions." *Epilepsy Res* 2000; 41:39-51.

5. Finucane AK. "Legal aspects of epilepsy." *Neurol Clin* 1999;17(2):235-243.

6. Von Oertzen J, Urbach H, et al. "Standard magnetic resonance imaging is inadequate for patients with refractory focal epilepsy." *J Neurol Neurosurg Psychiatry* 2002;73:643-647.

7. So EL. "Role of neuroimaging in the management of seizure disorders." *Mayo Clin Proc* 2002;77:1251-1264.

8. Browne TR, Holmes GL, *supra* note 1, at 1146.

9. Malow BA, Passaro E, et al. "Sleep deprivation does not affect seizure frequency during inpatient video-EEG monitoring." *Neurology* 2002;59:1371-1374.

10. Barry JJ. "Nonepileptic seizures: An overview." *CNS Spectrums* 2001;6(12): 956-962.

11. Luciano DJ. "Nonepileptic paroxysmal disorders." In: Ettinger AB, Devinsky O, eds. *Managing Epilepsy and Co-existing Disorders*. Boston: Butterworth-Heinemann; 2002:3-35.

12. *Id*. at 7.

13. Palac SM, Kanner AM. "Nonepileptic psychogenic spells: a neurologist's perspective." In: Ettinger AB, Devinsky O, *supra* note 11, at 329-342.

14. Reuber M, Pukrop R, et al. "Outcome in psychogenic nonepileptic seizures: 1- to 10-year follow-up in 164 patients." *Ann Neurol* 2003;53:305-311.

15. Harden CL, Burgut TF, Kanner AM. "The diagnostic significance of video-EEG monitoring findings on pseudoseizure patients differs between neurologists and psychiatrists." *Epilepsia* 2003;44:453-456.

16. Bowman ES. "Psychopathology and outcome in pseudoseizures." In: Ettinger AB, Kanner AM, eds. *Psychiatric Issues in Epilepsy: A Practical Guide to Diagnosis and Treatment*. Philadelphia: Lippincott Williams & Wilkins; 2001:355-377.

17. Fleisher W, Staley D, et al. "Comparative study of trauma-related phenomena in subjects with pseudoseizures and subjects with epilepsy." *Am J Psychiatry* 2002;159:660-663.

18. Quality Standards Subcommittee of the American Academy of Neurology and the American Epilepsy Society. "Practice advisory: The use of felbamate in the treatment of patients with intractable epilepsy." *Neurology* 1999; 52:1540-1545.

19. Berg AT, Shinnar S. "The risk of seizure recurrence following a first unprovoked seizure: A quantitative review." *Neurology* 1991;41:965-972.

20. Henry V. "Off-Label Prescribing." *J Legal Med* 1999;20:365-383.

21. *Id*. at 365.

22. O'Dell C, Shinnar S. "Initiation and discontinuation of antiepileptic drugs. *Neurol Clin* 2001;19:289-311.

23. Quality Standards Subcommittee of the American Academy of Neurology. "Practice parameter: A guideline for discontinuing antiepileptic drugs in seizure-free patients (summary statement). *Neurology* 1996;47:600-602.

24. Brodie MJ, French JA. "Management of epilepsy in adolescents and adults." *Lancet* 2000;336:323-329.

25. Berg AT, Shinnar S. "Relapse following discontinuation of antiepileptic drugs: A meta-analysis." *Neurology* 1994;44:601-608.

26. Holmes LB, Harvey EA, et al. "The teratogenicity of anticonvulsant drugs." *N Engl J Med* 2001;344:1132-1138.

27. Yerby MS. "Management issues for women with epilepsy: Neural tube defects and folic acid supplementation." *Neurology* 2003;61(Suppl 2):S23-S26.

28. Lindhout D, Schmidt D. "In-utero exposure to valproate and neural tube defects." *Lancet* 1986;1:1392-1393.

29. Cantrell DTC. "Reproductive issues or pregnancy and epilepsy." In: Ettinger AB, Devinsky O, *supra* note 11, at 317-326.

30. Engel JE. "A greater role for surgical treatment of epilepsy: Why and when?" *Epilepsy Currents* 2003;3(2):37-40.

31. Tomson T. "Mortality in epilepsy." *J Neurol* 2000;247:15-21.

32. Walczak TS, Leppik IE, et al. "Incidence and risk factors in sudden unexpected death in epilepsy: A prospective cohort study." *Neurology* 2001;56:519-525.

33. Carroll L. "Sudden unexplained death in epilepsy: To disclose or not disclose the risks." *Neurology Today* 2004;4(5):9-11,63.

34. Epilepsy Foundation of America: www.epilepsyfoundation.org, accessed December 24, 2004.

35. R.I. Gen. Laws §31-10-44(d)(e).

36. Drazkowski JF, Fisher RS, et al. "Seizure-related motor vehicle crashes in Arizona before and after reducing the driving restriction from 12 to 3 months." *Mayo Clin Proc* 2003;78:819-825.

37. Schacter SC. "Aggressive behavior in epilepsy." In: Ettinger AB, Kanner AM, *supra* note 16, at 201-213.

38. Treiman DM. "Violence and the epilepsy defense." *Neurol Clin* 1999;17(2): 245-255.

39. *Id*. at 251.

40. Luciano DJ, *supra* note 11, at 29.

41. Schacter SC, *supra* note 37, at 203.

42. Gerard ME, Spitz MC, et al. "Subacute postictal aggression." *Neurology* 1998;50:384-388.

43. Schacter SC, *supra* note 37, at 203-204.

44. Gupta AK, Ettinger AB, Weisbrot DM. "Psychiatric comorbidity in epilepsy." In: Ettinger AB, Devinsky O, *supra* note 11, at 343-387.

45. Treiman DM, *supra* note 38, at 252.

Additional Reading

American Epilepsy Society: www. aesnet.org, accessed December 24, 2004.

Epilepsy Foundation: www.epilepsyfoundation.org, accessed December 24, 2004.

Lüders HO, Noachtar S. *Epileptic Seizures: Pathophysiology and Clinical Semiology*. New York: Churchill Livingstone; 2000.

Wyllie E, ed. *The Textbook of Epilepsy: Principles and Practice*, 3rd. ed. Philadelphia: Lippincott, Williams & Wilkins; 2001.

Chapter 12

Stroke and Other Cerebrovascular Diseases

12.1 Introduction

Despite a 70 percent reduction in stroke mortality between 1950 and 1996,[1] stroke is still the third leading cause of death in the United States.[2] Much of the improvement in mortality is due to better survival rates for stroke victims; the number of strokes has actually been rising because of the growth in the population at risk, namely older individuals. Specialized hospital stroke services and stroke units contribute to the reduction in mortality. Indeed, one stroke expert regards these as "the most important therapeutic advance during the past decade in the treatment of patients with acute stroke."[3]

Stroke is caused by diminished blood flow to brain tissue, *ischemia*. An isolated blockage of the supply to a particular area of the brain is the most common cause; generalized circulatory failure due to cardiac arrest

209

or systemic low blood pressure is less frequent. Under normal circumstances the brain is able to maintain its blood supply through a wide range of systemic arterial pressures, a property known as *autoregulation.*

If the blood pressure rises high enough to breach the limits of cerebral autoregulation *hypertensive encephalopathy* occurs. Over several days the patient develops increasingly severe headache associated with nausea and vomiting, mental slowing, blurred vision, focal neurologic deficits, impaired consciousness or coma, and seizures. Control of the patient's hypertension is the main treatment. Hypertensive encephalopathy can occur with any disease that produces uncontrolled hypertension. Eclampsia (a complication of pregnancy) and acute nephritis are the most frequent causes.[4]

The brain derives its blood supply from the two internal carotid arteries supplying roughly the anterior two-thirds of the brain and the vertebrobasilar system supplying the posterior third. Each internal carotid artery divides into two major branches, the anterior cerebral and the middle cerebral arteries. The former supplies the anterior and medial parts of the cerebral hemisphere while the latter divides into branches that supply the lateral parts of the cerebral hemisphere. The two vertebral arteries join within the skull to form the basilar artery. The basilar artery splits, forming the posterior cerebral arteries supplying the occipital lobes. The vertebrobasilar system also supplies the brain stem and cerebellum.

There is a connection, or *anastomosis*, between the anterior and posterior circulations at the circle of Willis. The posterior cerebral arteries communicate with the internal carotid system through the posterior communicating arteries, and the anterior cerebral arteries connect through the anterior communicating artery. The main arteries in the brain are end-arteries. They supply a given territory but do not connect with other arterial systems. The venous blood drains from the brain into the jugular vein via the superior sagittal, the inferior sagittal, and the straight sinuses. Unlike the arterial supply, there are rich anastomoses within the venous systems of the brain, meninges, and other structures of the head.

12.2 Transient Ischemic Attack (TIA)

A TIA is a temporary neurologic disturbance caused by transient disruption of blood flow. By definition, TIAs resolve completely within twenty-four hours. However, most TIAs resolve in less than one hour, 90 percent in less than ten minutes.[5] The arbitrary duration-based definition of TIA does not reflect MRI findings. That is, there are patients who had transient deficits but actually suffered a stroke. Even more importantly, waiting for up to twenty-four hours to see if symptoms spontaneously resolve would eliminate patients from consideration for clot-busting (thrombolytic) stroke treatments. For these and other reasons the TIA Working Group proposed a new definition for TIA—an episode of neurologic dysfunction caused by ischemia lasting less than one hour without evidence of infarction.[6]

TIAs are very important because they are highly predictive of subsequent stroke.[7] Several hundred thousand TIAs occur annually in the United States; the risk of stroke within ninety days of a TIA is as high as 20 percent.[8] Thus, TIAs should be regarded as medical emergencies.

Not all transient neurologic dysfunction is due to TIA. Many other conditions cause focal deficits and can mimic TIAs. Demyelination, metabolic abnormalities such as hypoglycemia, migraines, partial seizures, subdural hematomas, and tumors are in the differential diagnosis. Usually, the history of an abrupt onset of symptoms that are maximal at onset serves to differentiate TIA from these other conditions. However, more extensive evaluation is often necessary for diagnostic certainty.

A. Manifestations

The symptoms and signs of TIAs depend on which brain tissue is deprived of its blood supply. The overwhelming majority of TIAs occur in the anterior circulation when blood flow in a carotid artery or one of its branches is blocked. Roughly 50 percent of patients will describe an abrupt onset of contralateral weakness or numbness.[9] If the language centers of the brain are involved the patient may be aphasic. Visual field defects, visuospatial abnormalities, cognitive deficits, and behavioral disorders are all well-known manifestations of TIA. Transient monocular blindness—*amaurosis fugax*—is another form of TIA that indicates ipsilateral carotid artery disease.

The manifestations of vertebrobasilar TIAs reflect involvement of the structures supplied by the posterior circulation—upper spinal cord, brain stem, occipital lobes, and posterior temporoparietal cortex. Interruption of the blood supply to the brain stem is likely to disturb function of several different structures and systems. The neurologic deficits can be complex.

Simultaneous bilateral symptoms usually indicate a vertebrobasilar TIA. Common manifestations include ataxia, vertigo, dysarthria, diplopia, unilateral or bilateral weakness or sensory loss, visual field defects, and confusion or altered consciousness. Single isolated findings—such as vertigo, syncope, diplopia, or incontinence—are unlikely to be due to a vertebrobasilar TIA.

B. Causation

TIAs are caused by the same mechanisms producing brain ischemia that cause strokes. The most common are artery-artery embolism, arterial thrombosis, cardiac embolism, and small vessel occlusion.[10] Among the rarer causes of TIA are vasculitis, arterial dissection, coagulation abnormalities, hyperviscosity of blood, and fibromuscular dysplasia.

Atherosclerosis is found in large blood vessels, especially where these split or *bifurcate*. Small pieces of the atherosclerotic plaques—microemboli of fibrin, platelets, or cholesterol particles—break off and travel into the brain. These artery-artery emboli are the most common cause of TIAs. If the emboli do not dissolve quickly they disrupt the blood supply and produce symptoms. Arterial blood clots—*arterial thrombosis*—besides shedding emboli, can extend distally and block blood flow in narrower diameter vessels, another major cause of TIAs.

Cardiac emboli may develop in patients with atrial fibrillation, recent heart attack, artificial heart valves, bacterial endocarditis, rheumatic heart disease, and left ventricular wall clots.[11] These emboli have a tendency to block the cerebral circulation at particular locations:[12]

- Junction of the anterior and middle cerebral arteries
- Posterior cerebral artery
- Posterior division of the middle cerebral artery
- Tip of the basilar artery

There is some evidence that longer TIAs, those lasting more than an hour, are more likely due to cardiac emboli than atherosclerotic emboli.[13]

Small-vessel occlusive disease affecting the deep penetrating arteries is especially common in patients with hypertension and diabetes. There are several well-known stroke syndromes produced by this mechanism (see §12.3A). Cardiac and arterial emboli can produce similar findings.

TIAs are warning signs for future strokes. The risk is highest in the first several weeks after a TIA; 15 percent of patients develop a stroke within twenty-four hours of the TIA.[14] Especially high-risk patients are those having increasing numbers of TIAs or those with recurrent TIAs despite medication. It is imperative to evaluate patients quickly in order to initiate appropriate preventative therapy. The TIA diagnosis is inappropriate for patients who have neurologic deficits; unless and until the deficits resolve the major diagnostic consideration is stroke. Usually, however, physicians see these patients after their deficits have resolved. Neurologists differ about whether or not they will hospitalize their TIA patients for evaluation.

C. Evaluation

Assessment begins with a detailed history of the event to determine whether or not it was a TIA. The medical history identifies risk factors for vascular disease. The general medical and neurologic examinations reveal signs of diseases that could produce the symptoms. The neurovascular examination—listening to the carotid and vertebral arteries for signs of abnormal flow and to the heart for evidence of murmurs—is critical. Screenings tests usually include a blood count with platelet count, coagulation studies, and blood chemistries including cholesterol and lipid levels. Electrocardiogram and chest x-ray evaluate the heart. Brain CT or MRI will exclude structural lesions such as tumors or subdural hematomas that can produce symptoms mimicking TIAs. Carotid artery ultrasound and, increasingly, magnetic resonance or CT angiography image the blood vessels.

If the examination and studies do not identify large-vessel disease the physician will search for other causes of the TIA. Cardiac emboli are the major consideration. In older patients with a history or signs of cardiac disease, a transthoracic echocardiogram is obtained. In younger TIA patients, and in others suspected of cardiac emboli but with normal routine diagnostic testing, the more invasive transesophageal echocardiography is performed. Children and young adults are prone to a host of less common causes of TIA and stroke.[15]

D. Management

Identification of vascular risk factors is an important part of the management of TIA patients. These are also the risk factors for stroke. The most important are smoking, hypertension, diabetes, elevated cholesterol and lipids, excessive intake of alcoholic beverages, and lack of exercise. Hypertension is the single most important modifiable risk factor. Management of these problems may include medications and efforts at lifestyle changes.

There are three main forms of stroke prevention therapy for TIA patients—antiplatelet therapy, anticoagulation, and surgery. Antiplatelet agents are the mainstay of preventative therapy for patients with atherothrombotic TIAs. Aspirin is the most economical and widely used antiplatelet agent though the ideal dosage is unclear. Ticlopidine, clopidogrel, and an aspirin-dipyridamole combination are the other FDA-approved antiplatelet choices. These are more effective than aspirin alone[16] but are significantly more expensive. Ticlopidine is associated with some serious side effects. Many neurologists will first prescribe aspirin. If the TIAs persist they will either switch to the aspirin-dipyridamole combination or add one of the other agents.

Oral anticoagulation with warfarin is recommended for patients with atrial fibrillation and other cardiac sources of emboli. There is a risk of bleeding, occasionally fatal, in anticoagulated patients. This most often involves the gastrointestinal and urinary tracts. Subdural or epidural hematomas can develop after apparently trivial head trauma. Regular blood testing is necessary to monitor the degree of anticoagulation. Therapy is complicated by the existence of many drug interactions with warfarin. Sometimes, anticoagulation is used in patients with atherothrombotic TIAs when antiplatelet therapy has failed and surgery is not possible.

Carotid endarterectomy is the most common procedure to remove a blockage. Patients with symptomatic severe narrowing—*stenosis* greater than 70 percent—of the carotid arteries in the neck benefit from carotid artery surgery compared to medical management.[17] There is a smaller benefit in patients with moderate stenosis—50 to 69 percent—but no proven benefit of surgery for stenosis less than 50 percent.[18] Carotid surgery for asymptomatic patients is controversial but may be a reasonable option for patients with severe stenosis and few surgical risks "when performed by experienced surgeons who have very low surgical morbidity and mortality profiles."[19]

The effectiveness and role of carotid angioplasty with stenting is under investigation. Stents are small metal meshes placed in arteries after clearing blockages by angioplasty. Some preliminary data suggest that this may be superior to endarterectomy.

12.3 Stroke

Stroke—*cerebral infarction*—refers to the death of brain cells. It can be caused by a lack of the glucose needed for energy metabolism—*hypoglycemia*—or by insufficient blood oxygen—*hypoxia*. However, the most common cause is insufficient blood flow—*ischemia*—leading to hypoxia and hypoglycemia as well as a buildup of metabolic waste products. There are more than four million stroke survivors alive in the United States.[20] The risk factors for stroke have been mentioned already. Most acute ischemic strokes are due to one of three mechanisms:

- Cardiac emboli
- Large-vessel atherosclerosis producing artery-artery embolism or diminished blood flow downstream from a critical narrowing of the artery
- Small-vessel disease of deep penetrating arteries causing *lacunar* strokes

The main arteries that supply the brain are "end-arteries" without significant overlap of the territories of brain tissue they supply. *Watershed* infarcts involving these boundary zones account for about 10 percent of ischemic strokes.[21] They usually occur as a result of sustained hypotension.

Nontraumatic spontaneous intracerebral hemorrhage—bleeding into the brain tissue—accounts for up to 15 percent of all strokes and has the highest mortality of stroke types, with only 38 percent of patients surviving one year.[22] Hypertension and amyloid angiopathy are the most common causes of damage to the walls of small blood vessels. These strokes tend to occur in the basal ganglia, thalamus, cerebellum, or pons. They are more likely to produce headache compared to ischemic strokes. The blood clot can cause rapid neurologic deterioration and requires close monitoring and aggressive management.[23]

A. Clinical manifestations

Strokes are characterized by a sudden onset of neurological deficits. This history may not be available if the stroke occurs while the patient is asleep. The clinical manifestations of stroke depend on the area of brain affected. Anterior circulation—carotid distribution—strokes are the most common. Typical features of middle cerebral artery distribution strokes are contralateral weakness, sensory loss, and visual field deficits. The weakness is usually more prominent in the arm than the leg. Additional features vary according to which hemisphere is involved. Anterior cerebral artery strokes usually produce contralateral weakness but with leg more involved than arm. Posterior cerebral artery strokes produce visual field deficits and related abnormalities.

Lacunar syndromes are due to small infarcts in the territory of deep penetrating arteries. The commonest cause is blockage of the arteries due to damage from hypertension. Lacunar strokes are sometimes seen on CT scans but are better visualized with MRI. These lesions occur in the deep white matter or brainstem, rather than in the cortex. Therefore, there are no visual field deficits or disturbances of higher intellectual function. There are several different lacunar syndromes:[24]

- Ataxic hemiplegia with pyramidal tract signs—corona radiata or ventral pons
- Dysarthria-clumsy hand syndrome—contralateral pons
- Pure motor stroke—anterior limb of the internal capsule, or pons
- Pure sensory stroke—posteroventral nucleus of the thalamus
- Sensorimotor stroke—ventral thalamus and internal capsule

There are numerous posterior circulation stroke syndromes, most named after the physicians who described them. These often produce a combination of brainstem and limb involvement.[25]

B. Initial management

Stroke is a medical emergency with only a few hours available for effective intervention. Accurate diagnosis and initiation of appropriate therapy must be carried out quickly in order to minimize the amount of brain damage. Heightened public awareness of stroke through educational efforts, akin to what has been done for heart attack, should lead to earlier recognition and more rapid activation of the emergency medical system. Anything that delays transportation of a suspected stroke patient to the emergency room—such as phone calls to physicians or family members, or waiting for symptoms to resolve—should be avoided.

Emergency or rescue personnel must be able to identify the symptoms of acute stroke. Stroke patients should be given a high rescue priority, comparable to possible heart attack. Once on the scene emergency personnel need to protect the airway and stabilize breathing and circulation. Most patients will need an intravenous line and oxygen. Additional interventions—examples are glucose for hypoglycemia, assisted ventilation, and cervical immobilization for suspected trauma—may be needed. Emergency personnel should also notify the receiving hospital about the patient.

Once the patient is stabilized medically the main goal of evaluation is accurate diagnosis. This will require an appropriate history, neurological and vascular examinations, and diagnostic testing. The history, if available, can identify conditions such as migraine, epilepsy, or drug abuse that can mimic stroke. Brain imaging, usually a CT scan, is performed to identify intracranial bleeding. CT is highly sensitive for acute bleeding but might miss subacute or chronic bleeds.[26] Increasingly, MRI scans using diffusion-weighted techniques are supplanting CT. Vascular imaging should also be performed in these patients, either by MR angiography, CT angiography, or ultrasound. The purpose of these tests is to establish the most likely mechanism causing the stroke.

General initial management of the acute stroke patient includes:

- Maintenance of normal cardiovascular, electrolyte, fluid, nutritional, and pulmonary status
- Management of systemic complications
- Minimizing the extent of irreversible brain damage

Regulation of hypertension during the acute phase of stroke is problematic. The stroke itself may cause hypertension and aggressive reduction can diminish blood flow to those areas of brain already at risk from ischemia. Nevertheless, elevations severe enough to pose a risk of hypertensive encephalopathy should be treated.[27]

C. Thrombolysis: Medical and legal aspects

Intravenous recombinant tissue plasminogen activator (rt-PA or TPA) is the only FDA-approved treatment for acute ischemic stroke. TPA is a "clot-busting" agent that can open a blocked artery, allowing *reperfusion* of brain tissue. There are considerable limitations and contraindications to the use of TPA. Most of these relate to conditions that might predispose to bleeding,[28] a significant complication of TPA. Furthermore, published guidelines recommend that treatment be initiated within three hours of onset—one major reason that only about 10 percent of eligible patients receive TPA.[29]

Use of TPA requires rapid identification of ischemic stroke patients without intracranial bleeding. The guidelines do not distinguish among strokes due to large-artery thromboembolic disease, cardiac emboli, or small-vessel disease. Treatment is more effective the sooner it is given, ideally within ninety minutes of onset.[30] CT scans are usually performed to identify bleeding or early signs of large stroke, contraindications to TPA. However, CT does not identify which patients have the type of blockage that TPA can clear, whether or not there is already irreversible brain damage, or even if the blockage has dissolved. Thus, some patients may receive TPA unnecessarily—and be exposed to a 5 to 10 percent risk of intracranial bleeding or death.[31]

On the other hand, rigid adherence to the three-hour rule excludes patients with ongoing ischemia who might benefit from TPA. MRI with perfusion and diffusion techniques can identify such patients. MR and CT angiography and other vascular imaging studies can demonstrate blockages amenable to TPA. Intraarterial thrombolysis—up to six hours after onset for anterior circulation blockages and twelve hours after posterior—may be justified in these cases.[32] Clearly, there must be room for individualized judgment because "patients do not magically change from Cinderellas to witches as the clock strikes three hours."[33]

The TPA stroke recommendations have generated criticism and skepticism. One journalist accused the American Heart Association of being unduly influenced by financial support from a TPA manufacturer.[34] A less inflammatory medical critique deals with the strength of the evidence behind the TPA recommendations.[35] However, in properly selected cases the weight of neurologic opinion favors use of TPA. Nevertheless, if there is a bad outcome there is ample room to question a physician's decision either to use or not use TPA.[36]

Physicians who do not give TPA must be able to demonstrate that the patient was not a good candidate for TPA. Conversely, if there is a bad result after using TPA the physician will need to prove that the patient was a good candidate and that the potential benefits outweighed the risks at the time the decision was made. In any case, patients and their families must be part of the decision-making process, and the physician needs to be meticulous about documentation.

12.4 Subarachnoid Hemorrhage (SAH)

Nontraumatic—or primary—SAH is usually due to a ruptured aneurysm. Aneurysms are abnormal weakened areas in the walls of blood vessels, present as incidental findings in 5 percent of autopsy studies.[37] The aneurysms tend to grow slowly, with a 5 percent annual rate of rupture once the diameter exceeds one centimeter.[38] Aneurysmal SAH accounts for up to 10 percent of all strokes, with a peak incidence in middle age, a female predominance, and fatal results in about half the patients.[39]

SAH usually strikes precipitously. Physical exertion—defecating, lifting, or sexual activity—may be a trigger in some patients. The most typical initial complaint is excruciating headache, different from any the patient ever had. Some patients describe a sensation of something snapping or popping in their heads before the headache. Nausea, vomiting, and altered consciousness are common. Other symptoms will depend on the location of the bleeding. Seizures are not unusual. A minority of patients have warning symptoms in the weeks before the bleed. The signs of these "sentinel" leaks include diplopia and visual obscurations, headaches, stiff neck, and unsteadiness. Unfortunately, many patients do not seek medical attention for these complaints or, if they do, the correct diagnosis is unsuspected.

The clinical examination of a patient with mild SAH may reveal only stiff neck. More severely affected patients will have impairments in consciousness or frank coma as well as focal neurologic deficits. *Preretinal—* or *subhyaloid*—hemorrhages can be seen within hours of the rupture. Cranial CT usually shows the blood. In the acute setting CT is superior to routine MRI for identification of SAH. If the study is negative but there is still suspicion of SAH examination of the cerebrospinal fluid by lumbar puncture for signs of bleeding is mandatory.

Once SAH has been confirmed its cause should be identified with angiography. If an aneurysm is seen surgical "clipping" is recommended. Although this is a risky procedure early in the course of SAH there is high morbidity should the aneurysm rebleed—up to 75 percent.[40] The medical management of SAH patients is also complex. Patients are prone to cerebral vasospasm and edema, hydrocephalus, cardiac and pulmonary complications, electrolyte imbalances (especially hyponatremia), and any of the consequences of prolonged bed rest. About half the patients who survive SAH are left with permanent neurologic deficits, especially cognitive problems.

12.5 Cerebral Venous Thrombosis

Clots can also develop in the venous sinuses, cortical veins, and deep veins. There are many different conditions that predispose to venous thrombosis.[41] Pregnancy, systemic malignancy, oral contraceptives, head injury, diabetes, autoimmune disease, and infection are the most important causes. Hypercoagulability of the blood may be the explanation for the clotting.

The clinical manifestations of venous thrombosis depend on the location of the clot. Headache is the most common symptom. Some patients have a syndrome that resembles benign intracranial hypertension (see §15.6). They have headache, nausea and vomiting, and papilledema. Thrombosis of cortical veins or the dural sinus, however, is likely to cause venous infarctions and focal deficits. These patients have a slowly developing encephalopathy with headache, seizures, confusion, altered consciousness, and focal signs such as hemiparesis. Cavernous sinus thrombosis has a more distinctive presentation. It usually develops after facial or paranasal sinus infection, with symptoms beginning in one eye and then spreading to the other.[42]

MRI and MRA is supplanting cerebral angiography for diagnosis of cerebral venous thrombosis. The main treatment for the clotting is anticoagulation. Underlying diseases must be treated appropriately. Decompressive surgery is reserved for severe cases.

12.6 Temporal (Giant Cell) Arteritis

This is a vasculitis with a predilection for the ophthalmic artery and branches of the external carotid artery. Early detection and treatment is important in order to avoid blindness. Diagnostic criteria for temporal arteritis include:[43]

- Age over fifty years
- Erythrocyte sedimentation rate greater than fifty millimeters per hour
- New-onset headache or scalp tenderness
- Pain with chewing (jaw claudication)
- Tenderness or nodularity of the temporal artery
- Visual loss

Temporal arteritis may occur in isolation or in association with polymyalgia rheumatica. Generalized malaise, fever, and fatigue are other common symptoms. The pain of temporal arteritis is usually in or near the temples. Patients often complain that the temporal arteries themselves are exquisitely tender to touch.

Patients are treated as soon as possible with corticosteroids if there is a high degree of clinical suspicion for temporal arteritis. They are referred for temporal artery biopsy to confirm the diagnosis. If the biopsy is negative consideration should be given to biopsy of the other temporal artery. This is done to avoid exposing patients unnecessarily to the serious side effects of long-term corticosteroid use. If bilateral temporal artery biopsies are normal the diagnosis of temporal arteritis is unlikely.[44]

Some clinicians rely on the sedimentation rate and response to corticosteroids to make the diagnosis. They feel that if there has been no response after forty-eight hours temporal arteritis is unlikely. If there has been a dramatic response the diagnosis is confirmed. A repeat sedimentation rate will then show a reduction. The rationale for this approach is that the risks of corticosteroids for two days are less than the risks of temporal artery biopsy.

There are serious potential side effects from chronic use of steroids. Therefore, once the symptoms resolve and the sedimentation rate becomes normal the medication is tapered. This must be done very gradually to avoid recurrence. Some patients may be able to stop the steroids within several months but others will require more prolonged treatment. If steroids are ineffective or not tolerated immunosuppressant agents can be used.

Endnotes

1. Centers for Disease Control. "Achievements in public health, 1900-1999: Decline in deaths from heart disease and stroke-United States, 1900-1999." *Morbid Mortal Weekly Rep* 1999;48: 649-656.

2. National Center for Health Statistics. "Deaths and death rates for the 10 leading causes of death in specified age groups, by race and sex: United States, 1998." *Nat Vital Stat Rep* 2000;48:26-36.

3. Caplan LR. "Treatment of patients with stroke." *Arch Neurol* 2002;59:703-707.

4. Toole JF. "Lacunar syndromes and hypertensive encephalopathy." In: Toole JF, ed. *Cerebrovascular Disorders*, 5th edition. Philadelphia: Lippincott Williams & Wilkins; 1999:342-355.

5. Fisher CM. "Perspective: Transient ischemic attacks." *N Engl J Med* 2002;347: 1642-1643.

6. Albers GA, Caplan LR, et al. "Transient ischemic attack - proposal for a new definition." *N Engl J Med* 2002;347:1713-1716.

7. Toole JF. "Transient ischemic attacks: Pathogenesis and clinical features." In: Toole JF, *supra* note 4, at 60-70.

8. Johnston SC. "Transient ischemic attack." *N Engl J Med* 2002;347:1687-1692.

9. Toole JF, *supra* note 7, at 61.

10. Skalabrin EJ, Albers GW. "Transient ischemic attack." In: Johnson RT, Griffin JW, McArthur JC, eds. *Current Therapy in Neurologic Disease*, 6th edition. St. Louis; Mosby: 2002;195-199.

11. *Id*. at 196.

12. *Id*. at 195.

13. Toole JF, *supra* note 7, at 62.

14. Toole JF. "Transient ischemic attacks: Evaluation and management." In Toole JF, *supra* note 4, at 71-82.

15. Biller J. "Strokes in the young." In: Toole JF, *supra* note 4, at 283-316.

16. Caplan LR, *supra* note 3, at 706.

17. Skalabrin EJ, Albers GW, *supra* note 10, at 199.

18. *Id.*

19. Caplan LR, *supra* note 3, at 705.

20. American Heart Association. *2001 Heart and Stroke Statistical Update*. Dallas; American Heart Association: 2000.

21. Toole JF, "Brain infarction: Pathophysiology, clinical features, and management." In: Toole JF, *supra* note 4, 193-232.

22. Qureshi AI, Tuhrim S, et al. "Spontaneous intracerebral hemorrhage." *N Engl J Med* 2001;344:1450-1460.

23. *Id.* at 1455-1458.

24. Toole JF, *supra* note 4, at 347-348.

25. Toole JF. "Vertebrobasilar syndromes: Clinical features." In: Toole JF, ed., *supra* note 4, at 160-192.

26. Packard AS, Kase CS, et al. "'Computed tomography-negative' intracerebral hemorrhage: case report and implications for management." *Arch Neurol* 2003;60:1156-1159.

27. Saver JL. "Acute ischemic stroke." In: Johnson RT, et al., *supra* note 10, at 200-205.

28. Meschia JF, Miller DA, Brott TG. "Thrombolytic treatment of acute ischemic stroke." *Mayo Clin Proc* 2002;77:542-551.

29. Caplan LR, *supra* note 3, at 703.

30. Marler JR, Tilley BC, et al. "Early stroke treatment associated with better outcome: The NINDS rt-PA stroke study." *Neurology* 2000;55:1649-1655.

31. Caplan LR, *supra* note 3, at 703.

32. Saver JL, *supra* note 27, at 203-204.

33. Caplan LR, *supra* note 3, at 703.

34. Lenzer J. "Alteplase for stroke: Money and optimistic claims buttress the 'brain attack' campaign." *BMJ* 2002;324:723-729.

35. Warlow C, Wardlaw J. "Therapeutic thrombolysis for acute ischaemic stroke: What is good for heart attacks is still not good enough for brain attacks." *BMJ* 2003;326:233-234.

36. Kroger EJ. "Medical-legal scenarios: Acute thrombolysis of stroke patients." *Stroke Interventionalist* 2001; II(3):8-11.

37. Varelas PN, Ulatowski JA. "Aneurysmal subarachnoid hemorrhage." In: Johnson RT, et al., *supra* note 10, at 215-218.

38. Toole, JF. "Intracranial arterial aneurysms." In: Toole JF, ed., *supra* note 4, at 420-434.

39. Varelas PN, Ulatowski JA, *supra* note 37, at 215.

40. *Id.* at 217.

41. Nagaraja D. "Brain veins and their diseases." In: Toole JF, ed., *supra* note 4, at 481-506.

42. *Id.* at 490.

43. Lee AG, Brazis PW. "Temporal arteritis and central nervous system vasculitis." In: Johnson RT, et al., *supra* note 10, at 225-227.

44. *Id.* at 225.

Additional Reading

American Heart Association: www.americanheart.org, accessed December 24, 2004.

American Stroke Association: www.strokeassociation.org, accessed December 24, 2004.

National Stroke Association: www.stroke.org, accessed December 24, 2004.

Chapter 13

Multiple Sclerosis and Demyelinating Diseases

13.1 Introduction

Demyelinating diseases encompass a wide range of conditions characterized by destruction of normal myelin. Central nervous system myelin differs structurally and immunochemically from peripheral nervous system myelin. This chapter will discuss CNS myelin disorders, also known as white matter diseases. There are many rare childhood degenerative disorders with abnormal myelin formation caused by congenital metabolic defects; these *dysmyelinating* diseases will not be reviewed.

Most of the acquired demyelinating diseases are mediated by abnormalities in the immune system. Loss of myelin impairs nerve conduction. *Remyelination* is the process of regrowth that can produce functional recovery. However, if there is also axonal destruction and cellular degeneration the damage may be irreversible.

13.2 Generalized Multiple Sclerosis (MS)

Multiple sclerosis is a slowly progressive or relapsing chronic CNS white matter disease mostly striking young adults. It is the most common disabling neurologic condition in this population,[1] affecting about 400,000 people in the United States.[2] There is both an environmental risk and genetic susceptibility to MS. MS is more prevalent in temperate climates than tropical, with as many as 100 cases per 100,000 population in the former compared to under 5 per 100,000 in the latter.[3] The risk related to geographic origin is acquired during the first fifteen years of life. However, despite extensive investigation there is no proven link to specific infectious or environmental causative factors.

Different lines of evidence indicate some hereditary predisposition to MS, with contribution from several different genes:[4]

- Approximately one-fifth of MS patients have a relative with the disease
- The risk of MS in patients' adopted relatives is similar to the general population
- There is an increased risk of MS in family members of MS patients
- Twin studies show higher rates of concordance in identical compared to fraternal twins of subjects, roughly 30 percent versus 3–5 percent

Since even identical twins are concordant in only about 30 percent of cases the genetic contribution to MS is modest.

The underlying pathology of MS is destruction of myelin in the CNS. MS *plaques* are lesions containing inflammatory cells and damaged myelin. An abnormal immune response leads to the attack on myelin. Without normal myelin nerve impulses are slower or blocked completely. This is the cause of clinical abnormalities. Damage to axons can occur, and may explain permanent deficits.

A. Trauma, stress, vaccines, and multiple sclerosis

The relationship of physical trauma and emotional stress to multiple sclerosis is controversial. Proponents of a causative connection provide a plausible explanatory mechanism: CNS trauma can damage the blood brain barrier (BBB) and alterations of the BBB are a necessary step in the process leading to formation of MS plaques. This topic is the subject of a detailed review by the American Academy of Neurology.[5] There are several weaknesses with the claim that trauma causes the onset of MS or exacerbations of the disease. First, there is recent evidence that BBB breakdown may not be a critical factor in plaque formation. Second, the various studies suffer from a variety of inconsistencies and biases. Rigorous analysis of the available data is more suggestive of a lack of association between trauma and MS.

Stress is also blamed as a cause of MS. However, defining and measuring stress is problematic at best. There are studies that support a causative connection but other data are negative. At best, current understanding suggests that psychological stress is only a possible cause of MS onset or exacerbations.

There have been several case reports suggesting that hepatitis B, influenza, and other vaccinations can cause or exacerbate MS. Typically, signs and symptoms of demyelination develop a short time after the vaccine. Since MS involves immune mechanisms, stimulating the immune system through vaccination apparently seems to put susceptible individuals at risk. However, detailed epidemiologic analysis indicates that there is probably not a causal connection between the vaccinations and demyelinating disease.[6]

B. Clinical manifestations

The clinical symptoms of MS depend upon the site of the CNS damage (Figure 13.1). Almost any kind of neurologic disturbance has been described in conjunction with MS.[7] In general, symptoms and signs develop in a few days, plateau for several weeks, and then resolve. There may be complete recovery or variable residual disability. In the early stages of the disease most patients recovery completely. Increasing residual disability tends to occur in the later stages of the disease. The most common symptoms are weakness, visual loss, and sensory impairment.

Fatigue is a frequently overlooked but major source of impairment in MS patients. It is not merely a manifestation of depression or muscle weakness. Bladder dysfunction due to spinal cord involvement is also common. Symptomatically, patients complain of urinary urgency and frequency, often progressing to incontinence. Urodynamic studies characterize the disorder and exclude other bladder disturbances. Sexual dysfunc-

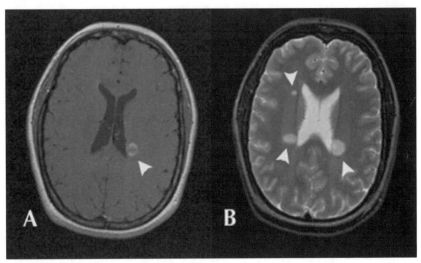

Courtesy of Dr. Roman Klufas.

Figure 13.1 *MS Plaques in Brain. Note that only one plaque is seen with FLAIR imaging (A) while three appear in a T2-weighted sequence (B). Plaques indicated by arrowheads.*

tion is a common cause of reduced quality of life in MS, though many patients do not volunteer information about this. Cerebellar plaques can cause gait abnormalities and limb incoordination. Movements become awkward and slow. Speech may become slurred—*dysarthria*—with patients sounding as if they are intoxicated.

Cognitive dysfunction and psychiatric disorders are increasingly recognized in MS patients. Typical difficulties include slowed information processing, inattention, and forgetfulness. Frank aphasia, agnosia, or other "cortical" cognitive syndromes are rare. The majority of patients with MS develop some symptoms of depression.[8] It is difficult to determine whether the depression is reactive—a consequence of the diagnosis and the burden of illness—or a primary sign of brain dysfunction. Inappropriate unconcern or indifference to the disease, but rarely euphoria, also occurs in MS patients with frontal lobe lesions.

Disorders of eye movement are common in multiple sclerosis, indicating involvement of the brainstem. Double vision (diplopia) occurs on lateral gaze due to damage to the *medial longitudinal fasciculus* (MLF) in the brainstem, causing *internuclear ophthalmoplegia* (INO). When this occurs, the ability of the eyes to move together as a pair is lost. Clinical examination of INO reveals a characteristic pattern of eye movement: on looking to the side opposite the damaged MLF, the leading eye does not move fully into the corner of the eye and it develops nystagmus, while the other eye does not cross the midline. There can be bilateral INO and other extraocular movement disorders in MS. Many patients complain of jerking movements of their vision; this is known as *oscillopsia*—subjective awareness of nystagmus.

MS plaques in the brainstem trigeminal pathways can cause trigeminal neuralgia. MS patients develop this at an earlier age than patients with "idiopathic" trigeminal neuralgia, usually a disorder of middle age. However, the same diagnostic procedures to exclude vascular compression and other causes are recommended.

Spinal cord involvement in MS causes dysfunction of the descending motor and ascending sensory pathways. Cervical spinal cord involvement is especially common (Figure 13.2). The patients complain of diffuse paresthesia or numbness in the hands, along with loss of dexterity and re-

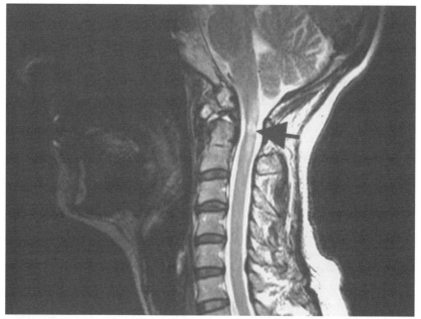

Courtesy of Dr. Roman Klufas.

Figure 13.2 Cervical Spine. T2-weighted sagittal image with MS plaque in upper cervical cord at arrowhead.

duced grip strength. Depending on the degree of descending motor pathway involvement there will be increased muscle tone (*spasticity*) and weakness. Involvement of the sensory pathways from the lower limbs may be confined to the spinothalamic pathways or may also include the dorsal columns. It is not unusual to discover signs of cord involvement that the patient has not reported in the history.

C. Course and prognosis

MS is an extremely variable disease. MRI studies show that MS plaques develop much more frequently than clinical attacks. Patients are usually categorized into one of four subtypes according to the pattern of their clinical course.

Relapsing-remitting MS is the most common presenting pattern. There are clear attacks of neurologic dysfunction followed by either complete or partial recovery. Relapses develop over hours and days. Some patients have long gaps between relapses; others have a series of relapses over a short period of time. As the disease progresses, full recovery from a relapse is less likely and progressive disability accumulates after each subsequent relapse.

Most relapsing-remitting patients eventually enter a *secondary progressive* stage of MS. They develop steadily increasing neurologic impairment, even in the absence of additional discrete relapses. Secondary progressive MS patients may still have relapses and even plateaus of apparent stability. The transition from relapsing-remitting to secondary progressive disease occurs over many years.

There is a small group of patients in whom the disease is progressive from the onset. *Primary progressive* MS is characterized by a gradual, fluctuating but nearly continuous deterioration from the onset. There are no acute relapses. This subtype is more likely to affect older patients and to present with spinal cord involvement. *Progressive relapsing* MS is a recently developed category that describes the rare patient with a progressive onset of disease who also experiences clear relapses.

The common question asked by a newly diagnosed patient regards the long-term prognosis. With such a variable disease this can be very difficult to predict. Perhaps 15 percent of patients have a benign course, with long intervals between the relapses and no significant neurological disability. However, years or decades of observation are needed to determine whether a particular patient will have this favorable outcome. Unfortunately, after fifteen years or more of illness most MS patients require assistance for ambulation. With proper medical care lifespan is not reduced.

There are several favorable prognostic indicators:[9]

- Age of onset under forty years
- Female sex
- Infrequent attacks early in the illness
- Rapid and complete recovery from exacerbations
- Relapsing-remitting subtype
- Sensory symptoms or optic neuritis as first episode

D. Diagnosis

Now that there are effective disease-modifying treatments for MS early and accurate diagnosis is more critical than it once was. Diagnosis depends upon identifying factors suggestive of MS and factors that are inconsistent with the disease. There are published diagnostic criteria that are particularly important for research purposes.[10] These include both clinical and laboratory evidence of disease. Most important is evidence of neurologic abnormalities separated in time and space—that is, attacks occurring at different times and in different anatomic locations.

Clinical abnormalities indicative of lesions separated in space are found by neurologic examination. MRI, evoked potentials, and urodynamic studies elicit *paraclinical* findings of anatomic dissemination. MRI is particularly useful in diagnosis of suspected MS. T1 and T2 hyperintensities are traditional markers of MS pathophysiology and disease activity, but with only modest correlation to long-term disability.[11] Persistent hypointense T1 lesions—known as *black holes*—probably indicate tissue destruction and are better markers of functional impairment and long-term disability.[12]

Evoked potentials, especially visual, can detect clinically silent lesions. Analysis of the cerebrospinal fluid usually reveals abnormal intrathecal antibody production (oligoclonal bands, increased IgG index and synthesis rate). During acute attacks, there may also be abnormal levels of *myelin basic protein* in the spinal fluid.

Misdiagnosis of MS occurs occasionally. One source of error is relying too heavily on MRI findings in the context of equivocal clinical findings. Also, since the manifestations of MS are so protean the range of diseases that can mimic MS is quite extensive. Clues suggesting a different diagnosis include:

- Attacks with abrupt onset
- Family history suggestive of other inherited disease
- Involvement of other organ systems
- Normal clinical examination, MRI, and spinal fluid
- Onset before age ten or after age fifty-five
- Peripheral neuropathy

Signs of prominent "gray matter" disease including seizures, aphasia, or dementia

E. Treatment

Therapeutic efforts are directed towards managing acute exacerbations, modifying the course of the disease, and providing symptomatic relief. Unfortunately, many of the manifestations of this disease do not respond well to any attempted intervention and there is no cure for MS.

High-dose intravenous methylprednisolone (0.5-1 gram daily for several days) is used to shorten the duration of relapses. It is not clear if the steroid improves the long-term outlook. Also undetermined is the ideal duration of the intravenous therapy and whether or not it should be followed by oral prednisone.

At the time of this writing, there are now four immunoregulatory medications approved in the United States for treatment of relapsing-remitting MS—three beta-interferons (Avonex, Betaseron, and Rebif) and glatiramer acetate (Copaxone). Avonex is administered weekly by intramuscular injection. The others are injected subcutaneously: Betaseron every other day, Rebif three times weekly, and Copaxone daily. Current practice is to recommend use of one of these agents early in the course of illness.[13] Accumulating evidence indicates that these drugs reduce the frequency of attacks and probably also reduce irreversible axonal damage. There is no compelling proof that one is significantly better than the others.

However, the situation is uncertain when dealing with patients with milder disease or who have had only one attack and are classified as having probable MS. Since some may have a benign course, treatment exposes them unnecessarily to the costs and risks of these agents. Interferon side effects include flu-like symptoms, pain, liver and bone marrow dysfunction, skin breakdown (necrosis) at the injection site, and significant depression. Some patients develop neutralizing antibodies to the interferon and the agent may lose its efficacy. Glatiramer may be better tolerated than the interferons. It can produce local irritation as well as a systemic injection reaction, but it does not cause the flu-like symptoms or depression. However, glatiramer does require daily injections.

The role of the newer immunomodulatory agents in progressive forms of MS is unclear. Immunosuppressant drugs including azathioprine, cyclophosphamide, and methotrexate are used in these patients but with limited benefits. Recently, mitoxantrone (Novantrone) gained approval for this patient population. There are prominent potential side effects with all these agents.[14]

Symptomatic therapy for MS symptoms is a major part of providing care to these individuals. A spastic bladder usually responds to medication such as oxybutinin. The hypotonic bladder may require self-catheterization. Several medications are used to treat muscle spasms and spasticity. In very severe cases baclofen, delivered directly to the spinal cord by an implanted pump, is effective.

MS fatigue is difficult to treat. Stimulant medications, amantadine, and the recently introduced wakefulness promoting agent modafanil are helpful for some patients. Paroxysmal pain and unpleasant sensations may respond to antiepileptic medications.

13.3 Isolated Demyelinating Syndromes

There are white matter diseases that can occur in isolation but may, in fact, represent a first episode of multiple sclerosis. Ninety percent of MS patients present with a clinically isolated syndrome,[15] and 30 percent of them develop clinically definite MS within a year.[16] Normal brain MRI and spinal fluid at presentation are good prognostic signs, suggesting a lower risk of subsequent MS.

Conversely, the presence of antibodies to myelin basic protein and myelin oligodendrocyte glycoprotein at the time of initial illness "predicts early conversion to clinically definite multiple sclerosis."[17] This has obvious implications for patient counseling including decisions about immunomodulatory treatment. Also, there are some MRI abnormalities that are highly predictive of subsequent disease in these syndromes.[18]

A. Optic neuritis

This typically presents with painful eye movements accompanied, or soon followed, by blurred or distorted vision. Some patients complain of loss of color vision. Typically, there is visual loss in the center of the visual field—*central scotoma*—with preservation of peripheral vision. Visual loss ranges from mild blurring to complete blindness. The symptoms develop over a period of a few days; then the pain usually subsides and there is improvement in vision. Recovery is complete, or nearly so, within a few months. However, visual evoked response testing will reveal residual abnormality.

The differential diagnosis of optic neuritis includes compressive lesions of the optic nerve, either from invasion from the nearby sinuses, tumors within the orbit, or tumors within the nerve itself. In an older patient, *anterior ischemic optic neuropathy* due to vascular disease may be confused with optic neuritis. There is also an inherited form of optic atrophy (Leber's disease) expressed predominately in males caused by a mutation of maternal mitochondrial DNA. The visual loss in *Leber's disease* develops more quickly and is almost always painless.[19]

Treatment of optic neuritis is determined by its cause. In the case of isolated disease there is considerable debate as to whether or how corticosteroids alter the subsequent course of the disease. Some argue that the prospect for good recovery of vision is enhanced by using intravenous steroids. Others feel that steroids should be given only if the unaffected eye is already compromised by concurrent ocular disease or previous optic neuritis. The optic neuritis treatment trial revealed more relapses of optic neuritis in patients treated with oral prednisone compared to placebo or high-dose intravenous steroids.[20]

Since half or more of MS patients will have involvement of the optic nerve at some time during their disease, there is considerable anxiety over the risk of developing MS after an isolated episode of optic neuritis. The risk is increased with:

- Brain MRI lesions at presentation
- Recurrence of optic neuritis, either in the same or the other eye

- Spinal fluid abnormalities

A patient presenting with optic neuritis has a 30 to 60 percent risk of developing MS.[21]

B. Transverse myelitis

This is an inflammatory spinal cord syndrome with involvement of the descending motor pathways and ascending sensory pathways. Associated bladder dysfunction is common. The lesion is typically in the thoracic region; cervical spine involvement is more likely in MS. Transverse myelitis may be related to infection, vasculitis, or an autoimmune response. There is ascending weakness from the feet upwards to the trunk, usually evolving over a period of a few days. The weakness is usually profound and interferes with walking. Sensory defects accompany the motor disturbance, with numbness gradually ascending from the feet to a variable position on the trunk. The transition zone from abnormal to normal sensation localizes the level of the lesion.

Investigation of transverse myelitis is done with spine imaging, preferably by MRI, to exclude compressive lesions and inflammatory disorders. Blood tests and cerebrospinal fluid analysis can identify evidence of infection, inflammation, or multiple sclerosis. Recovery requires weeks to months, and may be incomplete. The risk of subsequently developing generalized MS is low in patients with transverse myelitis unless brain MRI also reveals lesions. In that case, there is a greater than 50 percent chance of MS.[22]

C. Neuromyelitis optica (Devic's disease)

This uncommon condition is characterized by optic neuritis and transverse myelitis or other spinal cord symptoms, developing either simultaneously or within two years of each other. The symptoms and signs are similar to the individual disorders described above. However, neuromyelitis optica can relapse.[23] There is considerable debate regarding the relationship between Devic's disease and MS. Some feel that there is a very low conversion rate to generalized disease, whereas others feel that this is simply the initial presentation of what will eventually become generalized MS. Normal brain MRI and spinal fluid help to distinguish this from MS.

As with other causes of optic neuritis and transverse myelitis, alternative diagnoses should be considered. In the case of suspected Devic's disease with symptoms confined to the nervous system there is a possibility of a localized vasculitis; if there are signs of disease outside the nervous system a generalized vasculitis is possible.

13.4 Other Demyelinating Syndromes

Acute disseminated encephalomyelitis typically occurs in children and young adults following a viral infection or vaccination. An immune reaction causes demyelination around blood vessels in brain and spinal cord. Neurologic symptoms and signs develop within a few weeks of the infection and vary according to the sites of greatest destruction. This can be a severe disease, sometimes producing seizures and coma. Corticosteroids are the main treatment but plasmapheresis and immunoglobulins are also used. Mortality can be as high as 30 percent.[24]

HTLV-associated myelopathy (HAM)[25] is a slowly progressive infectious disease that produces bilateral spastic leg weakness. This condition is found in tropical regions throughout the world and is also known as *tropical spastic paraparesis*. It can be confused with the progressive spinal form of MS. The cause is a retrovirus—human T-lymphotropic virus type I—that attacks nerve tissue. Spinal cord white matter is the main target but brain and peripheral nerve involvement are not unusual. The weakness and spasticity develop steadily over many years. MRI scans reveal diffuse spinal cord atrophy and, often, white matter lesions in the brain. The brain abnormalities further contribute to confusion with MS. Diagnosis requires detection of HTLV-I antigens or antibodies. There is no cure for HAM.

Endnotes

1. Noseworthy JH, Lucchinetti C, et al. "Multiple sclerosis." *N Engl J Med* 2000; 343:938-952.

2. National Multiple Sclerosis Society: www.nmss.org, accessed December 24, 2004.

3. Kurtzke JF. "MS: changing times." *Neuroepidemiology* 1991;10:1-8.

4. O'Connor P, ed. "Key issues in the diagnosis and treatment of multiple sclero-

sis: An overview." *Neurology* 2002;59(suppl 3):S1-S33.

5. Goodin DS, Ebers GC, et al. "The relationship of MS to physical trauma and psychological stress." *Neurology* 1999;52:1737-1745.

6. DeStefano F, Verstraeten T, et al. "Vaccinations and risk of central nervous system demyelinating diseases in adults." *Arch Neurol* 2003;60:504-509.

7. Paty DW, Ebers GC. "Clinical features." In: Paty DW, Ebers GC, eds. *Multiple Sclerosis*. Philadelphia: F.A. Davis; 1997:135-191.

8. Diaz-Olavarrieta C, Cummings JL, et al. "Neuropsychiatric manifestations of multiple sclerosis." *J Neuropsychiatry Clin Neurosci* 1999;11:51-57.

9. Ebers GC, Paty DW. "Natural history studies and application to clinical trials." In: Paty DW, Ebers GC, eds., *supra* note 7, at 192-228.

10. McDonald WI, Compston A, et al. "Recommended diagnostic criteria for multiple sclerosis: Guidelines from the International Panel on the Diagnosis of Multiple Sclerosis." *Ann Neurol* 2001;50:121-127.

11. Filippi M, Grossman RI. "MRI techniques to monitor MS evolution." *Neurology* 2002;58:1147-1153.

12. McFarland HF, Barkhof F, et al. "The role of MRI as a surrogate outcome measure in multiple sclerosis." *Mult Scler* 2002;8:40-51.

13. Keegan BM, Noseworthy JH. "Multiple sclerosis." In: Johnson RT, Griffin JW, McArthur JC, eds. *Current Therapy in Neurologic Disease*, 6th ed. St. Louis: Mosby; 2002:181-187.

14. *Id.* at 185-186.

15. O'Riordan JI, Thompson AJ, et al. "The prognostic value of brain MRI in clinically isolated syndromes of the CNS: A 10-year follow-up." *Brain* 1998; 121:495-593.

16. Berger T, Rubner P, et al. "Antimyelin antibodies as a predictor of clinically definite multiple sclerosis after a first demyelinating event." *N Engl J Med* 2003;349:139-145.

17. *Id.* at 143.

18. Frohman EM, Goodin DS, et al. "The utility of MRI in suspected MS: Report of the Therapeutics and Technology Assessment Subcommittee of the American Academy of Neurology." *Neurology* 2003;61:602-611.

19. Brazis PW, Lee AG. "Optic neuropathy." In: Evans RW, ed. *Saunders Manual of Neurologic Practice*. Philadelphia: Saunders; 2003:375-383.

20. Beck RW, Cleary PA, et al. "A randomized controlled study of corticosteroids in the treatment of acute optic neuritis." *N Engl J Med* 1992;326:581-588.

21. Rolak LA. *Neurology Secrets*. 3rd ed. Philadelphia: Hanley & Belfus; 2001.

22. *Id*. at 115.

23. Wingerchuk DM, Hogancamp WF, et al. "The clinical course of neuromyelitis optica (Devic's syndrome)." *Neurology* 1999;53:1107-1114.

24. Davis LE, Bleck TP, et al. "Postinfectious syndromes." *Continuum* 2002; 8(3):89-109.

25. Byrne TN, Benzel EC, Waxman SG. *Diseases of the Spine and Spinal Cord*. New York: Oxford University Press; 2000.

Additional Reading

Burke JS, Johnson KP. *Multiple Sclerosis: Diagnosis, Medical Management, and Rehabilitation*. New York: Demos; 2000.

Herndon RM. *Multiple Sclerosis: Immunology, Pathology and Pathophysiology*. New York: Demos; 2002.

McDonald WI, Noseworthy JH, eds. *Multiple Sclerosis 2*. Boston: Butterworth-Heinemann; 2003.

Multiple Sclerosis Association of America: www.msaa.com, accessed December 24, 2004.

Multiple Sclerosis Foundation: www.msfacts.org, accessed December 24, 2004.

National Multiple Sclerosis Society: www.nmss.org, accessed December 24, 2004.

Chapter 14

Brain and Spinal Cord Tumors

14.1 Introduction

The brain is the site of tumors arising from tissues of the nervous system—*primary brain tumors*—as well as elsewhere in the body—*metastatic* disease. The nervous system may also be affected indirectly by systemic cancers—*paraneoplastic syndromes*. Chemotherapy and radiation therapy may damage the nervous system. *Neuro-oncology* is the subspecialty of neurology that focuses on these problems.

There are approximately 20,000 new primary brain tumor patients and 100,000 to 150,000 new brain metastasis patients annually in the United States.[1] Molecular techniques have revealed genetic or chromosomal abnormalities in many types of primary brain tumors. Identification of these has diagnostic, therapeutic, and prognostic significance.[2]

14.2 Clinical Presentations

Brain tumors cause symptoms by:

- Infiltrating normal tissue and destroying brain cells
- Proliferating and causing mass effect
- Producing swelling from fluid leaking out of cells—*cerebral edema.*

Nonfocal symptoms such as headache, nausea and vomiting, and sedation are common results of increased intracranial pressure (ICP) from mass effect and edema. Cognitive abnormalities can occur with increased ICP (and also with focal damage, especially from frontal tumors). For unknown reasons the signs and symptoms of raised ICP usually precede focal signs.

Headache is the most common initial symptom of brain tumors, occurring in 35 percent of patients.[3] These headaches can be dull and steady like muscle contraction headaches or throbbing like migraines. Activities that raise intracranial pressure such as physical exertion, coughing, sneezing, vomiting, stooping, intercourse, or straining during defecation usually worsen the headache. Some patients find that lying down exacerbates the pain.

Headaches due to tumors above the membrane separating the cerebellum and posterior fossa from the cerebral hemispheres—*supratentorial*—are usually located frontally. Tumors in the posterior fossa—*infratentorial*—produce occipital and posterior cervical pain. Tumor headaches can awaken patients at night and tend to be worse in the morning, improving within several hours. However, this is not the only possible pattern, nor is it unique to brain tumors. Since headaches are so common generally the clinician must be alert to a history of change in a patient's usual headache pattern. The headaches may be associated with *papilledema*—swelling of the optic nerve head seen through an ophthalmoscope. Papilledema and any focal neurologic deficits indicate a need for neuroimaging, preferably MRI.

Focal or generalized epileptic seizures are also common, particularly with slowly growing tumors such as oligodendrogliomas, low-grade astrocytomas, and meningiomas. They are the presenting feature in roughly one-third of brain tumor patients; up to 20 percent of adults with new-onset seizures have brain tumors.[4] A postictal paralysis may suggest the location but neuroimaging is essential to evaluate these patients.

Elevated ICP can displace parts of the brain and cause several different *herniation* syndromes.[5] For example, temporal lobe tumors can push the temporal lobe uncus medially and compress the midbrain. This can produce an ipsilateral dilated pupil, hemiparesis, cardiovascular and respiratory abnormalities, strokes in the distribution of the posterior cerebral arteries, and altered consciousness or coma.

Focal signs and symptoms depend on tumor location. Only some of the possible abnormalities are noted here. Frontal lobe lesions can cause cognitive and behavioral changes, gait disturbances, urinary dysfunction, aphasia, loss of the sense of smell, weakness, or gaze abnormalities. Temporal lobe tumors are associated with language and memory abnormalities, seizures, and visual field defects. Parietal lobe tumors can cause sensory deficits and sensory neglect syndromes, apraxia, and visual field deficits. Occipital lobes lesions also produce visual field defects as well as higher level visual processing disturbances.

Brain stem tumors produce cranial nerve abnormalities and complex patterns of motor and sensory deficits. Tumors in and around the pineal gland and third ventricle may cause hydrocephalus, gaze and pupillary abnormalities, and autonomic dysfunction. Cerebellar tumors cause headache, nystagmus, and different types of ataxia depending on location. Endocrine disturbances are common with tumors in or near the pituitary gland and hypothalamus.

14.3 Basics of Treatment

Details of treatment vary according to tumor type, pathologic grade, and individual patient factors. Cerebral edema is controlled with corticosteroids, osmotic diuretics, and hyperventilation. Most brain tumors are managed with a combination of surgery, radiation therapy, and chemotherapy. Biologic and immunologic therapies are emerging.

Surgery is part of the treatment plan for almost all brain tumors, either for diagnostic biopsy or tumor resection. For circumscribed benign tumors complete resection can produce a cure. For malignant tumors surgical debulking probably prolongs survival. Radiation therapy is the most effective treatment available for malignant tumors. Unfortunately, there are serious potential long-term side effects (see Chapter 21). Chemotherapy offers additional benefit to some patients but is also associated with significant side effects.

14.4 Primary Intracranial Tumors
A. Gliomas

Gliomas arise from the glial cells of the brain. They are named for the cell type of origin. Thus, there are astrocytomas derived from *astrocytes*, oligodendrogliomas from *oligodendrocytes*, and ependymomas from *ependymocytes*. Gliomas are the most common type of primary brain tumor. They are classified and graded according to World Health Organization criteria.[6] Treatment and prognosis depend on accurate pathologic grading of the tumor so a tissue sample is needed. This is obtained either by biopsy or during tumor resection.

Astrocytomas are the most common gliomas. They can occur in any age group and may develop in either the cerebral or cerebellar hemispheres. Low-grade astrocytomas are relatively benign, particularly the childhood form of cerebellar astrocytoma. Survival with low-grade astrocytomas is 40 to 65 percent at five years and 20 to 40 percent at ten years.[7] Many clinicians will avoid radiation therapy in these patients because of the high risk of subsequent cognitive dysfunction. Unfortunately, many low-grade tumors undergo transformation into more malignant forms. The most malignant glioma, *glioblastoma multiforme*, is the most common type of astrocytoma and has a much grimmer outlook—a median survival after surgery and radiation of only thirty-seven weeks,[8] and a five-year survival rate less than 5 percent.[9]

Oligodendrogliomas are slowly growing, relatively benign tumors occurring in the cerebral hemispheres of young adults. Seizures are very common with oligodendrogliomas. Unlike most gliomas these are quite sensitive to chemotherapy. Given their slow progression detection of an oligodendroglioma often presents a dilemma. In a patient whose only symptom is epilepsy, it is unclear whether the potential benefits outweigh the risks of surgery.

Ependymomas arise from cells lining the ventricles of the brain. These tumors occur mainly in children. Surgery is the main treatment, with five-year survival rates of 50 to 60 percent following gross total tumor resection.[10]

Generally, treatment of high-grade gliomas is disappointing and has not improved significantly for many years. Standard treatment consists of surgery, radiation, and chemotherapy. The more complete the surgical removal, the better the survival; radiation is the single most effective means of prolonging survival.[11] There are significant risks and side effects that must be considered. These tumors often produce cerebral edema. This is usually managed with dexamethasone. However, long-term use of corticosteroids also creates serious side effects. Many new treatment approaches are under investigation.[12]

B. Meningiomas

These tumors arise from the arachnoid cells that form part of the lining around the brain. Strictly speaking, meningiomas are intracranial tumors but not brain tumors. However, meningiomas are located intracranially and produce neurologic symptoms and signs. They are fairly common, rarely malignant, more frequent in women, symptomatic in about two per 100,000 people, and account for approximately 20 percent of all primary intracranial tumors.[13]

Meningiomas are often found near the intracranial venous sinuses. The common locations are parasagittal, cerebral convexity, and sphenoid ridge. Meningiomas grow slowly, compressing the brain rather than invading it. They can reach prodigious size before symptoms lead the patient to evaluation. Symptoms depend upon tumor location but headache, weakness, behavior changes, and seizures are common. Many meningiomas are asymptomatic and are identified as incidental findings either by neuroimaging performed for other reasons or at autopsy. Surgical removal is the usual treatment. Radiation therapy is needed if there is regrowth or incomplete removal.

C. Primary central nervous system lymphoma (PCNSL)

Immunodeficiency increases the risk of this highly malignant form of lymphoma. However, in recent decades there has been a threefold increase in incidence in immunocompetent patients.[14] PCNSL occurs mostly in middle-aged and older individuals. Behavior and personality changes are common initial manifestations. The tumors usually enhance diffusely with contrast MRI scanning. Diagnosis should be confirmed with a biopsy tissue sample.

Steroids often produce a temporary resolution of the tumor. Unlike most other brain tumors surgery has little to offer. Chemotherapy, usually including methotrexate, is the primary treatment modality. Radiation therapy can be highly effective but because of side effects, particularly in patients over sixty years, is usually reserved for those who did not respond to chemotherapy or refuse it. Chemotherapy plus radiation therapy produces a median survival of up to forty-five months, and a five-year survival rate of roughly 25 to 45 percent.[15]

D. Acoustic neuromas (vestibular schwannomas)

These benign tumors arise from the Schwann cells of the vestibular division of the eighth cranial nerve. The tumors spread into the space between the cerebellum and pons—the *cerebellopontine angle*. Acoustic neuromas (or neurinomas) are usually unilateral; bilateral neuromas in young persons may indicate an inherited disorder known as neurofibromatosis type II. These tumors produce symptoms by compressing cranial nerves VIII, VII, and V. Slowing worsening hearing is the most common symptom. Patients also complain of dizziness, tinnitus, ear pain or fullness, and facial pain. Large acoustic neuromas can compress the brain stem and cerebellum, producing dysfunction in those structures.

Diagnosis is usually made with a contrast enhanced MRI. Hearing tests and brainstem auditory evoked responses are done to measure hearing and serve as a baseline for monitoring purposes. Treatment is surgical removal, typically with intraoperative monitoring of the seventh and eighth cranial nerves. Gamma knife radiation is an option for smaller tumors.

E. Pituitary tumors

These tumors arise within the pituitary gland itself. They are classified as *microadenomas* if less than 1.0 centimeter in diameter, *macroadenomas* if larger. Pituitary tumors are further defined as either secreting or nonsecreting according to whether or not they produce pituitary hormones.

Nonsecreting pituitary tumors produce symptoms by virtue of mass effect, compression, and invasion of nearby structures. Headache is typical. The pituitary is near the optic chiasm. Therefore, visual field and optic nerve abnormalities are common. Destruction of normal pituitary tissue leads to endocrine deficiencies. The secreting adenomas can produce similar symptoms as well as additional problems due to excessive hormone production. Most symptomatic pituitary tumors are removed surgically but some secreting adenomas respond to drug therapy alone.

14.5 Metastatic Brain Tumors

These occur more frequently than primary brain tumors. Lung cancer is the most common source of brain metastases; breast carcinoma, renal cell cancer, and malignant melanoma are other significant sources.[16] In approximately 10 percent of patients the brain lesion is the first manifestation of the cancer.[17] Metastatic brain tumors are seen at autopsy in almost one-fourth of all cancer patients.[18] The neurologic signs and symptoms of metastases are due to mass effect, cerebral edema, and focal brain dysfunction.

Treatment and prognosis of brain metastases depends upon a number of factors. These include the size and number of brain lesions, patient age and condition, extent of systemic disease, and the responsiveness of the underlying cancer to therapy.[19] Surgical removal and radiation therapy improve and preserve neurologic function but are not curative. Without treatment survival is measured in weeks or a few months. Surgery and radiation increase survival by months, rarely longer.[20]

14.6 Paraneoplastic Syndromes

These are disorders of the nervous system that arise as remote effects of neoplasms in other parts of the body.[21] Paraneoplastic syndromes are much rarer than metastatic disease or complications of cancer and its treatment. However, they must be considered in any cancer patient who develops neurologic dysfunction. Even more importantly, a paraneoplastic syndrome is the presenting feature of an undiscovered tumor in about 60 percent of cases.[22] Recognition of a paraneoplastic syndrome must trigger a search for the underlying tumor because early diagnosis improves outcome.

A few neurologic paraneoplastic syndromes are caused by substances secreted by the tumor but most are autoimmune diseases.[23] The tumor produces an antigen and the body reacts by producing an antibody. The antigen resembles normal molecules in particular nervous system tissues. The neurologic manifestations develop when the antibody attacks these normal molecules. Several of these *autoantibodies* are known.[24] Small cell lung cancer, breast, thymoma, and gynecologic cancers are frequent sources.

There are paraneoplastic syndromes of the peripheral and central nervous systems. Some involve a single element of the nervous system (*limbic encephalopathy* and *cerebellar degeneration*) while others are more diffuse (*paraneoplastic encephalomyelitis*). Symptoms develop over weeks or months. Treatment of the underlying cancer usually leads to improvement. Immunosuppression is helpful in some paraneoplastic syndromes.

14.7 Spinal Tumors
A. Background
The spinal cord, like the brain, is the site of primary and metastatic tumors. Tumors growing outside of the dura are called *extradural* or *epidural*. Almost all metastatic spinal tumors are epidural. Tumors arising beneath the dural covering are intradural. Intradural tumors arising outside of the spinal cord are termed *extramedullary*. These develop from blood vessels, connective tissue, and the meninges. Intradural *intramedullary* tumors arise within the spinal cord; most are gliomas.

B. Epidural metastases
These are the most common tumors of the spinal column, occurring in between 60,000 and 160,000 of the roughly 400,000 individuals who die of cancer each year in the United States.[25] Back pain, with or without radicular pain, is the initial symptom in 95 percent of cases.[26] It may be present for weeks or months and can be excruciating. The tumor produces symptoms either directly by damaging the spinal cord and nerve roots, or indirectly by interfering with the vascular supply to the cord. The thoracic spine is the most common site for epidural metastasis.[27]

Spinal cord compression is an ominous complication that occurs in as many as 12 percent of patients with systemic cancers.[28] Weakness, sensory deficits, bowel and bladder dysfunction, and other manifestations of spinal cord compression can occur precipitously. Early diagnosis is essential to avoid permanent neurologic complications because patients with neurologic deficits at the time of diagnosis are unlikely to recover completely.

Known cancer patients with back pain require imaging studies because they often have normal neurologic examinations. MRI or CT myelogram is needed to identify tumor within the epidural space. Unfortunately, most patients with epidural metastases already have neurologic deficits at the time of diagnosis.[29] Therefore, when faced with an at-risk patient with back pain clinicians need to have a high index of suspicion in order to diagnose epidural metastases. Standard treatment of the metastatic tumor includes radiation therapy and glucocorticosteroids to reduce swelling. Surgical decompression can be useful in selected patients.[30]

Endnotes

1. Groves MD. "Epidemiology and pathophysiology in neuro-oncology." In: Evans RW, ed. *Saunders Manual of Neurologic Practice*. Philadelphia: Saunders; 2003:266-267.

2. Hildebrand, J, Baleriaux D, et al. "Clinical relevance of advances in molecular biology." *Continuum* 2001;7(6):9-27.

3. Tummala S, Groves MD. "Clinical presentations." In: Evans RW, *supra* note 1, at 268-271.

4. *Id.* at 269.

5. Hildebrand, J, Baleriaux D, et al. "Neuroradiology and brain tumors." *Continuum* 2001;7(6):28-44.

6. Kleihues P, Cavenee W, eds. *World Health Organization Classification of Tumours*. Lyon, France: IARC Press; 2000.

7. Mazzoni P, Rowland LP, eds. *Merritt's Neurology Handbook*. Philadelphia: Lippincott Williams & Wilkins; 2001.

8. *Id.* at 176.

9. Hsu S. "Glial tumors." In: Evans RW, *supra* note 1, at 272-276.

10. Janss AJ. "Childhood brain tumors." In: Johnson RT, Griffin JW, McArthur JC, eds. *Current Therapy in Neurologic Disease*, 6th ed. St. Louis: Mosby; 2002:247-252.

11. Fathallah-Shaykh HM. "Darts in the dark cure animal, but not human, brain tumors." *Arch Neurol* 2002;59:721-724.

12. Rich JN. "Malignant neural tumors." In: Johnson RT, et al., *supra* note 10, at 253-256.

13. De Angelis, LM. "Brain tumors." *N Engl J Med* 2001;344:114-123.

14. Schabet M. "Epidemiology of primary CNS lymphoma." *J Neurooncol* 1999; 43:199-201.

15. Tremont-Lukats IW. "Other tumors." In: Evans RW, *supra* note 1, at 290-295.

16. Hildebrand, J, Baleriaux D, et al. "Therapy of brain metastases." *Continuum* 2001;7(6):76-85.

17. Moriarty JL, Storm PB, Olivi A. "Central nervous system metastases." In: Johnson RT, et al., *supra* note 10, at 257-260.

18. Groves MD. "Metastatic brain tumors. "In: Evans RW, *supra* note 1, at 300-303.

19. *Id.* at 301.

20. *Id.* at 303.

21. Dropcho EJ. "Remote neurologic manifestations of cancer." *Neurol Clin* 2002;20:85-122.

22. Dalmau J. "Paraneoplastic neurologic syndromes." In: Evans RW, *supra* note 1, at 309-316.

23. Darnell RB, Posner JB. "Mechanisms of disease: Paraneoplastic syndromes involving the nervous system." *N Engl J Med* 2003;349:1543-1554.

24. *Id.* at 1548.

25. Byrne TN, Benzel EC, Waxman SG. *Disease of the Spine and Spinal Cord.* New York: Oxford University Press; 2000.

26. Grossman SA. "Epidural cord compressions and neoplastic meningitis." In: Johnson RT, et al., *supra* note 10, at 267-272.

27. Byrne TN, et al., *supra* note 25, at 177.

28. Grossman SA, *supra* note 26, at 267.

29. *Id*. at 268.

30. Byrne TN, et al., *supra* note 25, at 192-193.

Additional Reading

American Brain Tumor Association: www.abta.org, accessed December 24.

Brain Tumor Society: www.tbts.org, accessed December 24, 2004.

Kaye AH, Laws Jr ER, eds. *Brain Tumors. An Encyclopedic Approach*, 2nd ed. London: Churchill Livingstone; 2001.

National Brain Tumor Foundation: www.braintumor.org, accessed December 24, 2004.

Posner JB. *Neurologic Complications of Cancer*. Philadelphia: F.A. Davis; 1995.

Chapter 15

Headache

15.1 Introduction

Headache is an extraordinarily common complaint. Frequently disabling, it interferes with educational, vocational, and social activities. Rare is the individual who has never suffered from a headache of some type. Most people attempt to treat their headaches without formal intervention. When they do seek medical attention it is usually with a primary care physician. Nevertheless, headache is one of the most common complaints made to a neurologist. More neurologists provide long-term care for headache patients than any other condition.[1] Most headaches are benign but some indicate potentially life-threatening diseases. The first challenge for any physician is to distinguish *primary* headaches—migraine, tension-type, or cluster—from *secondary* headaches—those due to specific neurologic or non-neurologic diseases.

Although the experience of pain arises in the brain, the brain tissue itself is insensitive to pain. Head pain arises in one or more pain-sensitive cranial structures. These include the scalp, head and neck muscles, blood vessels, teeth, sinuses, cervical nerve roots, and pain receptor fibers in certain cranial nerves. A particular pain can have different causes and pain in one location may be referred there from a remote source.

251

Headache can be a symptom of brain abscess, brain tumor, cranial nerve dysfunction, dental disease, glaucoma and other ocular disturbances, intracranial bleeding, meningitis, metabolic derangements, severe hypertension, sinus infection, systemic infections, temporal arteritis, trauma, vascular malformations, and other conditions. Sleep apnea and even mere snoring can be significant triggers for headache.[2] A careful history and focused physical examination usually lead to a correct diagnosis. Particular danger signs suggestive of a serious underlying problem include:

- Coexisting fever, stiff neck, focal neurologic deficits, altered mental status, personality changes, papilledema
- Headache with precipitous onset ("thunderclap")
- New headaches after age fifty

Physicians should be particularly concerned about a patient with an excruciating first headache or "the worst headache of my life." Some of these patients may have a subarachnoid hemorrhage (SAH) due to rupture of an intracranial aneurysm (see §12.4). In addition to pain there may be altered or lost consciousness, nausea and vomiting, neurologic deficits, and stiff neck. Many SAH patients have had prior severe "sentinel" headaches, suggesting leaks from the aneurysm. SAH has a high mortality and morbidity, making accurate diagnosis essential. Brain CT scan is very sensitive to the subarachnoid bleeding early after the event. If the scan is normal but there is still suspicion of a ruptured aneurysm, lumbar puncture is done to look for blood in the cerebrospinal fluid.

It is always important to ask what is meant by headache since patients mean different things when they use this word. Furthermore, many patients will have more than one type of headache. Since the vast majority of headache patients have normal neurological and general physical examinations the history is supremely important in reaching the diagnosis. The headache history should address:

- Age of onset
- Anxiety, depression, or other psychological illness
- Associated visual alterations or neurologic abnormalities
- Association with vomiting or nausea

- Exacerbating or alleviating factors
- History of recent head or neck trauma
- History suggestive of cervical spine degenerative disease
- If intermittent or recurrent, time of day headache occurs
- Medication usage, including over-the-counter and herbal products
- Occupational history
- Presence of local scalp tenderness
- Quality of the pain—aching, bursting, knife-like, pounding, pressure-like, squeezing, stabbing, or throbbing
- Sleep pattern
- Temporal pattern—is the headache constant, intermittent, or recurrent
- Whether the headache is improving, stable, or worsening

Management of headache patients, especially those with chronic daily headaches, can be extremely difficult. Treatment failure can be due to inaccurate or incomplete diagnosis, unrecognized exacerbating factors, inadequate pharmacologic or nonpharmacologic treatment, unrealistic patient expectations, or serious coexisting conditions.[3]

15.2 Migraine

There is considerable confusion surrounding the diagnosis of migraine. Patients, and even some clinicians, often diagnose migraine even though the headache does not have any of the characteristics of the condition. Migraine is not a synonym for severe headache. Migraines can be only mildly to moderately painful whereas some tension headaches may be severe. Migraine affects approximately 18 percent of women and 6 percent of men.[4] Although these headaches usually cause moderate to very severe pain, only about half of all sufferers have a formal diagnosis and even fewer receive specific treatment.[5]

Migraine usually begins in teenagers or young adults, rarely in middle age or later. Most patients who suffer from migraine have a family history of the condition. One rare form of migraine—*familiar hemiplegic migraine*—has an associated gene abnormality. However, the precise pathophysiology of migraine is not clearly understood. Several comorbidities have been recognized in migraineurs including:

- Anxiety disorders
- Asthma
- Environmental allergies
- Epilepsy
- Irritable bowel syndrome
- Mitral valve prolapse
- Mood disorders
- Stroke

Most migraine headaches are unilateral, but bilateral headaches are common. Pain can occur over any part of the face or head. Frequently, the pain spreads into the posterior cervical region leading to confusion with muscle contraction or tension-type headaches. When the migraines are unilateral the location tends to switch from side to side. In a minority of patients, all of the migraines occur on the same side of the head. The lack of alternation should raise suspicion of an underlying structural lesion.

The typical quality of pain in migraine is throbbing. However, steady or constant pain is far from unusual. Headaches usually develop gradually and, untreated, last from a few hours to a few days. Physical exertion exacerbates the headache. Frequent associated symptoms include nausea, *photophobia* (sensitivity to light), *photophobia* or *hyperacusis* (sensitivity to sound), and mood changes. Many migraineurs experience a *prodrome* in the hours or days before a headache. Common manifestations include excessive yawning, unusual fatigue or restlessness, food cravings, impaired concentration, changes in appetite, and abnormal mood. Fluid retention may occur, particularly in women.

In the roughly 20 percent of patients who have migraine with aura (also known as *classic* migraine), the headache is preceded by symptoms of brain dysfunction. The aura is usually visual—flashing lights, blind spots surrounded by scintillations (*scintillating scotomata*), and visual distortions. Somatosensory auras are also fairly common. These most often consist of numbness or paresthesia in the arm and hand. Auras typically last between fifteen minutes and an hour and then disappear. When patients experience their first aura they may believe they are having a stroke. There is usually an interval between the termination of the aura and the onset of the headache phase. Sometimes, auras occur without a succeeding headache—*acephalic migraine* or *migraine equivalent*. In older persons these can be confused with transient ischemic attacks.

Many untreated patients are unable to continue with normal activities because their migraine symptoms are so severe. Most take to their beds for the duration of the headache phase, preferring a dark, quiet location. Following the attack, many patients feel drained and must rest for several hours.

Diagnosis of migraine is straightforward in most cases. When there are unusual or worrisome features diagnostic testing is necessary. MRI scanning is the most useful tool. Indications include:

- Headaches with precipitous onset
- Migraines lasting more than three days (*status migrainosus*)
- Migraines with onset after age fifty
- Posttraumatic migraines
- Progressively worsening headaches
- Prolonged or persistent auras

Nonspecific white matter abnormalities are common in migraineurs' MRI scans and are of uncertain significance.[6]

Identification and avoidance of migraine triggers is a major aspect of treatment. Patients are particularly sensitive to missed meals, too much or too little sleep, stress, and fatigue. The trigger can be emotional, physical, or a combination of both. Often, the migraine occurs immediately after a period of stress or intense activity. Many patients have particular sensory triggers—certain aromas, bright or flickering lights (especially fluorescent), and noises. Alcohol and many foods trigger migraines. Many women have their migraines before or during their menses. Occasionally, migraines occur only in association with menses—*catamenial migraine*. Migraine may develop for the first time following mild head injury or whiplash.

Patient education plays a major role in treatment. Patients need to be reassured of the benign nature of their migraines. They must learn to recognize their individual triggers in order to avoid these. Medications are used to abort or alleviate headache attacks and to prevent headaches. Symptomatic or acute medication treatment is most effective when initiated early, when the headache is milder. The selection of agents is based on individual factors including the severity of the typical headache and coexistence of complicating features such as nausea and vomiting.

Overuse of acute medications, especially those containing butalbital, can lead to frequent *rebound* or *medication overuse* headaches. This can occur both with over-the-counter agents as well as prescription medications. Patients at risk are those who in one week use: [7]

- Narcotics or ergots on more than two days
- Simple analgesics three or more times daily on five or more days
- Triptans or analgesics containing barbiturates or sedatives on more than three days

The physician needs to re-evaluate the treatment plan and consider use of daily preventative therapy for such patients. *Transformed migraine* and *chronic migraine* are terms used to describe chronic daily headache syndromes that began with intermittent migraines.

Triptans—selective 5-hydroxytryptamine receptor agonists—are a new class of very effective migraine medications. There are oral, nasal, and subcutaneous forms of these drugs. Chest and neck tightness and flushing are common side effects. Coronary artery disease, uncontrolled high blood pressure, and vascular disease are contraindications. Overuse can produce rebound headaches.

Several different classes of medications are effective migraine prophylactic agents. All have potential side effects. The most commonly used are tricyclic antidepressants, beta-blockers, and anticonvulsants. Often, a prophylactic agent is selected based on the presence of comorbid conditions that might also respond to the particular medication. Methysergide is an older medication that is highly effective but has significant contraindications and risks.

Some patients respond to alternative preventive strategies including magnesium supplementation, high doses of riboflavin (vitamin B2), or herbs such as butterbur and feverfew. Relaxation techniques and cognitive-behavioral therapies are of uncertain benefit. Botulinum toxin appears to be a promising treatment.[8]

15.3 Cluster Headaches

Cluster headaches are probably the most painful of all primary headaches. Fortunately, these are far less common than migraines, with a prevalence of only 0.02 to 0.06 percent of the population.[9] Unlike migraine, cluster headaches occur more often in men than women. *Episodic cluster* headaches usually begin when the patient is in his twenties. As the name suggests, the patient tends to suffer clusters of attacks occurring over several weeks or a few months. The clusters tend to recur periodically, with headache-free intervals between clusters. Most patients have one or two headaches per day. Each usually lasts between thirty and ninety minutes, rarely up to three hours. Frequently, these occur at the same time each day. Nocturnal cluster headaches that awaken the patient in the early morning hours are common.

A small number of cluster patients have daily attacks without a headache-free interval—*chronic cluster* headache. If these develop after a more typical episodic onset they are known as secondary chronic cluster; if there is never a remission after onset, they are primary chronic cluster. Chronic cluster develops at a later age, especially in women, and is associated with heavy cigarette use.[10] Neuroimaging should be performed in chronic cluster patients to identify structural lesions in the head and neck, particularly if the headaches are progressively worsening or if there are focal neurologic deficits.

The pain of the cluster headache can be excruciating. It is usually located in or around one eye. The pain develops over several minutes. It is associated with signs of autonomic dysfunction—red eye, tearing, nasal congestion, drooping eyelid, constricted pupil, and increased forehead sweating. Unlike migraine sufferers cluster headache patients are restless and agitated during their headaches, rarely able to lie down. Alcohol, often only small amounts, is a potent trigger of cluster headaches. Most patients quickly learn to avoid alcohol, especially when they are in the midst of a cluster.

Trigeminal neuralgia, sinus infections, and other structural lesions can mimic cluster headache but the usual periodicity will be absent. *Chronic paroxysmal hemicrania* consists of frequent, brief cluster-like headaches. These last only a few minutes and are seen mainly in women. Chronic paroxysmal hemicrania responds dramatically to indomethacin, an agent that is rarely helpful for cluster. There are individuals whose headaches have features of migraine and cluster, *cluster-migraine*. Cluster headaches can also occur in conjunction with trigeminal neuralgia, *cluster-tic*.

Treatment for an individual attack must be fast-acting. Oxygen inhalation, topical nasal lidocaine and other anesthetics, subcutaneous triptan injections, and intravenous dihydroergotamine are effective options. Corticosteroids given at the onset of a headache cycle may ameliorate the cluster. Lithium, verapamil, and methysergide are effective prophylactic agents for many patients. Refractory patients may require surgical intervention. Procedures to cut the trigeminal sensory nerve roots are effective but cause loss of sensation and destroy the protective corneal reflex.

15.4 Tension-type Headaches

Tension headache, also known as muscle contraction headache, is the most common type of headache. Surprisingly, the causes and pathophysiology of tension headache are poorly understood. Stress, anxiety, depression, and sleep deprivation are all blamed for tension headaches. It is not clear whether excessive scalp muscle contraction explains these headaches. Some patients develop chronic tension headaches, defined as at least six months with headaches fifteen or more days per month. This can be seen with or without analgesic overuse.

Patients describe a tight, band-like sensation around the head up to the vertex. The pain is characterized as heavy and squeezing. It tends to worsen as the day goes on. Unlike migraine, episodic tension headache is not associated with nausea or vomiting nor is it aggravated by physical activity. Chronic tension headaches, however, may have some migrainous features. Many patients have considerable anxiety regarding the possibility of serious underlying disease such as a brain tumor. Often, reassurance is insufficient to address this concern. Only a neuroimaging procedure satisfies the patient.

Most simple tension headaches respond to over-the-counter analgesics, particularly nonsteroidal anti-inflammatory medications. Prescription agents containing butalbital are quite effective, but if used too frequently may lead to overuse, *rebound* headaches, and chronic daily headaches.[11] The concept of medication overuse as a cause of chronic daily headache is widely recognized, even in the popular media.[12] However, a great deal is not understood about this. For example, many patients using analgesics daily for other illnesses such as arthritis do not develop such headaches, even if they have a history of migraine or tension-type headache.[13] Also, some chronic daily headache patients do not overuse medication.

Discontinuation of the offending agent—easier said than done—is a critical part of treatment for chronic daily headache patients. Withdrawal of some medications must be done gradually. Occasionally, inpatient detoxification is needed. Treatment of these patients is complex and difficult.[14] Though there are claims of success rates as high as 80 percent, there is some controversy about how well these patients actually do in the long-term.[15]

15.5 Cervicogenic Headache

This is a controversial entity, originally described in 1983.[16] The term is often used synonymously for post-whiplash headache or occipital neuralgia. Cervicogenic headache shares features with migraine, and current diagnostic criteria do not completely distinguish the two.[17] Pain is usually unilateral, radiating from the posterior cervical region to the forehead and orbit. Pressure over the greater and lesser occipital nerves usually reproduces the radiating pain; nerve blocks should abolish the pain of a typical attack.[18] There may be blurred vision and tearing, sensitivity to light and noise, and gastrointestinal upset—features that suggest migraine. Cervicogenic headache after a whiplash injury may be bilateral, chronic, and disabling.[19]

The ideal treatment for cervicogenic headache is unknown. Many patients overuse analgesics. There is some evidence that migraine medications are ineffective,[20] but there are no controlled studies of the newer abortive or prophylactic agents. Physical modalities directed toward the neck stiffness and reduced mobility may be useful.

15.6 Pseudotumor Cerebri (Benign Intracranial Hypertension)

This is due to elevated intracranial pressure not caused by malignancy or other mass lesions. Headache and visual abnormalities are the usual manifestations. Pseudotumor cerebri is most common in overweight women in their childbearing years. It is associated with excessive intake of vitamin

A, several endocrine diseases, and use of tetracycline and other antibiotics. Neurological examination is usually normal except for papilledema and, sometimes, cranial nerve VI palsy. Brain MRI and CT are also usually normal. The diagnosis is confirmed by detection of elevated opening pressure during lumbar puncture.

The headache can have a pulsating quality. In some patients the headache worsens as the day goes on and can awaken the patient during the night. Certain positions or activities can exacerbate the headache. If not treated properly pseudotumor can lead to optic nerve atrophy and blindness. Most patients respond to the carbonic anhydrase inhibitor acetazolamide, an agent that reduces cerebrospinal fluid production. Headaches are treated symptomatically. Surgical intervention is necessary when there are signs of deteriorating vision. Optic nerve sheath fenestration and lumboperitoneal shunt are the two options. It is not clear which is superior.

Endnotes

1. Swarztrauber K, Lawyer BL, AAN Practice Characteristics Subcommittee. *Neurologists 2000: AAN Member Demographic and Practice Characteristics*. St. Paul: American Academy of Neurology; 2001.

2. Scher AI, Lipton RB, Stewart WF. "Habitual snoring as a risk factor for chronic daily headache." *Neurology* 2003;60:1366-1368.

3. Lipton RB, Silberstein SD, et al. "Why headache treatment fails." *Neurology* 2003;60:1064-1070.

4. Lipton RB, Scher AI, et al. " Migraine in the United States: Epidemiology and patterns of health care use." *Neurology* 2002;58:885-894.

5. Goadsby PJ, Lipton RB, Ferrari MD. "Migraine: Current understanding and treatment." *N Engl J Med* 2002;346:257-270.

6. Swartz RH, Kern RZ. "Migraine is associated with magnetic resonance imaging white matter abnormalities: A meta-analysis." *Arch Neurol* 2004; 61:1366-1368.

7. Silberstein SD, Welch KMA. "Painkiller headache." *Neurology* 2002;59:972-974.

8. Argoff CE. "The use of botulinum toxin for chronic pain and headaches." *Curr Treat Options Neurol* 2003;5(6):483-492.

9. Finkel AG. "Epidemiology of cluster headache." *Curr Headache Reports* 2003;2:50-55.

10. *Id*. at 52.

11. Silberstein SD. "Chronic daily headaches." *Continuum* 2003;9(1):121-143.

12. Jauhar S. "Over-the-counter headache." *N.Y. Times*, January 12, 2003, §6 (Magazine), at 40.

13. Bahra A, Walsh M, et al. "Does chronic daily headache arise de novo in association with regular use of analgesics?" *Headache* 2003;43:179-190.

14. Silberstein SD, *supra* note 11, at 134-139.

15. McBride G. "Why medication overuse is a big headache - and what to do about it." *Neurology Today* 2003;9(3):49-55.

16. Sjaastad O, Saunte C, et al. "Cervicogenic headache: A hypothesis." *Cephalalgia* 1983;3:249-256.

17. Fishbain DA, Lewis J, et al. "Do the proposed cervicogenic headache diagnostic criteria demonstrate specificity in terms of separating cervicogenic headache from migraine?" *Curr Headache Reports* 2003;2:165-172.

18. Sjaastad O, Fredriksen TA, Pfaffenrath V. "Cervicogenic headache: Diagnostic criteria." *Headache* 1998;38:442-445.

19. Drottning M. "Cervicogenic headache after whiplash injury." *Curr Headache Reports* 2003;2:162-164.

20. Bovim G. Sjaastad O. "Cervicogenic headache: Responses to nitroglycerin, oxygen, ergotamine and morphine." *Headache* 1993;33:249-252.

Additional Reading

American Council for Headache Education: www.achenet.org, accessed December 24, 2004.

Evans RW, Mathew NT. *Handbook of Headache*. Philadelphia: Lippincott Williams & Wilkins; 2000.

National Headache Foundation: www.headaches.org, accessed December 24, 2004.

Silberstein SD, Lipton RB, Goadsby PJ. *Headache in Clinical Practice*, 2nd ed. London, UK: Martin Dunitz; 2002.

Chapter 16

Infectious Diseases

16.1 Introduction

Infections of the nervous system have been recognized since antiquity. Before the development of antibiotics, infection was the most common cause of serious neurologic illness. Indeed, bacterial meningitis was usually a fatal disease. In the late twentieth century hopes that drug therapies would eliminate infectious diseases were dashed. Instead, the spectrum of disease changed. Syphilis was a major part of neurology before the discovery of penicillin (and is still to be reckoned with). For example, the 1939 edition of one well-regarded neurology textbook[1] devoted sixty of its 838 pages—roughly 7 percent—to neurosyphilis. Early in the AIDS epidemic, the seventh edition of another standard text[2] contained only eight pages on neurosyphilis out of 774—just over 1 percent.

New diseases and dramatic increases in previously rare infections are more likely to face neurologists today. Human immunodeficiency virus attacks the nervous system directly. In addition, patients with compromised immune systems due to HIV infection and other causes are subject to a host of previously rare *opportunistic* infections. Lyme disease is endemic in much of the United States and often involves the nervous system. The spread of bovine spongiform encephalopathy ("mad cow" disease) to people (new variant Creutzfeld-Jakob disease) is another example of the challenge posed by infectious disease.

Infectious organisms can attack any part of the nervous system, its coverings, and its blood vessels. *Meningitis* refers to infections of the lining of the spinal cord and brain—the *meninges*. Bacterial meningitis is also known as *septic* meningitis. *Aseptic* meningitis has nonbacterial causes, mostly viral. *Encephalitis* indicates an infection of the brain itself. A few of the main categories of disease are discussed here.

16.2 Acute Meningitis

Three membranes (meninges)—the *dura mater*, the *arachnoid mater* and the *pia mater*—cover the brain and spinal cord. The dura is a thick fibrous structure closely applied to the inside of the skull. The pia mater is a delicate membrane that adheres closely to the surface of the brain. The arachnoid mater lies between the dura and the pia, bridging the sulci of the brain. The space between the arachnoid and pia (*subarachnoid space*) contains cerebrospinal fluid (CSF). Meningitis involves the arachnoid, pia, and subarachnoid space.

The clinical features of viral meningitis vary little regardless of the causative virus. There is usually sudden intense headache, fever, neck stiffness, and drowsiness or confusion. Malaise, listlessness, myalgia, nausea, and vomiting are typical. Patients do not look as ill as those with bacterial meningitis. The symptoms generally resolve within a few days and most patients recover within a couple of weeks. Long-term neurological sequelae are uncommon. Frequent viral causes of meningitis are coxsackie, echo, and mumps.

Bacterial meningitis is an acute purulent (pus-forming) infection of the subarachnoid space. There may also be inflammation of the brain—*meningoencephalitis*—or spinal cord tissue—*meningomyelitis*—and blood vessels. This is a medical emergency. Early diagnosis and treatment is critically important. Despite advances in antibiotic therapy and improvements in general management mortality rates are still high, up to 37 percent in patients older than sixty years.[3] Meningitis survivors may have serious complications including deafness, epilepsy, and brain damage. Morbidity may be as high as 60 percent.[4]

The bacteria causing meningitis most frequently enter the subarachnoid space through the bloodstream. Some infections spread to the nervous system from other nearby infected structures—sinuses, bone, and middle ear. Finally, bacteria can enter through defects in the bone or spinal column. This occurs with skull fractures and penetrating wounds, and can happen iatrogenically (lumbar puncture, epidural injections).[5]

The most common bacterial species producing community-acquired meningitis are *Neisseria meningitidis*—meningococcus—and *Streptococcus pneumoniae*—pneumococcus. Vaccines have led to a sharp decline in *Haemophilus influenzae* meningitis, previously a leading cause of childhood meningitis. *Listeria monocytogenes* is a common cause of meningitis in neonates and older patients, and in those with defective T-cell-mediated immunity. *Staphylococcus aureus* is not rare in any patient group but is an especially important cause of infections after neurosurgical procedures and in patients with penetrating head injuries.[6]

Bacterial meningitis usually presents with a few days of worsening nonspecific symptoms—fever, malaise, nausea, confusion, and irritability. The patient then develops signs of meningeal irritation, namely headache and stiff neck. Sensitivity to light and altered level of consciousness—sometimes even coma—are common. The rare fulminant cases develop in a few hours.

The headache is severe, steadily progressive, made worse by movement, and associated with nausea and vomiting. As the meningitis develops there is cerebral swelling with increased intracranial pressure, causing altered consciousness and coma. Seizures occur in many patients. The neck resists passive flexion by stiffening—*nuchal rigidity*. *Brudzinski's sign* consists of flexion of the knees and hips by the patient in response to the examiner's attempts at neck flexion. *Kernig's sign* is patient resistance to the examiner attempting to extend the leg at the knee with the hip flexed.

Meningitis may present with atypical features. Infants are said to have a particular high pitched cry. The youngest and the oldest patients, as well as any immunocompromised individuals, may not have signs of meningeal irritation. Since there are many more common causes of fever clinicians might not suspect bacterial meningitis in such cases. Typical features are also difficult to elicit in inebriated or post-surgical patients.

Definitive diagnosis is achieved with blood cultures and lumbar puncture, the latter being the most important. Depending on the timing of the lumbar puncture the CSF may vary from being only mildly abnormal to containing frank pus. If there is any evidence of focal neurological abnormality, some form of imaging (brain CT or MRI) is usually performed prior to the lumbar puncture. However, since waiting even for a readily available CT scan delays management decisions, it is important to recognize that lumbar puncture is probably safe in patients who lack certain clinical features predictive of significant mass effect. These warning signs include:[7]

- Abnormal language function
- Age greater than sixty years
- Altered level of consciousness
- CNS disease—stroke, mass lesion, focal infection
- Gaze palsy
- Impaired immunity
- Limb weakness
- Seizure within one week of presentation
- Visual field defects

Once the CSF is available for testing immediate therapy with antibiotics is mandatory. Classic CSF abnormalities in bacterial meningitis include:[8]

- Glucose less than 45 milligrams per deciliter
- Opening pressure greater than 180 millimeters H_2O
- Positive culture in 80 percent of cases
- Positive Gram's stain in 70–90 percent of untreated cases
- Protein greater than 45 milligrams per deciliter
- White blood cells, 10–10,000 per cubic millimeter, mostly neutrophils

Even if an organism cannot be identified in the CSF broad-spectrum antibiotics should be given to treat the most common causes of meningitis in the patient's age group. The empiric regimen usually includes a third or fourth generation cephalosporin plus vancomycin.[9] Since fever and confusion are also produced by viral and tick-borne agents acyclovir and doxycycline may also be given before test results are available.[10] More definitive treatment depends on identification of the specific organism and measurement of its antibiotic sensitivities. The role of corticosteroids such as dexamethasone to reduce the inflammatory response that underlies some of the tissue damage in bacterial meningitis is unclear.[11]

A. Pneumococcal meningitis

The pneumococcus bacterium is the most common cause of bacterial meningitis in adults and in children under two years. The bacteria colonize the nasopharynx and spread in respiratory droplets. Transmission is increased in crowded conditions. Meningitis often results from bacteremia—bacteria in the bloodstream—secondary to a focus of infection in the lungs, ear, or sinuses. Risk factors include diabetes mellitus, splenectomy, and liver disease. Many patients also have a pneumococcal pneumonia. Mortality in adults with pneumococcal meningitis is 21 percent compared to 3 percent for meningococcal meningitis.[12] Treatment of pneumococcal meningitis is complicated by the rise of penicillin-resistant strains. These usually respond to a combination of vancomycin and a cephalosporin.

B. Meningococcal meningitis

The meningococcus bacteria is the most common cause of meningitis in children two- to eighteen-years old and also accounts for about one-third of cases in children one- to twenty-three-months old. Across all age groups it is responsible for a quarter of bacterial meningitis cases.[13] A red, maculopapular rash develops into a rash with tiny bleeds (*petechiae*) in most patients suffering from meningococcal meningitis. It is most prominent on the trunk and legs but may be difficult to detect in early stages of the disease. Meningococcal sepsis—spread of toxins throughout the body—can cause disseminated intravascular coagulopathy. This will lead to coalescence of the rash into large hemorrhagic areas known as *purpura fulminans*—a very poor prognostic sign.

Penicillin or ampicillin is the drug of choice for meningococcal meningitis. Contacts of patients with proven meningococcal meningitis should be treated prophylactically with rifampin, since their risk of developing the disease increases 500-fold or more.[14]

C. Haemophilus influenzae meningitis

Before widespread vaccination drastically reduced its incidence this was predominantly a disease of infants and young children, nearly all cases occurring under the age of four. Now, *H. influenzae* meningitis is seen more often in adults. The onset of the clinical features is usually less dramatic than other forms of meningitis. Lethargy and mild evidence of meningeal irritation may be the early symptoms. It may take up to forty-eight hours for signs of cerebral irritation to develop. Management is similar to other forms of meningitis.

16.3 Chronic Meningitis

This syndrome refers to meningoencephalitis that develops more gradually than acute purulent meningitis, usually over one or more weeks. In the immunocompetent individual the most important cause is tuberculosis; in the immunocompromised individual, fungal infections assume greater importance.

Chronic meningitis can present with very subtle manifestations. Typical features include changes in mental status, general malaise, headache, low-grade fever, and weight loss. Seizures and focal neurologic deficits may occur as the disease progresses. Some patients exhibit bizarre behavior and are sent for psychiatric evaluation. Untreated, the disease progresses to coma and death.

Neuroimaging should ordinarily be performed before lumbar puncture. Gadolinium-enhanced brain MRI is the recommended procedure. Definitive diagnosis depends on identification of the causative organism in the CSF. Anti-tuberculosis treatment requires a multiple drug regimen because resistant strains are becoming more common. Certain fungal infections are difficult to treat and may require *intrathecal* medication—delivery directly into the spinal fluid. Antifungal treatments must be monitored closely because of toxicity.

16.4 Syphilis and Lyme Disease

These two diseases are caused by bacteria in the spirochete family, *Treponema pallidum* and *Borrelia burgdorferi* respectively. (A third genus of spirochete, Leptospira, can produce meningitis and other infections.) Both *T. pallidum* and *B. burgdorferi* have an affinity for the nervous system and are difficult to eradicate.

A. Neurosyphilis

Syphilis is a widespread, mostly sexually transmitted disease. The incidence decreased sharply during the antibiotic era but rebounded with the rise of HIV infection in the 1980s. Incidence has fallen since then but there are still about 2.5 cases per 100,000 population with 5 to 10 percent of untreated individuals developing CNS infection.[15] *Primary syphilis* refers to the initial infection, which produces a painless genital ulceration that can go unobserved. The spread of bacteria throughout the bloodstream—*secondary syphilis*—follows and is associated with a generalized rash. Next, there is a latent phase that can last for years or decades. *Tertiary syphilis* refers to the manifestations that follow the latent phase.

Neurosyphilis can be asymptomatic. This common state is diagnosed by examination of the cerebrospinal fluid. Such patients are at risk for symptomatic neurosyphilis. Therefore, the clinician needs to have a high degree of suspicion whenever neurosyphilis is a possibility, particularly in HIV positive individuals. Diagnosis of neurosyphilis requires a history of typical signs and symptoms, a positive serum test, and characteristic CSF abnormalities.[16]

Early neurosyphilis affects the meninges and blood vessels. *Syphilitic meningitis* usually occurs within a year or two of infection. Patients have the usual signs of meningeal irritation along with cranial neuropathies. *Cerebrovascular neurosyphilis* develops an average of seven years after infection.[17] Inflammation of the arteries leads to occlusion of the blood vessels and inadequate perfusion of the brain. Patients present with signs and symptoms of focal brain or spinal cord damage. Treatment with high-dose intravenous penicillin prevents these complications but does not reverse deficits due to vascular insufficiency and tissue destruction.

Late neurosyphilis develops years or decades after infection and affects the brain or spinal cord. *Tabes dorsalis* develops an average of twenty-one years after infection.[18] There is demyelination of the spinal cord dorsal columns, posterior nerve roots, and sensory ganglia. Patients experience lightning-like or lancinating pains, usually traveling into the legs. The damage to the sensory structures causes severe loss of sensation and incoordination.

General paresis (also known as dementia paralytica or general paralysis of the insane) is a progressive, chronic dementing process that produces mostly frontotemporal degeneration. Psychiatric symptoms are common. The memory deficits and other cognitive problems can resemble Alzheimer's disease. Penicillin therapy can halt the progression of both tabes and general paresis, but return of function is unlikely. Treated patients should be monitored periodically, including repeat CSF examination, for treatment failure.

B. Lyme neuroborreliosis (LNB)

Lyme disease is a multi-system infection endemic to large parts of the United States and Europe. There are approximately fifteen thousand cases annually in the United States.[19] Species of the deer tick *Ixodes* are the vectors for transmission of the *Borrelia* bacteria. A spreading red rash with a bull's-eye appearance at the tick's feeding site is almost pathognomonic of Lyme disease but is sometimes missed or not present. If untreated, the disease spreads to other organs and produces symptoms within weeks or months. Joint, muscle, cardiac, and neurologic involvement are common. Details of the epidemiology, transmission, and clinical manifestations were reviewed recently.[20]

Like neurosyphilis, there are both early and late forms of LNB. Radiculoneuropathies and cranial neuropathies, especially facial nerve palsies, are common in early LNB.[21] The facial palsy can be confused with idiopathic Bell's palsy if the patients do not have other Lyme symptoms or laboratory testing for Lyme disease is omitted. Lyme meningitis, a chronic basilar meningitis, is typical of Lyme in the United States; there may be relatively mild symptoms despite prominent spinal fluid findings.[22] A painful radiculoneuropathy is more typical of early LNB in Europe.[23] This difference is attributed to diversity in the causative *Borrelia* species.

Radiculopathy and neuropathy are the most common late LNB manifestations. Pain and sensory symptoms predominate but objective findings are rarely detected. Antibiotic treatment usually alleviates these complaints. Cognitive difficulties related to a chronic Lyme encephalopathy are also seen. Impaired memory and concentration occur in conjunction with malaise, fatigue, and joint pains. This syndrome is rare but has given rise to controversy about "chronic Lyme disease" and the need for long courses of intravenous antibiotics.

There are Lyme patients who report persistent fatigue, cognitive dysfunction, muscle and joint pain, and other subjective complaints following standard antibiotic treatment. Some physicians recommend prolonged antibiotic treatment. However, several double-blinded studies reveal that in the absence of objective signs of infection such patients do not benefit from antibiotics as compared to placebo.[24,25,26] This is an important issue because inappropriate use of antibiotics in these patients has had fatal consequences.[27] Simultaneous infection with *Babesia* and *Ehrlichia* bacteria can occur with Lyme disease and may explain ongoing symptoms in some patients.

16.5 Brain Abscess

This is a localized area of infection within the brain tissue. It can be due to bacterial, fungal, or parasitic infection. Abscesses are uncommon in developed nations with effective antibiotic treatment of sinusitis and other infections. Bacterial abscesses have different causes than bacterial meningitis. Also, a brain abscess can be caused by more than one infectious organism. They can occur in isolation or along with other nervous system infections. There can be multiple abscesses. Abscesses arise most often from infections elsewhere, spreading to the brain via the blood or by direct extension from nearby structures (sinuses, mastoid, and middle ear). The frontal and temporal lobes harbor most abscesses arising from other cranial structures.

Brain abscesses produce symptoms and signs of raised intracranial pressure—headache, altered mental status—as well as localized brain injury—seizures, weakness, aphasia, and other focal deficits. However, the classic initial presentation of fever, headache, and focal deficits is present in less than half the patients.[28] Symptoms develop over weeks in most cases. Stiff neck is less common than with meningitis. Many patients do not have laboratory findings suggestive of systemic infection such as elevated white cell counts or positive blood cultures.

Fortunately, neuroimaging with CT or MRI is quite sensitive for brain abscess. Lumbar puncture should not be performed because it can cause brain herniation and death. Also, the cerebrospinal fluid may not add significant diagnostic information because the responsible organism will not be recovered unless the abscess had ruptured.[29]

Large abscesses require a combination of surgical and antibiotic treatment. The goal of surgery is to reduce the mass effect produced by the abscess. Aspiration and excision are options. Early abscesses do not contain pus and cannot be drained. At this stage—*cerebritis*—antibiotics alone are used. Tissue swelling around the abscess—*edema*—responds to hyperventilation and corticosteroids. Initial choice of antibiotics depends on identifying the most likely source of the abscess. If there is neurosurgical intervention or the primary source is found, pus is obtained and specific microbes are identified. In some cases stable patients can be treated with antibiotics alone and their condition monitored by serial brain scanning.

The mortality of cerebral abscesses ranges from 10 percent in patients who were not comatose when diagnosed to 82 percent in those who did not respond to pain when first examined.[30] Neurological sequelae are frequent in survivors and, often, disabling. Epilepsy develops in as many as half and focal neurological deficits such as hemiparesis are very common.[31] In general, the more severe the neurological presentation, the more likely there will be a permanent focal deficit. Changes in higher intellectual functions occur in the vast majority of patients who have had raised intracranial pressure.

16.6 Acute Viral Encephalitis

This is an infection of the brain tissue itself, usually characterized by headache, fever, and altered mental status. Seizures and focal neurologic deficits are common. The distinction between acute meningitis and encephalitis is not always clear-cut. In patients with encephalitis the disease reflects the predominant involvement of brain tissue. Signs of meningeal irritation are less marked than in meningitis. *Meningoencephalitis* indicates a syndrome with elements of both meningitis and encephalitis.

There are dozens of viruses known to cause encephalitis. *Arthropodborne* viruses—arboviruses—are transmitted by bites of infected mosquitoes and ticks. These cause *epidemic* encephalitis in particular geographic regions at particular times of the year. Manifestations vary among the different infections and there is a wide range in morbidity and mortality. *Eastern equine encephalitis* is probably the most severe arbovirus encephalitis but is, fortunately, rare. *St. Louis encephalitis* is less severe but more common and, therefore, a more frequent cause of impairment and death. *West Nile* virus is a recent arrival to the western hemisphere. Identified initially as a cause of mass bird deaths, this virus has a high propensity to infect humans. It produces CNS disease—especially meningoencephalitis—in 1 in 150 infected persons and can also cause a polio-like weakness.[32] There is no specific treatment for the arboviruses.

The most common cause of *sporadic* encephalitis is herpes simplex virus 1 (HSV-1), accounting for 20 to 30 percent of sporadic encephalitis cases in immunocompetent adults.[33] This is a complication of infection with that ubiquitous agent. The virus enters the body during primary infection, either without symptoms or with pharyngitis, and then establishes a latent infection in the trigeminal ganglion. HSV encephalitis represents a reactivation of the latent virus.

Many patients have an upper respiratory or gastrointestinal illness before they develop the encephalitis. There is usually an abrupt onset of fever, headache, and vomiting. Decreased level of consciousness and seizures are common in the early stages. Coma can occur within days. The virus has a predilection for the temporal and inferior frontal lobes, the explanation for the characteristic neuropsychiatric features. These include bizarre behaviors, disorientation, and severe memory loss. Auditory or olfactory hallucinations and aphasia are very frequent, reflecting involvement of the areas of the brain serving those functions. Hemiparesis and visual field disorders develop as the encephalitis progresses.

The mortality of untreated HSV encephalitis is extremely high, up to 70 percent. Even with treatment long-term neurological sequelae are the rule.[34] Any patient presenting with acute encephalitis should be treated with the antiviral agent acyclovir until HSV infection is excluded.

16.7 Human Immunodeficiency Virus

Neurologic disease is a common part of HIV infection, either directly from the virus or indirectly, due to opportunistic infections. The virus is *neurotropic*, entering the nervous system after initial infection. Patients often develop an *aseptic meningitis* or *acute inflammatory demyelinating neuropathy* (Guillain-Barré type syndrome) at that time. Neurologic manifestations are seen in 20 to 55 percent of HIV-infected persons, with the risk increasing with survival time and immunosuppression.[35]

Later in the course of infection HIV is also associated with dementia, myelopathy, and peripheral neuropathy. *HIV-associated dementia* is seen in 15 percent of patients.[36] Typical features include mental slowing, impaired attention and concentration, and memory disturbances. Psychiatric symptoms are common. The mechanism of damage is not clear. Many symptoms can be reversed with antiretroviral therapy. Encephalitis in HIV patients can be caused by rare infections such as *Toxoplasma gondii* or the JC virus (the cause of *progressive multifocal leucoencephalopathy*). *Cytomegalovirus* can cause a polyradiculitis. In advanced HIV infection peripheral neuropathies can be a direct result of the virus, a medication side effect, or due to opportunistic infections.[37]

16.8 Prion Diseases

Kuru is a rapidly progressive dementing illness previously found among the Fore people in New Guinea when cannibalism was still practiced.[38] Under the microscope the brain tissue resembled that of sheep suffering from a neurodegenerative disease known as scrapie. These became known as *transmissible spongiform encephalopathies*. The causative agent was thought to be an atypical or "slow" virus. These and several related conditions are actually caused by an abnormal form of the *prion* protein found in the brain.[39] Prion diseases can be inherited or sporadic. These diseases are all progressive and fatal.

Creutzfeldt-Jacob disease (CJD) accounts for the vast majority of human prion infections but is still quite rare, with an annual incidence of one per million.[40] The mean age of onset is sixty-two years.[41] There may be a nonspecific prodrome with headache, fatigue, decreased appetite, and sleep disturbance. Neurologic manifestations include ataxia, myoclonic jerks, and cognitive disturbances that progress to dementia. The EEG will usually reveal typical abnormal periodic discharges, though mainly in middle and late stages of disease. MRI may reveal hyperintensities in the basal ganglia;[42] there is also evidence that diffusion-weighted MRI abnormalities may be the most sensitive test for early diagnosis of CJD.[43] Death occurs within six months in most cases. There is no known treatment.

Iatrogenic CJD can be caused by cornea transplants, human growth hormone injections, and neurosurgical procedures utilizing contaminated instruments. *New variant CJD* is the name given to the human prion disease transmitted from cattle infected with bovine spongiform encephalopathy—so-called mad cow disease. It occurs in younger individuals and has a more protracted course than classic CJD. There is some worry about *chronic wasting disease* spreading from deer or elk to man but this has not occurred yet.

Endnotes

1. Bing R, Haymaker W. *Textbook of Nervous Diseases*. St. Louis: C.V. Mosby; 1939.

2. Rowland LP, ed. *Merritt's Textbook of Neurology*, 7th ed. Philadelphia: Lea & Fibiger; 1984.

3. Kaplan SL. "Clinical presentation, diagnosis, and prognostic factors of bacterial meningitis." *Infect Dis Clin North Amer* 1999;13:570-594.

4. Quagliarello VJ, Scheld WM. "Treatment of bacterial meningitis." *N Engl J Med* 1997;336: 708-716.

5. Leib SL, Tauber MC. "Pathogenesis of bacterial meningitis." *Infect Dis Clin North Amer* 1999;13:527-547.

6. Roos KL, Tunkel AR, et al. "Acute bacterial meningitis in children and adults." In: Scheld WM, Durack DT, Whitley RJ, eds. *Infections of the Central Nervous System*. Philadelphia: Lippincott-Raven; 1997:335-401.

7. Hasbun R, Abrahams J, et al. "Computed tomography of the head before lumbar puncture in adults with suspected meningitis." *N Engl J Med* 2001; 345:1727-1733.

8. Roos KL. "Bacterial meningitis." In: Evans RW, ed. *Saunders Manual of Neurologic Practice*. Philadelphia: Saunders; 2003:699-703.

9. *Id.* at 701-702.

10. Roos KL. "Fever and confusion." *Continuum* 2003;9(3):32-46.

11. Davis LE, Bleck TP, et al. "Bacterial meningitis." *Continuum* 2002;8(3):7-26.

12. Schuchat A, Robinson K, et al. "Bacterial meningitis in the United States in 1995." *N Engl J Med* 1997;337:970-976.

13. Spach DH, Jackson LA. "Bacterial meningitis." *Neurologic Clinics* 1999; 17(4):711-735.

14. *Id*. at 725.

15. Gelderblom H, Pachner AR. "Spirochetal infections (neurosyphilis and Lyme neuroborreliosis). In: Evans RW, *supra* note 8, at 730-735.

16. *Id*. at 731-732.

17. Merritt HH, Adams RD, Solomon HC. *Neurosyphilis*. New York: Oxford; 1946.

18. *Id*.

19. Steere AC. "Lyme disease." *N Engl J Med* 2001;345:115-125.

20. *Id*.

21. Halperin JJ. "Lyme disease and the peripheral nervous system." *Muscle Nerve* 2003;28:133-143.

22. Clintron R, Pachner AR. "Spirochetal diseases of the nervous system." *Curr Opin Neurol* 1994;7:217-222.

23. Steere AC, *supra* note 19, at 116.

24. Klempner MS, Hu LT, et al. "Two controlled trials of antibiotic treatment in patients with persistent symptoms and a history of Lyme disease." *N Engl J Med* 2001;345:85-92.

25. Kaplan RF, Trevino RP, et al. "Cognitive function in post-treatment Lyme disease: Do additional antibiotics help?" *Neurology* 2003;60:1916-1922.

26. Krupp LB, Hyman LG, et al. "Study and treatment of post Lyme disease (STOP-LD): A randomized double masked clinical trial." *Neurology* 2003; 60:1923-1930.

27. Patel R, Grogg KL, et al. "Death from inappropriate therapy for Lyme disease." *Clin Infect Dis* 2000;31:1107-1109.

28. Tunkel AR, Wispelwey B, Scheld WM. "Brain abscess." In: Mandell GL, Bennett JE, Dolin R, eds. *Principles and Practice of Infectious Diseases*, 5th ed. NewYork: Churchill Livingstone, 2000:1016-1028.

29. Davis LE, Bleck TP, et al. "Brain abscess." *Continuum* 2002;8(3):38-47.

30. Greenlee JE. "Brain and spinal abscess." In: Evans RW, *supra* note 8, at 724-729.

31. Davis LE, Bleck TP, et al., *supra* note 29, at 45-46.

32. Sampathkumar P. "West Nile virus: Epidemiology, clinical presentation, diagnosis, and prevention." *Mayo Clin Proc* 2003;78:1137-1144.

33. Crumpacker CS, Gonzalez RG, Makar RS. "Case 26-2003: A 50-year-old Colombian man with fever and seizures." *N Engl J Med* 2003;349:789-796.

34. Baringer JR. "Herpes simplex virus encephalitis." In: Davis LE, Kennedy PGE, eds. *Infectious Diseases of the Nervous System*. Oxford: Butterworth-Heinemann, 2000:139-164.

35. Bartt R. "Human immunodeficiency virus and human T-lymphotropic virus type 1." In: Evans RW, *supra* note 8, at 714-723.

36. *Id*. at 714.

37. Brew BJ. "The peripheral nerve complications of human immunodeficiency virus (HIV) infection." *Muscle Nerve* 2003;28:542.

38. Gajdusek DC, Zigas V. "Degenerative disease of the central nervous system in New Guinea: The endemic occurrence of 'kuru' in the native population." *N Engl J Med* 1957;257:974-978.

39. Prusiner SB. "Shattuck Lecture - Neurodegenerative diseases and prions." *N Engl J Med* 2001;344:1516-1526.

40. Weihl CC, Roos RP. "Creutzfeldt-Jakob disease, new variant Creutzfeldt-Jakob disease, and bovine spongiform encephalopathy." *Neurologic Clinics* 1999;17(4):835-859.

41. *Id*. at 838.

42. Case records of the Massachusetts General Hospital. Case 28-1999. *N Engl J Med* 1999;341:901-908.

43. Shiga Y, Miyazawa K, et al. "Diffusion-weighted MRI abnormalities as an early diagnostic marker for Creutzfeldt-Jakob disease. *Neurology* 2004; 63:443-449.

Additional Reading

Davis LE, Kennedy GE, eds. *Infectious Diseases of the Nervous System*. Boston: Butterworth-Heinemann; 2000.

Scheld WM, Whitley RJ, Marra CM, eds. *Infections of the Central Nervous System*, 3rd ed. Philadelphia: Lippincott Williams & Wilkins; 2004.

Chapter 17

Neuromuscular Diseases

17.1 Muscle Diseases

These are usually classified as either *inherited* or *acquired*. Some are degenerative, others not. They are distinguished from other neuromuscular disorders by their particular clinical manifestations and specific laboratory abnormalities. Weakness is the main complaint in most myopathies. Some muscle diseases are associated with other systemic disturbances such as cardiac disease or mental retardation.

The weakness can be intermittent (periodic paralyses and certain metabolic myopathies) or persistent (muscular dystrophies and inflammatory myopathies), rapidly (polymyositis and dermatomyositis) or slowly progressive (muscular dystrophies), or static (congenital myopathies). Some myopathies produce pain (myalgia), cramps, or stiffness. However, this can be misleading because other non-muscle disorders can cause myalgia and muscle cramps.

Elevated serum creatine kinase levels are characteristic of most myopathies but can be seen in other conditions. Also, normal levels do not exclude the possibility of a myopathy. EMG might reveal abnormal sponta-

279

neous electrical discharges including fibrillations, positive sharp waves, myotonic discharges, or complex repetitive discharges. Myopathy usually produces small, short-duration motor unit potentials. Nerve conduction velocities are normal.

Molecular genetic techniques are supplanting muscle biopsy for diagnosis of most inherited neuropathies. However, biopsy is still useful in many other myopathies. Large proximal limb muscles are usually selected; severely affected muscles should be avoided because these may not have enough muscle tissue left for proper analysis.

Most patients with muscle disease have a "limb girdle" distribution of weakness, that is, weakness around the shoulder girdle and the pelvis. The latter causes difficulty in getting off the floor or up from a chair. Many patients have to "walk up their legs" (Gower's maneuver) by forcing their hands against their thigh, using their arms as levers, and pushing the body up using their legs as braces. Proximal arm weakness will cause difficulty with lifting and carrying objects and elevating the arms to wash or brush hair.

A. Inherited myopathies

These include muscular dystrophies, congenital myopathies, myotonic disorders, mitochondrial myopathies, and metabolic myopathies. Even though these are genetic disorders symptoms do not necessarily present in childhood. Diagnosis and classification of the inherited myopathies is difficult. Inheritance patterns and clinical features are the basis of traditional schemes. However, identification of particular genetic defects and biochemical abnormalities is becoming more important.

Duchenne muscular dystrophy is the most common of the inherited dystrophies, occurring in roughly one of every 3,500 live male births.[1] It is an X-linked recessive disorder, manifested by the male and carried by the female. In about two-thirds of cases the genetic abnormality causes either a deficiency or a complete absence of *dystrophin*—a protein that is part of the muscle membrane. Spontaneous mutations account for the other cases. Elevations in serum creatine kinase are present within days of birth. Weakness becomes obvious by age three to five years. Proximal muscles are affected first. There is a waddling gait and exaggerated lumbar lordosis. The child has difficulty getting up from the floor, often doing so using Gower's maneuver. *Pseudohypertrophy* of muscles, especially the calves, is seen in younger boys but disappears as the weakness worsens and muscles atrophy.

Most of these boys are wheelchair-bound by their early teens and ventilator dependent by their early twenties. Heart failure and aspiration are common causes of death. Even with meticulous attention to pulmonary function and aggressive treatment of infections few survive into their thirties. Prednisone appears to slow the disease[2] but is not curative. *Becker's dystrophy* is a less common variant of Duchenne dystrophy. It is a milder disease with a later onset and slower progression. Survival is longer, usually into or beyond the thirties or forties. There is active research into gene therapy for these conditions.

Myotonic dystrophy is the most common adult genetic myopathy, with a prevalence of up to fourteen in 100,000.[3] It has an autonomic dominant mode of inheritance. The genetic defect is an unstable expansion of a trinucleotide sequence (cytosine, guanine, thymine) on chromosome 19. The greater the number of repeats of this sequence, the more severe the disease and the earlier the age of onset.[4] Symptoms usually develop in late adolescence or early adulthood. The distribution of weakness is unusual; distal limb, facial, neck, and pharyngeal muscles are involved. This creates a "hatchet-face" appearance. *Myotonia*, impaired or slow muscle relaxation, can be elicited by percussion of involved muscles or observed after forceful muscle contractions. Anesthesia can exacerbate myotonia and produce apnea. Mild mental retardation and other neuropsychiatric manifestations are common. Myotonic dystrophy is a multi-system disease. Cardiac abnormalities are present in most patients[5] and can be life-threatening. Cataracts, hormonal disturbances, and gastrointestinal dysfunction are also common.

Limb girdle muscular dystrophy refers to a group of less common inherited conditions characterized by progressive, mainly proximal weakness. There is a wide variation in severity. However, almost all patients have weakness in other muscle groups. In some variants the weakness may even begin in distal muscles. Several of these *distal myopathies* are recognized. Many are atypical variants of limb girdle dystrophies but others are of less certain etiology. Gene defects are known for the majority of the limb girdle dystrophies, but the protein product has not been as fully elucidated as in Duchenne dystrophy. Treatment is supportive.

Congenital muscular dystrophies are a heterogenous group of disorders that produce weakness and poor muscle tone in infants. The genetic defect is known in some. Clinical severity varies considerably and there is no effective treatment. Mental retardation occurs in some of the congenital dystrophies.

Congenital myopathies[6] usually produce weakness at birth or within the first year of life. These rare and poorly understood diseases are characterized by their appearance in muscle biopsies. *Central core disease*, *nemaline rod*, *centronuclear*, and *myotubular* myopathies are the most common congenital myopathies. In the most severe cases weakness can be present before birth. These infants can have feeding difficulties and respiratory failure. Less severe cases are associated with delayed motor milestones and milder degrees of weakness. Occasionally, the mildest congenital myopathies are not detected until adulthood. Except for the most severe cases life expectancy is good.

Mitochondrial myopathies are a group of rare diseases caused by abnormality in the mitochondria. These are cell structures responsible for production of energy. There are hundreds in every cell. Mitochondria contain their own genetic material. The mitochondrial DNA is more prone to mutation than chromosomal DNA. All mitochondria are derived from the mother. Therefore, mitochondrial DNA mutations can be passed to the offspring only from the mother. Males and females are equally likely to be affected. However, the mitochondrial proteins themselves are under the control of nuclear DNA. Therefore, there can be mitochondrial myopathies inherited in more typical fashion: autosomal dominant, autosomal recessive, or X-linked. The clinical expression of the mitochondrial abnormality is highly variable and depends upon the number of mutated mitochondria present.

Myoclonic epilepsy and ragged red fibers (MERRF) is a mitochondrial myopathy characterized by seizures, incoordination, dementia, hearing loss, optic nerve atrophy, and weakness. The ragged red fibers are seen under the microscope in muscle biopsy samples. *Mitochondrial encephalomyopathy with lactic acidosis and strokes* (MELAS) presents with stroke-like episodes often triggered by physical exertion. *Kearns-Sayre syndrome* usually develops before age twenty with progressive external ophthalmoplegia (weakness or paralysis of eye movements), retinitis pigmentosa, heart conduction defects, and other symptoms. There are several other mitochondrial myopathies.

Disturbances in glycogen, lipid, and nucleotide metabolism can produce *metabolic myopathies*.[7] There are dozens of these conditions with clinical manifestations ranging from very mild and nonprogressive weakness to infantile-onset rapidly progressive fatal disorders. Many metabolic myopathies have features that indicate exercise intolerance such as muscle cramping and pain. The muscle destruction produces excessive amounts of myoglobin in the urine and can lead to kidney failure. Other organs are affected in some of the metabolic myopathies.

Inherited abnormalities in the ion channels of muscle membranes can cause abnormal membrane excitability and produce the various *periodic paralysis* (PP) syndromes. In these rare diseases there are episodes of severe weakness lasting minutes to days. The ion channel abnormality probably produces the weakness by altering potassium concentration. When PP is triggered by low potassium (*hypokalemic* PP), treatment efforts are designed to maintain normal potassium levels. Preventative therapy includes a low carbohydrate diet and acetazolamide. With *hyperkalemic* PP preventative treatment with albuterol—a beta-adrenergic agonist inhalant used for asthma—may be helpful. The diuretic hydrochlorothiazide and carbonic anhydrase inhibitors like acetazolamide are also useful. Often, attacks can be aborted or prevented by ingesting high carbohydrate meals.

B. Acquired myopathies

These include conditions produced by infection, idiopathic inflammatory processes, various toxic exposures, and muscle disease occurring in association with other systemic illnesses.

There are inflammatory myopathies with focal involvement and others with diffuse manifestations. The common varieties are *polymyositis* (PM), *dermatomyositis* (DM), and *inclusion body myositis* (IBM). These are autoimmune disorders with distinct clinical and laboratory features, sometimes occurring in isolation, sometimes with other systemic diseases.[8]

DM can present at any age and is more common in women than men. Weakness usually develops over weeks to months and involves the neck flexors and other proximal muscles. A characteristic red rash has a "butterfly" distribution over the nose and cheeks, and can spread to the eyelids, neck, and upper chest. There may be lesions over the knuckles, elbows, knees, and ankles. Childhood DM is associated with subcutaneous calcifications and involvement of other organ systems. PM, in contrast, rarely occurs in children. The distribution of weakness is similar to that in DM. Both conditions are associated with an increased risk of underlying malignancy—DM more than PM.[9]

Serum creatine kinase is elevated in PM and DM. Muscle biopsy reveals characteristic features that distinguish the two diseases. Corticosteroids will help most patients but treatment usually requires administration for months or years. Steroid side effects are common. Intravenous immunoglobulin and immunosuppressant drugs (methotrexate, cyclosporine, and cyclophosphamide) are also effective.

Inclusion body myositis is the most common inflammatory myopathy in patients over 50.[10] It progresses more slowly than PM and DM, and there is more distal weakness. Inclusion body myositis is more common in men than women and there is no associated risk of malignancy. Corticosteroids and other immunosuppressant drugs are unlikely to be helpful but should be tried unless they are too risky for these older patients. Indeed, treatment resistance helps to distinguish IBM from the other inflammatory myopathies.

Muscle aches and pains are characteristic of *polymyalgia rheumatica*. This is a common condition in older adults, with a female predominance. It is not a true myopathy but can be confused with these conditions. Patients present with diffuse aching pain in the shoulder girdle and, to a lesser extent, pelvic girdle. The muscles may be tender to touch. However, there is no true muscle weakness, apparent weakness being due to pain. The symptoms are most prominent in the morning but wear off after a few hours and rarely recur later in the day. Needle EMG and muscle biopsies are normal or reveal nonspecific findings. Most patients require treatment with corticosteroids.

A minority of polymyalgia patients develop *temporal* (or *giant cell*) *arteritis*. This is a serious disorder that requires more aggressive management to avoid complications such as blindness. It may develop as an isolated syndrome. If there is any suspicion of temporal arteritis, treatment with corticosteroids must be started even before results of the temporal artery biopsy are available.

Infectious agents can invade muscle tissue directly. A variety of viral, bacterial, fungal, and parasitic organisms are known to cause *infectious myopathy*. Muscle swelling, pain, and myoglobinuria are typical manifestations. HIV causes an inflammatory myopathy of uncertain etiology, probably an immune reaction. Muscle is also susceptible to a wide range of toxins. Many medications have been implicated in production of *toxic myopathy*. These include several cholesterol-lowering drugs, cyclosporine, chloroquine, amiodarone, colchicine, vincristine, and corticosteroids. The muscle tissue can be damaged either by a direct action of the toxin or indirectly as a result of electrolyte imbalances or reduced delivery of nutrients and oxygen. Myopathy is a well-recognized manifestation of endocrine disorders of the thyroid, parathyroid, and adrenal glands.[11]

17.2 Neuromuscular Junction Diseases

Diseases affecting the neuromuscular junction are uncommon. Most general neurologists will have little direct experience with these conditions. However, proper diagnosis is essential for treatment and to avoid potentially grave complications.

A. Myasthenia gravis (MG)

This rare acquired autoimmune disease is characterized by fluctuating weakness and abnormal fatigability. The disease is due to an attack on postsynaptic muscle acetylcholine receptors (AchR) by antibodies. The trigger for this immune reaction is unknown but the thymus gland is involved. Acetylcholine is the neurotransmitter released by the presynaptic nerve at the neuromuscular juncture to produce a muscle contraction. The AchR antibody attack reduces the number of receptors and thereby impairs the ability of the muscle to contract in response to release of acetylcholine by the nerve.

Myasthenia gravis has unusual epidemiologic features. There is a bimodal distribution for age of onset. The peak for women is the late teens and twenties; for men, the fifties and sixties. Incidence seems to be rising, probably because of an increase in the number of older men diagnosed with MG. There are about twenty cases per 100,000 people, though this may be an underestimate.[12]

Patients initially complain of problems with particular muscles, especially intermittent drooping of the eyelids (*ptosis*) or double vision (*diplopia*). Indeed, some patients may seek cosmetic surgery for their droopy eyelids, unaware they actually have a neurologic disease. In roughly 15 percent of cases the disease does not progress, so-called *ocular myasthenia*.[13] Within two years of onset most patients will develop *generalized myasthenia*. This typically begins with weakness of oropharyngeal muscles causing problems with speaking, chewing, or swallowing. Most later develop fluctuating weakness in other skeletal muscles. Symptoms tend to worsen as the day proceeds. The involved muscles are abnormally fatigable; repetitive contraction leads to weakness while rest often restores strength. If respiratory muscles are involved the weakness can be fatal without appropriate supportive measures.

Diagnosing MG requires recognition of the typical clinical features and a high degree of suspicion for the disorder because many patients are asymptomatic when they present to their physicians. Therefore, obtaining a history of fluctuating weakness and abnormal fatigability is essential. The neurologist will try to elicit a history of unusual weakness provoked by different causes. Myasthenic symptoms can be unmasked by commonly used medications including certain antibiotics, cardiac antiarrhythmics, thyroid medications, and drugs used during anesthesia. Also, menstruation, pregnancy, high body temperature, stress, or systemic viral infections have all been reported to unmask MG.

A routine examination often does not reveal abnormalities. The neurologist must test strength repetitively in suspected muscles in order to demonstrate the abnormal fatigability. For example, the patient is asked to raise her eyes to the ceiling for two or three minutes in order to elicit ptosis or diplopia. Additional tests are needed to increase diagnostic accuracy. AchR serum antibodies are found in almost all patients with generalized myasthenia but there is a higher false negative rate in ocular myasthenia.

Administration of edrophonium, a short-acting anticholinesterase drug that improves neuromuscular transmission, produces a brief but dramatic improvement of strength in most MG patients. However, this test does carry some serious cardiorespiratory risks and should be performed only where emergency supportive measures are available. Also, the test is not specific for MG because edrophonium can improve strength in other neuromuscular diseases. Electrophysiologic testing is quite important for confirming this diagnosis. In many patients, repetitive nerve stimulation studies will show a reduction of the compound muscle action potential, sometimes in asymptomatic muscles. Single fiber EMG is even more sensitive to defects in neuromuscular transmission. However, it is technically more demanding and should be performed only by experienced examiners. Most general neurologists do not perform this test.

MG is a treatable disease. Therapeutic goals are to relieve symptoms and alter the underlying autoimmune process. Cholinesterase inhibitors (anticholinesterases) improve symptoms in many MG patients. Plasmapheresis improves strength by removing the circulating antibodies from the bloodstream. However, this is an expensive procedure that is generally reserved for *myasthenic* crises—short-lived exacerbations of MG—or other situations such as surgery where strength must be improved.

If these are not helpful there are other interventions designed to alter the course of the illness. Immunosuppressant and cytotoxic drugs including prednisone, azathioprine, and cyclosporine often produce sustained symptom reduction. However, there are serious potential side effects and these agents often must be used for long periods. Finally, there is thymectomy—surgical removal of the thymus gland. Surgery appears to improve symptoms even in MG patients without thymoma. Some evidence suggests that the sooner the thymus gland is removed the quicker the remission and the more complete the recovery. However, the available outcome studies have "serious methodological flaws that prevent definitive conclusions regarding the benefits of thymectomy."[14]

B. Lambert-Eaton myasthenic syndrome (LEMS)

This autoimmune condition is even rarer than MG. LEMS is the presynaptic counterpart of myasthenia gravis. That is, the defect is in the presynaptic side of the synapse—impaired release of acetylcholine from the nerve terminal. The reduced amount of acetylcholine available to the postsynaptic muscle receptors leads to fatigability of the muscle. Unlike MG, however, repetitive exercise improves muscle function in many patients. This is better seen during repetitive nerve stimulation testing than clinically.

Patients present with different kinds of weakness than in MG because limb muscles are more often involved than ocular and oropharyngeal muscles. Thus, there is difficulty in walking, climbing stairs, holding the arms up, and lifting objects. LEMS is usually associated with symptoms of autonomic dysfunction—dry mouth, postural hypotension, and impotence. About half of LEMS patients have an underlying malignancy, usually small cell lung cancer.[15] In the remaining cases the etiology is obscure. When the diagnosis is made there should be an extensive investigation for a malignancy.

Treatment for LEMS depends on whether or not the patient has cancer. In those without malignancy, options are evolving. The investigational drug 3-4 diaminopyridine improves symptoms for the majority of patients. There is some evidence that immunosuppressant agents and plasmapheresis are beneficial. When there is a cancer, therapeutic efforts should be directed toward the malignancy. Successful treatment of the malignancy leads to improved strength.

17.3 Motor Neuron Diseases

There are several diseases characterized by dysfunction of motor neurons, particularly spinal cord anterior horn cells and brainstem motor neurons. There are both inherited and acquired motor neuron diseases as well as some of unknown etiology. Many are relentlessly progressive and ultimately fatal. The list includes amyotrophic lateral sclerosis (ALS), the spinal muscular atrophies, and poliomyelitis. Despite numerous claims there is no compelling proof that antecedent trauma is a causative or provocative factor in motor neuron disease.

A. Amyotrophic lateral sclerosis (Lou Gehrig's disease)

ALS is the most common form of motor neuron disease. It is a progressive, fatal incurable disease of unknown etiology. ALS is more common in men and usually begins in middle age. A familial form of ALS accounts for up to 10 percent of cases. The incidence of ALS is two per 100,000, the prevalence, about six per 100,000.[16] Accurate diagnosis is essential given the poor prognosis. The emphasis is on identifying potentially treatable conditions that mimic motor neuron disease.

The clinical manifestations of ALS reflect dysfunction in both lower motor neurons (LMN) and upper motor neurons (UMN). ALS does not produce sensory symptoms though these can be present due to coexisting conditions such as neuropathy or degenerative spine disease. LMN dysfunction produces weakness, muscle atrophy, slurred speech, difficulty swallowing, and muscle fasciculations. UMN signs include spasticity, exaggerated and pathologic reflexes, and impaired motor control. Extraocular muscles and bowel and bladder functions are spared. Patients can present with either UMN or LMN signs, or a combination of both. ALS affects skeletal muscles supplied by all levels of the spine—cervical, thoracic, and lumbosacral—as well as the brainstem (*bulbar* muscles). If either UMN or LMN signs are not present at onset they usually develop as the disease progresses.

Progressive muscular atrophy is a pure LMN disease with a slower, more benign course than ALS. Isolated UMN involvement characterizes the very rare *primary lateral sclerosis*. This also carries a better prognosis than ALS. Unfortunately, most individuals who present with isolated UMN or LMN symptoms actually are in the early stages of ALS and eventually show more of the expected signs. In *progressive bulbar palsy* there are both UMN and LMN signs, but with involvement restricted to bulbar muscles. Bulbar LMN findings include slurred speech and tongue fasciculations with wasting; bulbar UMN signs include spastic speech, pathologic reflexes, and pathologic emotional lability termed *pseudobulbar palsy*. Chewing and swallowing are also impaired. Progressive bulbar palsy is also likely to represent an early stage of ALS and not a separate disease in most cases.

Most ALS patients present with asymmetric limb weakness. Misdiagnoses are common, usually other neurologic conditions that produce weakness such as radiculopathy or peripheral neuropathy. Surgery for carpal tunnel syndrome or herniated discs is not unheard of in these patients. Eventually, the inexorable progression of the disease produces additional complaints that cannot be explained by the initial (mis)diagnosis. An accurate diagnosis is not difficult when there are widespread upper and lower motor neuron findings, especially if there is also bulbar involvement. However, when symptoms and signs are more restricted the diagnosis is less obvious.

Cervical spondylosis can produce compression of the spinal cord with both UMN and LMN findings. Other structural lesions including syringomyelia and tumors in the foramen magnum and cervical region may do the same. The symptoms and signs can be difficult to distinguish from ALS occurring without bulbar involvement. However, unlike ALS these cervical lesions usually produce pain and other sensory complaints. Brain and cervical MRI scanning can help distinguish structural causes of these symptoms from ALS.

Myasthenia gravis without ocular motor weakness can resemble ALS, but there are no UMN abnormalities in myasthenia and there are distinctive EMG findings. When there are only LMN findings testing is done to exclude peripheral neuropathies, plexopathies, radiculopathies, and other neuromuscular diseases. Electrodiagnostic testing is especially useful for this purpose. Metabolic and endocrine derangements can produce some ALS-like symptoms but these are readily identified with appropriate laboratory tests.

ALS runs an inexorable downhill course with death usually occurring within two to five years of onset though survival for ten years is not rare. The classic teaching is that cognition is not affected and the patients are aware of their steady decline. However, there is evidence that many ALS patients have frontal executive deficits suggestive of frontotemporal lobar dementia.[17] Treatment of ALS is mostly supportive. Riluzole is the only drug approved for treatment of ALS. It increases survival by a few months.

B. Spinal muscular atrophies (SMA)

The SMA are a group of progressive inherited conditions characterized by weakness and muscle atrophy due to degeneration of the anterior horn motor cells. Almost all cases are inherited by autosomal recessive transmission and involve an absent or defective *survival motor neuron* (SMN1) gene located on chromosome 5.[18] There are three forms of childhood SMA, classified according to age of onset or developmental milestones reached. There is also a rarer adult-onset form of SMA. The childhood SMA are among the most common inherited causes of death. The earlier the age of onset, the worse the prognosis. Few infants with onset before age three months survive beyond two years of age. Death is usually due to respiratory failure or infection. Scoliosis and contractures are common. Children with symptoms beginning after age eighteen months and most of those with the adult-onset variation often have a very benign course. There is no specific treatment for SMA.

C. Acute poliomyelitis and postpolio syndrome

Prior to the introduction of effective vaccines infection with poliovirus was a dreaded common occurrence. Most poliovirus infections did not lead to paralytic disease. Nevertheless, until the mid-1950s, there were as many as 50,000 paralytic cases annually. Now, symptomatic infection with the poliovirus is rare except among unvaccinated populations. However, other enteroviruses can cause similar CNS inflammation. The West Nile virus also causes polio-like paralytic disease.[19]

A polio infection initially resembles a common viral syndrome—fever, sore throat, and myalgias. Some patients go on to develop signs of neurologic involvement including stiff neck, back pain, and severe headache. Paralytic disease develops within a few days in many of these patients. The distribution of flaccid paralysis is very focal and asymmetric. The diagnosis is confirmed by culturing virus and documenting antibody production. MRI scanning of the spinal cord may reveal anterior horn abnormalities.

Many polio survivors develop a *postpolio syndrome* decades after their acute illness. It includes symptoms of fatigue, pain, and new weakness in both previously involved as well as uninvolved muscles. Some symptoms may represent a failure of compensatory mechanisms due to the general effect of aging or arthritis. Also, since the surviving motor neurons innervate many more muscle fibers than normal they may be under greater metabolic stress and prone to deteriorate eventually, producing weakness years after the acute illness.[20]

Endnotes

1. Machkhas H. "Muscular dystrophies." In: Evans RW, ed. *Saunders Manual of Neurologic Practice*. Philadelphia: Saunders; 2003:663-669.

2. Mendell JR, Moxley RT, et al. "Randomized, double-blind six-month trial of prednisone in Duchenne's muscular dystrophy." *New Engl J Med* 1989;320: 1592-1597.

3. Machkhas H, *supra* note 1, at 667.

4. Redman JB, Fenwick RG, et al. "Relationship between parental trinucleotide CGT repeat length and severity of myotonic dystrophy in offspring." *JAMA* 1993;269:1960-1965.

5. Johnson ER, Abresch RT, et al. "Profiles of neuromuscular diseases. Myotonic dystrophy." *Am J Phys Med Rehabil* 1995;74:S104-S116.

6. Taratulo AL. "Congenital myopathies and related disorders." *Curr Opin Neurol* 2002;15:553-561.

7. Pourmand R. "Metabolic myopathies: A diagnostic evaluation." *Neurol Clin* 2000;18:1-13.

8. Mastaglia FL, Garlepp MJ, et al. "Inflammatory myopathies: Clinical, diagnostic and therapeutic aspects," *Muscle Nerve* 2003;27:407-425.

9. Sigurgeirsson B, Lindelof B, et al. "Risk of cancer in patients with dermatomyositis or polymyositis: A population-based study." *N Engl J Med* 1992; 326:363-367.

10. Griggs RC, Askanas V, et al. "Inclusion body myositis and myopathies." *Ann Neurol* 1995;38:705-713.

11. Horak HA, Pourmand R. "Endocrine myopathies." *Neurol Clin* 2000;18:203-213.

12. Myasthenia Gravis Foundation of America: www.myasthenia.org, accessed December 24, 2004.

13. Drachman MG. "Myasthenia gravis." *N Engl J Med* 1994;330:1997-1810.

14. Gronseth GS, Barohn RJ. "Practice parameter: Thymectomy for autoimmune myasthenia gravis (an evidence-based review). Report of the quality standards subcommittee of the American Academy of Neurology." *Neurology* 2000;55:7-15.

15. Benjamin RK, Das A, Hochberg F. "Metastatic neoplasms and paraneoplastic syndromes." In: Goetz CG, ed. *Textbook of Clinical Neurology*, 2nd ed. Philadelphia: Saunders; 2003:1041-1058.

16. Ross MA. "Clinical features and diagnosis of amyotrophic lateral sclerosis." *Continuum* 2002;8(4):9-31.

17. Lomen-Hoerth C, Murphy J, et al. "Are amyotrophic lateral sclerosis patients cognitively normal?" *Neurology* 2003;60:1094-1097.

18. Nicole S, Diaz CC, et al. "Spinal muscular atrophy: Recent advances and future prospects." *Muscle Nerve* 2002;26:4-13.

19. Sampathkumar P. "West Nile virus: Epidemiology, clinical presentation, diagnosis, and prevention." *Mayo Clin Proc* 2003;78:1137-1144.

20. Dalakas MC. "Pathogenetic mechanisms of post-polio syndrome: Morphological, electrophysiological, virological, and immunological correlations." *Ann NY Acad Sci* 1995;753:167-185.

Additional Reading

Karpati G, Hilton-Jones D, Griggs RC. *Disorders of Voluntary Muscle*, 7th ed. Cambridge: Cambridge University Press; 2001.

Katirji B, Kaminski HJ, et al., eds. *Neuromuscular Disorders in Clinical Practice*. Boston: Butterworth-Heinemann; 2000.

Muscular Dystrophy Association: www.mdausa.org, accessed December 24, 2004.

Pourmand R, Harati Y, eds. *Neuromuscular Disorders* (Advances in Neurology, Volume 88). Philadelphia: Lippincott Williams & Wilkins; 2002.

Chapter 18

Dementias

18.1 Introduction

Dementia is a clinical syndrome, not a discrete diagnostic entity. There are many different definitions of dementia but the term generally refers to an acquired, persistent loss of cognitive function severe enough to interfere with work, social functioning, and daily activities. Memory loss is a prominent feature of most dementias but is not the sole manifestation. In fact, dementia can occur in patients with well-preserved memory function. One example of this is *primary progressive aphasia*, a rare condition affecting language function.[1]

The dementia label does not suggest a specific etiology. There are several dozen causes of dementia though a handful account for almost all cases. Older terms such as senility or hardening of the arteries are inappropriate. Clinicians recognize age-related cognitive changes such as forgetfulness and mental slowing that do not interfere significantly with daily function. A more worrisome development is *mild cognitive impairment*, probably either a transition stage between normal aging and early Alzheimer's disease or the earliest stage of the latter.

Neurologists may speak of *primary* and *secondary* dementias. The latter are nondegenerative conditions that produce cognitive deficits by impairing neuronal function—examples are chronic meningitis, normal pressure hydrocephalus, subdural hematoma, toximetabolic derangements such as hypothyroidism, and vitamin B12 deficiency. Many secondary dementias are treatable or reversible if identified early enough.

Primary dementias are those due to degenerative processes arising in the brain cells themselves. Alzheimer's disease, frontotemporal or frontal lobe dementias, and dementia with Lewy bodies are examples. The dementing conditions are not undifferentiated or indistinguishable from each other. There is a particular pattern of brain tissue vulnerability in each condition that produces a different clinical picture. Careful review of the history combined with detailed cognitive evaluation should lead to a correct classification. This is increasingly important now that there are treatments for some dementias.

Dementia is an enormous public health issue. More than 95 percent of patients with mild deficits are not identified by their primary care physicians.[2] In 2000, there were 4.5 million people in the United States with Alzheimer's disease—by far the most common form of dementia—with 13.2 million expected in 2050.[3] Related healthcare costs are in the hundreds of billions of dollars. Dementia also shortens life expectancy.[4] Family education is essential. Patients who are still competent to make decisions about their welfare should be informed of the diagnosis so that they may participate in planning for the future.

A. Evaluation

The physician's role in the evaluation of a cognitively impaired patient is to characterize the deficits, exclude any treatable causes of the decline, identify and treat any confounding conditions, and make a specific diagnosis if possible. A thorough and orderly approach is needed. This will include a detailed history from the patient and other informants, mental status testing, neurologic examination, and appropriate additional investigations.[5] A practice parameter from the AAN addresses the diagnostic process.[6]

Thyroid function, vitamin B12 level, blood count, serum electrolytes and glucose, renal function, and liver function are standard tests. Neuroimaging with CT or MRI is recommended. EEG is useful if there is a question of seizures, fluctuating levels of consciousness, or suspicion of Creutzfeldt-Jacob disease. SPECT and PET scans are of limited use in most patients but have a role in certain circumstances, particularly in evaluation of frontotemporal dementias.

Dementia should be distinguished from *delirium*, a state of fluctuating arousal and consciousness with prominent attentional deficits. This is not always easy because demented individuals are at high risk for delirium. However, the more persistent nature of the deficits in dementia should help separate the two conditions. Dementia is also distinct from congenital or inherited cognitive disorders such as mental retardation.

Medication side effects and depression are both extremely common causes of cognitive difficulty in the population at risk, the elderly. *Pseudodementia* is a label given to the cognitive deficits found in depressed patients. However, this term is disfavored because of the implication that the deficits are feigned. Depressed patients do exhibit physical and mental slowing and put forth poor effort during cognitive testing. Unfortunately, long-term follow-up studies suggest that many such patients eventually develop dementia.

B. Mild cognitive impairment (MCI)

There is a continuum between normal cognitive function and dementia. In the most common form of MCI there is a measurable amnesic disturbance but no significant impairment in daily activities (such impairment would shift the diagnosis to dementia). There may be other functional deficits but these have not been studied extensively. MCI progresses to dementia in more than half the cases, at a rate of 10 to 15 percent annually compared to 1 to 2 percent in healthy control subjects.[7] Thus, in most cases MCI is probably a prodrome or early stage of Alzheimer's.

Risk factors for progression to dementia include hippocampal atrophy, older age, and presence of the apolipoprotein $\in 4$ allele. Early identification of these at-risk patients allows for potential interventions with disease-altering therapies at a stage where greater function is preserved. Also, there is an opportunity for patients to have an active role in life-planning decisions while they are still competent.

C. Cortical and subcortical dementias

Some clinicians classify dementias into those with predominantly *cortical* features and those with mostly *subcortical* findings. Strictly speaking, this is less of an anatomic than a functional division. A cortical dementia such as Alzheimer's is characterized by amnesia, aphasia, apraxia, and agnosia; there may be impairments in judgment and abstract thinking. Subcortical dementias such as progressive supranuclear palsy[8] are characterized by:

- Apathy or depression
- Impaired attention and concentration
- Motor and gait abnormalities
- Poor recall or retrieval but no frank amnesia
- Slowed thinking

Parkinson's disease, other movement disorders, and small-vessel hypertensive disease may produce subcortical dementia. Dementia develops in a significant number of Parkinson's disease patients and is common in several other rarer movement disorders. These are discussed in Chapter 19.

18.2 Alzheimer's Disease (AD)

This is the most common form of dementia, accounting for over half of all cases. It is a disease of middle and later life. Up to 10 percent of cases are familial; these tend to have an earlier onset. AD is not a diagnosis of exclusion. There are very typical clinical features and diagnostic criteria that allow the careful physician to diagnose almost all cases correctly.[9] Many people have heard about apolipoprotein E genotyping but this is not sensitive or specific enough "to be used alone as a diagnostic test for Alzheimer's disease."[10]

Typically, these patients present with memory impairment. Less commonly, language difficulties, apraxia, or other cognitive disturbances are the first signs of the disease. There is impaired learning of new information so patients might forget where they parked the car or placed objects, what they did earlier in the day, or what they were told. Some become frustrated and irritable when the problem is pointed out to them. Others begin to lose insight into their deficits and deny any such problems. It is essential that history be obtained from other sources. More remote memories are retained until late in the disease, and the difference in recall for these compared to recent events is striking.

In early stages the general neurological examination is essentially normal apart from the cognitive dysfunction. Prominent motor or gait abnormalities at onset suggest cerebrovascular disease or one of the dementia-parkinsonism syndromes. An abrupt onset and stepwise deterioration characterize vascular dementia. Early changes in behavior or personality without forgetfulness can indicate a frontotemporal dementia. A very rapid decline is typical of infection.

AD progresses slowly but steadily. Over time the memory impairment worsens and more and more cognitive functions are impaired. Patients get lost in previously familiar surroundings. They have frequent word-finding pauses and their speech becomes "empty" as they lose language function. Many exhibit odd, atypical, or inappropriate behaviors. Seizures occur in some 10 to 20 percent of patients late in the disease. Apathy, anxiety, delusions, and depression develop in many. A combination of medications and nonpharmacologic interventions are used to treat behavioral symptoms.

Cholinesterase inhibitors (donepezil, galantamine, rivastigmine, tacrine) appear to slow the progression of the disease modestly, preserving function and delaying the need for skilled care or a nursing home. The N-methyl-D-aspartate (NMDA) receptor blocker memantine, a leading dementia treatment in Germany, is now approved in the United States for use in moderate to severe disease. It can be used in conjunction with the cholinesterase drugs.

Many pharmacologic agents are being studied for their ability to prevent AD. Studies are looking at antioxidants such as vitamin E and gingko biloba, statins (the cholesterol-lowering agents), ampakines (agents that stimulate the hippocampal glutamate receptors), nonsteroidal anti-inflammatory drugs, and anti-amyloid agents. There is no cure for AD; median survival is eight years though some patients live much longer.

18.3 Vascular Dementia

Cognitive deficits can occur as a result of stroke, other cerebrovascular diseases, cardiac dysfunction, and circulatory disorders. Manifestations of vascular dementia vary according to the location of the strokes. *Multi-infarct dementia* refers to a vascular dementia syndrome that develops suddenly and has a fluctuating, step-wise progression. The strokes can be cortical or subcortical. Somewhat controversial is the diagnosis of *Binswanger's disease*. This refers to small-vessel hypertensive subcortical white matter damage without actual strokes.[11]

Vascular dementia patients usually have focal neurologic signs, unusual in most AD patients. However, AD often coexists with vascular dementia. These *mixed dementia* patients steadily decline between strokes. Diagnosis of vascular dementia requires evidence of vascular lesions in the brain by CT or MRI scanning. There is no unique lesion; there may be one or more large or small cortical or subcortical strokes. Extensive white matter damage can also support this diagnosis. Single strokes in critical areas of the brain (e.g., angular gyrus) can produce dementia.[12]

The main goal of vascular dementia treatment is prevention through modification of the risk factors for the underlying vascular disease, especially hypertension. This is critically important because even "silent" lacunar strokes double the risk of dementia in the elderly.[13] The cholinesterase inhibitors used for treating AD appear helpful for cognition in vascular dementia.

18.4 Frontotemporal Dementia

This refers to a group of non-AD dementias caused by frontal or temporal lobe degeneration.[14] The typical presentation is different from AD.[15] The usual age of onset is younger than AD, ranging from the forties to the sixties. Nearly half the cases are familial. Behavior and personality changes predominate, indicating executive and cognitive dysfunction due to frontal lobe involvement. Patients have inappropriate or bizarre behaviors and lack insight. Social interactions are impaired and patients lose the ability to regulate their conduct in response to social cues. Not surprisingly, many receive a psychiatric diagnosis. If anterior temporal lobe involvement predominates patients present with language output problems—decreased fluency, echolalia (repeating what they hear), and mutism.

Early in the course of frontotemporal dementias, and quite unlike AD, memory and other cognitive functions are intact. Pathologically, most patients have frontotemporal lobar degeneration without specific microscopic findings. A few have unique pathologic features that meet criteria for *Pick's disease*. There is no proven treatment. Management is directed toward control of the behavioral symptoms. Patients survive for several years.

18.5 Dementia with Lewy Bodies (DLB)

This is a more recently identified neurodegenerative disorder associated with a microscopic abnormality—the Lewy body. Lewy bodies are common in the brains of both AD and Parkinson's disease patients. Isolated DLB is a dementia syndrome characterized by fluctuations in level of consciousness, visual hallucinations, and parkinsonism.[16] It may be the second most common cause of dementia, ahead of vascular dementia. Early psychiatric symptoms are typical and patients are unusually sensitive to the extrapyramidal side effects of antipsychotic medications.

There is disagreement as to whether DLB is a unique disease or a subtype of AD or Parkinson's. Although DLB may be the second most common form of dementia, diagnostic accuracy is rather poor. AD is a frequent misdiagnosis.[17] This is probably due to the high rate of coexisting Alzheimer's pathology in these patients.[18]

18.6 Legal and Ethical Implications

Dementia has devastating emotional and financial consequences for patients and their families. It is clear now that dementia is not an inevitable part of aging. Since there are treatments to slow the progression of AD and possibly help other dementias, the standard of care has changed. Physicians who miss the opportunity to intervene early could be liable for their failure to diagnose dementia.[19] Advantages of early diagnosis include:

- Ability of patient to participate in medical decisions and personal planning
- Education for caregivers to improve their coping skills
- Identification and treatment of comorbid conditions such as agitation and depression
- Initiation of disease-modifying medications to slow the cognitive decline
- Referral to social services
- Timely financial and legal planning

The first issue for the physician is presenting the diagnosis. A competent patient has the right of self-determination; the exercise of autonomy requires sufficient information for decision-making. Physicians generally do not have the right to withhold this information. Some family members may not want the patient to hear the "Alzheimer's" label. The physician should make it clear that the patient does have a right to know the diagnosis, unless he or she waives that right. If psychiatric difficulties make learning the specific diagnosis too demoralizing or harmful it is probably acceptable to speak about a memory disorder in more general terms. In the absence of such concerns the availability of approved treatments makes the case for telling the truth to competent patients quite strong.[20]

Frequently, physicians speak first to family members to learn how the patient might react. However, some patients are evaluated without family members or significant others present, or insist on complete confidentiality. If the patient is competent to understand the nature and significance of the diagnosis the physician should not violate a request for confidentiality.

Dementia raises issues about competency, decision-making, and financial planning. Most patients and families will need legal advice during the course of the disease. Clearly, it is better to anticipate these problems and seek counsel early, while the patient is still able to make decisions. Families can also benefit from early diagnosis by learning about available social services, respite care, and nursing homes long before these are needed.

Many members of the public are aware of genetic testing for AD. The apolipoprotein E (ApoE) gene on chromosome 19 is a susceptibility or risk gene for AD. There are three forms, or *alleles*, or the gene: $\in 2$, $\in 3$ (the most common), and $\in 4$. Each person carries two ApoE alleles. The $\in 4$ allele lowers the age of onset of AD and increases the risk of the disease two- or three-fold in individuals without an AD family history.[21] The $\in 2$ allele appears to be protective. While there is some evidence that ApoE testing may increase diagnostic accuracy in symptomatic persons it "is not useful for cognitively normal individuals."[22] This is because the genotype cannot predict at what age the disease might occur. Furthermore, less than half of AD patients have the $\in 4$ allele.[23]

Endnotes

1. Mesulam M-M. "Current concepts: Primary progressive aphasia-a language-based dementia." *N Engl J Med* 2003;349:1535-1542.

2. Gifford DR, Cummings JL. "Rating dementia screening tests: Methodologic standards to rate their performance." *Neurology* 1999;52:224-227.

3. Hebert LE, Scherr PA, et al. "Alzheimer disease in the US population: prevalence estimates using the 2000 census." *Arch Neurol* 2003;60:1119-1122.

4. Wolfson C, Wolfson DB, et al. "A reevaluation of the duration of survival after the onset of dementia." *N Engl J Med* 2001;344:1111-1116.

5. Knopman DS, Boeve BF, Petersen RC. "Essentials of the proper diagnoses of mild cognitive impairment, dementia, and major subtypes of dementia." *Mayo Clin Proc* 2003;78:1290-1308.

6. Knopman DS, DeKosky ST, et al. "Practice parameter: Diagnosis of dementia (an evidence-based review). Report of the Quality Standards Subcommittee of the American Academy of Neurology. *Neurology* 2001;56:1143-1166.

7. Griffith HR, Belue K, et al. "Impaired financial abilities in mild cognitive impairment: A direct assessment approach." *Neurology* 2003;60:449-457.

8. Albert ML, Feldman RG, Willis AL. "The 'subcortical dementia' of progressive supranuclear palsy." *J Neurol Neurosurg Psychiatry* 1974;37:121-130.

9. Kawas CH. "Early Alzheimer's disease." *N Engl J Med* 2003;349:1056-1063.

10. Mayeux R, Saunders AM, et al. "Utility of the apolipoprotein E genotype in the diagnosis of Alzheimer's disease." *N Engl J Med* 1998;338:506-511.

11. Bennett DA, Wilson RS, et al. "Clinical diagnosis of Binswanger's disease." *J Neurol Neurosurg Psychiatry* 1990;53:961-965.

12. Amar K, Wilcock G. "Vascular dementia." *Brit Med J* 1196;312:227-231.

13. Vermeer SE, Prins ND, et al. "Silent brain infarcts and the risk of dementia and cognitive decline." *N Engl J Med* 2003;348:1215-1222.

14. McKhann GM, Albert MS, et al. "Clinical and pathological diagnosis of frontotemporal dementia." *Arch Neurol* 2001;58:1803-1809.

15. Levy ML, Miller BL, et al. "Alzheimer disease and frontotemporal dementias: Behavioral distinctions." *Arch Neurol* 1996;53:687-690.

16. McKeith I, Galaski D, et al. "Consensus guidelines for the clinical and pathologic diagnosis of dementia with Lewy bodies (DLB): Report of the consortium on DLB international workshop." *Neurology* 1996;47:1113-1124.

17. Lippa CF, McKeith I. "Dementia with Lewy bodies: Improving diagnostic criteria." *Neurology* 2003;60:1571-1572.

18. Merdes AR, Hansen LA, et al. "Influence of Alzheimer pathology on clinical diagnostic accuracy in dementia with Lewy bodies." *Neurology* 2003;60: 1586-1590.

19. Kapp MB. "Legal standards for the medical diagnosis and treatment of dementia." *J Legal Med* 2002;23:359-402.

20. Drickamer MA, Lachs MS. "Sounding board: Should patients with Alzheimer's disease be told their diagnosis?" *N Engl J Med* 1992;326:947-951.

21. Seshadri S, Drachman DA, Lippa CF. "Apolipoprotein E $\in$ 4 allele and the lifetime risk of Alzheimer's disease. *Arch Neurol* 1995;52:1074-1079.

22. Roses AD. "Genetic testing for Alzheimer disease." *Arch Neurol* 1997;54: 1226-1229.

23. *Id*. at 1227.

Additional Reading

Alzheimer's Association: www.alz.org, accessed December 24, 2004.

Alzheimer's Disease Education and Referral Center: www.alzheimers.org, accessed December 24, 2004.

Mendez MF, Cummings JL. *Dementia: A Clinical Approach*, 3rd ed. Boston: Butterworth-Heinemann; 2003.

Chapter 19

Movement Disorders

19.1 Introduction

Conditions characterized by abnormal speed, size, and form of movements are known as movement disorders. Abnormal or involuntary movements—*dyskinesias*—may be the sole manifestation of a disease or part of a syndrome with other symptoms. Basal ganglia disturbances cause most movement disorders. These structures lie deep in the cerebrum and the upper brainstem:

- Globus pallidus
- Striatum—caudate nucleus, putamen, and ventral (or limbic) striatum
- Substantia nigra
- Subthalamic nucleus

The basal ganglia act as a damping system between impulses generated in the cortex and the final input to the motor neurons in the spinal cord and brainstem. The basal ganglia monitor input from the cortex and provide feedback to the frontal motor cortex via the thalamus. Abnormalities of basal ganglia function can lead to reduced movement—*akinetic-rigid* or *hypokinetic syndromes*—or excessive movement—*hyperkinetic* disorders.

The neurologist evaluating a patient with a movement disorder must obtain a detailed history that includes:

- A clear and comprehensive description of the movements
- Current and past medications
- Family history
- Past medical history, especially infections
- Toxic exposures

The neurological examination will focus on the abnormal movements, speech, eye movements, gait and station, coordination, strength, reflexes, and facial expression. Diagnostic testing will include routine laboratory studies and specialized tests selected according to clinical suspicions. Brain MRI may reveal abnormalities that narrow the differential diagnosis. PET scans are also helpful in certain conditions.

The frontal lobes have extensive links with the basal ganglia and other related subcortical structures. Therefore, it is not surprising that many movement disorders are associated with prominent neurobehavioral and neuropsychiatric disorders. These include cognitive impairments, mood changes, psychosis, disinhibition, anxiety, and inappropriate behavior.

Hypokinetic symptoms include *bradykinesia* (slowness of movement), rigidity, and postural instability. *Parkinsonism* refers to a combination of tremor, rigidity, bradykinesia, and impaired postural reflexes. Parkinson's disease is the most common cause of this symptom complex. However, drug effects and many rarer movement disorders also cause parkinsonism.

19.2 Parkinson's Disease (PD)

This is the prototypical akinetic-rigid syndrome. PD is a slowly progressive, age-related neurodegenerative disorder. For the vast majority of patients with sporadic PD (as opposed to the rarer familial cases) the cause is unknown. Risk factors include increasing age, male sex, rural residency, exposure to herbicides and pesticides, and other toxic exposures. A recent careful epidemiologic study indicates that severe head trauma is also a risk factor.[1] (See §19.6 for more details about trauma and movement disorders.) Cigarette smoking appears to reduce the risk of PD, though whether this is a direct effect or reflects other factors is unclear.[2] Dysfunction within the basal ganglia, particularly a reduction in dopamine-producing cells, causes the clinical manifestations of PD.

PD is a common disorder, probably affecting 500,000 people in the United States. Onset is usually between the ages of fifty and sixty though younger people can be affected. In the majority of patients there is an insidious onset of tremor, stiffness, and clumsiness, typically first affecting an upper limb. The voice becomes softer and even slurred (dysarthria), and there may be difficulty in walking. Although the disease may remain confined to one side of the body for many years, usually it spreads to the other side within a few years. Cognitive slowing is common, and exceeds what is expected from aging alone.[3] Depression and dementia develop in many patients.

A typical patient has a mask-like expression, speaks in a soft monotone, and walks with slow small steps and decreased arm swing. There is great difficulty initiating movement, such as starting to walk or getting up from a chair. Many patients "freeze" when trying to go through an open door or when pivoting. The majority of PD patients have a slow tremor in their hands, often described as "pill rolling" because of its appearance. It is important to remember that not everyone with tremor has PD.

The diagnosis of PD is entirely clinical. There are no biological markers or pathognomonic diagnostic test findings. Pathologically, there is loss of pigmented dopaminergic neurons in the substantia nigra and elsewhere, and abnormal cytoplasmic inclusions—Lewy bodies. Diagnosis is not difficult if a patient has a typical tremor with unilateral onset that responds well to levodopa. Presentation with prominent atypical features— ataxia, autonomic dysfunction, dementia, myoclonus—should raise suspicion of another diagnosis. PD is often confused with benign essential tremor, discussed in §19.4C.

Treatment of PD is largely symptomatic and must be individualized. There are some neuroprotective and disease-modifying therapies but the benefits of these have not been confirmed. Anticholinergic agents are helpful in reducing tremor but have many side effects, especially in older patients. The antiviral agent amantadine has some anti-parkinsonian effects but these usually fade within a year. Most treatment efforts are directed toward replacing the missing dopamine. The dopamine precursor levodopa is the most effective agent for treatment of PD but does produce long-term motor complications. In the early stages of the disease this causes few difficulties. However, the longer drug therapy is continued the more drug-induced side effects will develop.

Therefore, many clinicians prefer to begin treatment with direct-acting dopamine receptor agonists, especially in younger patients who will need treatment for many years. Some proponents believe the agonists have a neuroprotective effect as well. Levodopa is then held in reserve for the time when symptoms worsen and no longer respond to the agonists. This is the recommended approach of a published guideline.[4] However, these medications—bromocriptine, pergolide, pramipexole, and ropinirole—are less potent than levodopa. The question of which approach to follow has not been answered definitively though some recent data seems to favor starting treatment with levodopa.[5] Treatment strategies will continue to evolve as our understanding of the disease and medications increases.

The role of surgical intervention is also unclear. Deep brain stimulation and ablative procedures can be useful for some of the motor abnormalities but are risky. Fetal dopaminergic cell implantation is an experimental approach with unclear long-term benefits.

There are many potential side effects with all of the medications used for PD. As the disease progresses there are increasing motor, neuropsychiatric, and other nonmotor problems. Nevertheless, with currently available medications life span is almost identical to a control group without PD.[6] Pharmacologic management is difficult. This implies that management of patients with PD should only be undertaken by those with interest and expertise in the field.

19.3 Parkinsonism-Plus Syndromes

There are several neurologic conditions with parkinsonian features plus other manifestations. These can be confused with PD. The correct diagnosis may become obvious only after atypical features develop or when the neurologist finds that the usually effective medications for PD are not helpful.

Progressive supranuclear palsy (PSP) is the most common parkinsonism-plus syndrome. It is also known by the eponym, Steele-Richardson-Olszewski syndrome. There is rigidity, bradykinesia, and postural instability, but no resting tremor. The rigidity affects axial—posterior neck and back—rather than limb muscles, causing the head to turn upwards. This is combined with a characteristic impairment of eye movement, particularly of downward gaze. Thus, the patient cannot move the eyes downward to compensate for the extended head position; the result is frequent trips and falls, often the presenting complaint. The absence of tremor is a key point in differentiating this from PD. PSP causes a dementia with prominent frontal executive dysfunction, the paradigm for *subcortical dementia* as described in an historic paper.[7] There is no cure for PSP; symptomatic treatment is unsatisfactory. Median survival from onset is less than ten years.[8]

Multiple system atrophy (MSA) is a slowly progressive degenerative disease of unknown cause with varying degrees of autonomic, cerebellar, and parkinsonian features. The subtypes are known as *Shy-Drager syndrome* (MSA with dysautonomia), *striatonigral degeneration* (mainly parkinsonian features), and *olivopontocerebellar atrophy* (prominent cerebellar features, often with dementia).

Autonomic dysfunction, especially postural hypotension producing lightheadedness or fainting, is also common in PD. However, autonomic dysfunction in MSA is more severe and occurs earlier in the disease, sometimes preceding the motor abnormalities. Nevertheless, it is not always easy to distinguish between PD and MSA with parkinsonian features. A recent report indicates that brain MRI may be a helpful diagnostic tool.[9]

There is no cure for MSA and survival is also under ten years.[10] PSP and MSA are much less common than PD, with prevalences about 5 and 3 percent that of PD respectively.[11] Other parkinsonism-plus syndromes are even rarer.

19.4 Hyperkinetic Disorders

There are several types of hyperkinetic movement disorders. More than one type of abnormal movement can occur in the same patient, making diagnosis difficult. Movement disorders specialists often videotape their patients to help with analysis.

A. Dystonia

Dystonias are involuntary, sustained muscle contractions that produce twisting, repetitive movements, or abnormal postures. Dystonias may be primary (idiopathic) or secondary (symptomatic), associated with neurodegenerative diseases of the brain, head injury, drugs, and metabolic disorders. Dystonias are also classified according to the distribution of abnormality:

- Focal—blepharospasm, torticollis, writer's cramp
- Generalized—idiopathic torsion dystonia
- Hemidystonia—one side of the body
- Multifocal—affecting noncontiguous regions
- Segmental—affecting two or more contiguous body regions such as arm and neck

The often bizarre appearance of dystonia and the fluctuations in symptoms may lead to a psychiatric diagnosis. Indeed, psychogenic dystonia due to somatization does occur. Conscious and deliberate productive of dystonia is also possible (see §19.5).

Benzodiazepines, anticholinergics, and baclofen have some efficacy in reducing dystonia. Many patients require multiple agents. Patients who develop dystonia before age thirty should have a trial of levodopa therapy to exclude the possibility of a rare dopa-responsive dystonia. Many focal dystonias—particularly blepharospasm and torticollis—respond to botulinum toxin injections to paralyze the overactive muscles. Brain surgery and deep brain stimulation are reserved for the severest dystonia cases.

B. Chorea

Chorea is defined as irregular, flowing, purposeless, unpredictable, brief jerking movements that appear to flit randomly from one part of the body to another. Some patients try to incorporate the movements into seemingly normal actions. Chorea can occur as an isolated syndrome or as one part of a neurological disorder.

Huntington's disease (HD) is a progressive, autosomal dominant inherited neurodegenerative disease affecting about five to ten of every 100,000 people world-wide,[12] or about 30,000 in the United States. Symptoms usually appear insidiously in early to mid-adulthood. Manifestations include a movement disorder dominated by chorea, a progressive subcortical dementia, and a variety of psychiatric and behavioral problems. Depression is quite common and there is a heightened risk of suicide. HD is caused by an abnormal trinucleotide repeat in a gene on chromosome 4 that codes for the *huntingtin* protein. At-risk relatives of HD patients can be screened to determine whether or not they carry the defective gene. This should only be done at centers with psychologic and genetic counseling available. Since there is no means to prevent the disease a positive test result raises serious ethical dilemmas and may create considerable emotional turmoil.

Sydenham's chorea occurs in childhood due to an autoimmune reaction triggered by rheumatic fever. Chorea developing in pregnancy—*chorea gravidarum*—may be a recurrence of Sydenham's chorea. Chorea is also caused by many different toxic, metabolic, and inflammatory conditions.

C. Tremor

This is defined as oscillations of a body part, caused by rhythmical or alternating contractions of agonist and antagonist muscles. *Physiologic tremor* is normal and is seen in outstretched arms. Anxiety, infection, or drug therapy enhances this tremor. Differentiation between a normal and a pathological tremor may be difficult.

Essential tremor (ET) is probably the most common movement disorder. It is often familial. Although often called benign, the tremor can interfere significantly with daily activities. Some patients develop social anxiety and avoid situations where the tremor draws attention. The tremor usually involves the arms and is predominantly *postural*. That is, the tremor is present when the arms are held away from the body, as when drinking or eating. However, legs, head, jaw, tongue, and voice can be affected.

Most patients find that small amounts of alcohol reduce the tremor though this is not a standard recommended treatment. The tremor usually responds to primidone or beta blockers. Many other medications are helpful as second-line treatments. Some forms of ET respond to botulinum toxin injections.

Tremor occurring as a limb moves nears a target is known as *intention tremor*; this is often a sign of cerebellar disease. *Resting tremor*, typical of PD, is most prominent in stationary, supported limbs.

D. Myoclonus

Myoclonus is defined as rapid, brief, involuntary shock-like muscle jerks which are frequently repetitive and sometimes rhythmical. Normal myoclonic movements occur in almost all individuals and include hiccup—due to myoclonus of the diaphragm—and the 'jerk' that occurs when falling asleep at night. Unlike tremor, there are clear pauses between movements. Myoclonus does not flow or resemble normal movements like chorea.

Myoclonus is classified by distribution—focal, segmental, or generalized—and by origin—cortical, brainstem, or spinal. *Epileptic myoclonus* can be focal or generalized. Several progressive childhood epilepsies have prominent generalized myoclonus. *Epilepsia partialis continua* is a focal seizure disorder that causes myoclonic jerks. It is often due to irritative lesions of the cortex. *Palatal myoclonus* is usually idiopathic but may be seen in conjunction with tumor or multiple sclerosis. Myoclonus also occurs in a variety of degenerative, toximetabolic, and infectious conditions.

E. Tics

Tics are irregular, stereotyped, repetitive nonrhythmic movements or vocalizations that can usually be imitated and briefly suppressed. Simple motor tics include eye blinks, facial grimaces, or shoulder shrugs. Complex motor tics resemble normal purposeful movements including throwing, touching, or gesturing, but occur in inappropriate situations. Simple vocal tics include throat-clearing, coughing, sniffing, grunting, or hissing. Complex vocal tics include words or phrases. Many people have an occasional tic.

Tourette's syndrome is a chronic tic disorder characterized by simple and complex motor and vocal tics, usually associated with behavioral abnormalities.[13] Onset is almost always in childhood. The tics vary in location and severity over time. A minority of patients exhibit *coprolalia*—

obscene language. There is a high incidence of obsessive-compulsive disorder and attention deficit hyperactivity disorder. The tics may respond to benzodiazepine medications such as clonazepam or alpha adrenergic agonists—clonidine, guanfacine. However, dopamine receptor blockers are the most effective agents. The potential benefits of these must be weighed against the risk of drug-induced movement disorders.

19.5 Psychogenic Movement Disorders

These are not rare and can mimic any type of movement. There are diagnostic criteria for the following categories of psychogenic movement disorders: documented, clinically established, probable, and possible.[14] Clinical and historical features suggestive of a psychogenic movement disorder or an attempt to deceive include:[15]

- Abrupt onset
- Distraction eliminates the movement
- False sensory complaints or weakness in involved areas
- Fluctuating character of movements
- Inconsistent movements over time
- Litigation and compensation issues
- Movements or postures not consistent with physiologic patterns
- Other signs of somatization or obvious psychiatric illness
- Secondary gain
- Spontaneous remission

Employment in the healthcare and insurance industries should also raise suspicions.

Diagnosis of a psychogenic origin is difficult because the above-mentioned clues are not exclusive or always definitive. Indeed, some movement disorders share these characteristics. For example, there may be spontaneous remissions in certain dystonias and tic disorders. Conversely, abrupt onset of abnormal movements can occur after stroke, anoxia, or severe brain trauma. Surprising impairments or retained abilities not predicted by examination occur in both psychogenic and organic disorders. Also, voluntary control of the movements is possible in some organic movement disorders. Finally, there are these additional complications: psychogenic movements can occur in conjunction with "real" abnormal movements and psychiatric symptoms can be the presenting features of some movement disorders.

19.6 Posttraumatic Movement Disorders: Legal Implications

Can trauma cause PD or other movement disorders? Can trauma worsen an existing movement disorder? Direct traumatic damage to the basal ganglia and connected structures can produce abnormal movements but this a rare phenomenon. Predisposing factors include family history of a movement disorder and coexisting movement disorders. Trauma severe enough to cause the brain damage will likely produce other neurological signs; isolated traumatic damage to the midbrain is rare and usually fatal.[16]

If abnormal movements begin soon after a trauma severe enough to produce visible lesions in brain structures known to relate to motor function then causation is probable. However, if there is no such damage or the abnormalities begin years later the answer is less obvious. Late inflammatory changes and CNS reorganization might explain movements that develop months or years after injury but these are only theoretical possibilities. If the trauma is peripheral the situation is even less clear. Presumably, in such cases altered sensory input to the spinal cord somehow leads to changes in the brain's motor centers—also an unproven hypothesis.

Patients with basal ganglia or midbrain damage may be parkinsonian, but this is not idiopathic PD. The diagnosis of *posttraumatic parkinsonism* requires:

- Absence of parkinsonism before the trauma
- Concussion or other evidence of brain trauma
- Development of symptoms soon after trauma, probably within days or weeks
- Imaging or pathologic evidence of midbrain or basal ganglia damage

Another form of posttraumatic parkinsonism develops after repeated closed head injury—boxer's encephalopathy or *parkinson pugilistica*. Cognitive and behavioral problems develop along with the parkinsonism in these patients.

Head trauma does not cause idiopathic PD[17] but can cause an exacerbation of existing symptoms in patients with PD.[18] However, head trauma is probably a risk factor for subsequent PD. Some of the supporting studies rely on patients' reports, raising the issue of *recall bias*—a tendency to remember those incidents apparently connected to the issue in question while forgetting similar events without such a relationship. Recall bias is avoided by using historical documentation of head injury before onset of PD. This was done in one recent study, and results indicate that severe head injury did appear to increase the risk of PD, though possibly accounting only for 5 percent of cases.[19] Likely mechanisms for the increased risk include:[20]

- Disruption of the blood-brain barrier allowing toxic or immune damage leading to the neurodegenerative condition
- Trauma-induced overexpression of proteins that triggers a cascade of events leading to formation of Lewy bodies and cell death

Risk, however, is not medical causation. Both environmental and genetic components contribute to the pathogenesis of idiopathic PD. It is unlikely that any single factor, including trauma, causes the disease. The trauma might simply precipitate symptoms sooner in people who would have developed the disease eventually anyway. The physician must express medical causation in terms of reasonable medical certainty (it is more probable than not or more than 50 percent probable) under either the "but for" test or the looser "substantial factor" analysis of legal causation. The medical and scientific literature only supports a possibility rather than a probability that trauma "causes" PD.

Severe head injury can cause dystonia, chorea, tremors, and other abnormal movements. Patients usually have basal ganglia abnormalities visible on imaging studies. The movements appear within days or weeks of injury, though delays of months or years can occur with posttraumatic dystonias.[21] Minor head injury should not be accepted as a cause of these movements.

Dystonias, tremors, and other movements are also reported after peripheral trauma, frequently in conjunction with pain.[22] There is considerable controversy about this, with doubts relating to the lack of a proven causative mechanism.[23] Many of these posttraumatic movement disorders, especially dystonias, occur in association with complex regional pain disorder (the current preferred term for reflex sympathetic dystrophy and causalgia). However, the movements are often atypical, differing from the idiopathic or classic form of the particular movement disorder.[24] Many of these patients may actually have a psychogenic movement disorder.

The neurologist can have an important role in elucidating these issues. First, it is critical that precise language be used. If the patient is parkinsonian, the neurologist must differentiate between idiopathic PD and posttraumatic parkinsonism. Next, an accurate and detailed history is critical. Were there actually subtle signs of a movement disorder even before the trauma? The abnormalities could have contributed to the injury. Such history might be suppressed in the face of litigation. Many patients are taking medications that can cause abnormal movements; the neurologist must consider a drug-induced disorder. Finally, the differential diagnosis must address the possibilities of idiopathic and psychogenic movement disorders.

Endnotes

1. Bower, JH, Maraganore DM, et al. "Head trauma preceding PD: A case-control study." *Neurology* 2003;60:1610-1615.

2. Hernán MA, Takkouche B, et al. "A meta-analysis of coffee drinking, cigarette smoking, and the risk of Parkinson's disease." *Ann Neurol* 2002;52:276-284.

3. Tachibana H, Aragane K, et al. "P3 latency change in aging and Parkinson disease." *Arch Neurol* 1997;54:296-302.

4. Miyasaki JM, Martin W. et al. "Practice parameter: Initiation of treatment for Parkinson's disease: An evidence-based review. Report of the Quality Standards Subcommittee of the American Academy of Neurology." *Neurology* 2002;58:11-17.

5. Wooten GF. "Agonists vs levodopa in PD." *Neurology* 2003;60:360-362.

6. Uitti RJ, Ahlskog JE, et al. "Levodopa therapy and survival in idiopathic Parkinson's disease: Olmsted County project." *Neurology* 1993;43:1918-1926.

7. Albert ML, Feldman RG, Willis AL. "The 'subcortical dementia' of progressive supranuclear palsy." *J Neurol Neurosurg Psychiatry* 1974;37:121-130.

8. Golbe LI, Davis PH, et al. "Prevalence and natural history of progressive supranuclear palsy." *Neurology* 1988;38:1031-1034.

9. Bhattacharya K, Saadia D, et al. "Brain magnetic resonance imaging in multiple-system atrophy and Parkinson disease." *Arch Neurol* 2002;59:835-842.

10. Wenning GK, Ben Shlomo Y, et al. "Clinical features and natural history of multiple system atrophy: An analysis of 100 cases." *Brain* 1994;117:835-845.

11. Schrag A, Ben Shlomo Y, Quinn NP. "Prevalence of progressive supranuclear palsy and multiple system atrophy: A cross-sectional study." *Lancet* 1999; 354:1771-1775.

12. Conneally PM. "Huntington's disease: Genetics and epidemiology. *Am J Hum Genet* 1984;36:506-526.

13. Jankovíc JJ. "Tourette's syndrome." *N Engl J Med* 2001;345:1184-1192.

14. Fahn S. "Psychogenic movement disorders." In: Marsden CD, ed. *Movement Disorders 3*. Boston: Butterworth-Heinemann; 1994.

15. Cummings JL, Mega MS. *Neuropsychiatry and Behavioral Neuroscience*. New York: Oxford University Press; 2003.

16. Rosenblum WI, Greenberg RP, et al. "Midbrain lesions: Frequent and significant prognostic feature in closed head injury." *Neurosurgery* 1981;9:613-620.

17. Goetz CG, Pappert EJ. "Movement disorders: Post-traumatic syndromes." In: Evans RW, ed. *Neurology and Trauma*. Philadelphia: Saunders; 1996:569-580.

18. Goetz CG, Stebbins GT. "Effects of head trauma from motor vehicle accidents on Parkinson's disease." *Ann Neurol* 1991;29:191-193.

19. Bower JH, Maraganore DM, et al., *supra* note 1, at 1613.

20. *Id.*

21. Lee MS, Rinne JO, et al. "Dystonia after head trauma." *Neurology* 1994;44: 1374-1378.

22. Jankovic J. "Controversy. Can peripheral trauma induce dystonia and other movement disorders? Yes!" *Mov Dis* 2001;16:7-12.

23. Weiner WJ. "Controversy. Can peripheral trauma induce dystonia? No!" *Mov Dis* 2001;16:13-22.

24. Bhatia KP, Bhatt MH, Marsden CD. "The causalgia-dystonia syndrome." *Brain* 1993;116:843-851.

Additional Reading

American Parkinson Disease Association: www.apdaparkinson.org, accessed December 24, 2004.

Factor SA, Weiner WJ, eds. *Parkinson's Disease: Diagnosis and Clinical Management*. New York: Demos; 2002.

Jankovíc JJ, Tolosa E, eds. *Parkinson's Disease and Movement Disorders*. Philadelphia: Lippincott Williams & Wilkins; 2002.

The National Parkinson Foundation, Inc.: www.parkinson.org, accessed December 24, 2004.

Society for Progressive Supranuclear Palsy: www.psp.org, accessed December 24, 2004.

Watts RL, Koller WC, eds. *Movement Disorders: Neurologic Principles and Practice*, 2nd ed. New York: McGraw-Hill; 2004.

Chapter 20

Attention Deficit Hyperactivity Disorder (ADHD)

20.1 Introduction

In 1902, British pediatrician Dr. George Still described a group of children who were disinhibited, inattentive, and overly defiant.[1] They did not have general physical or intellectual impairments and did not come from notably dysfunctional homes. Still concluded that there was a biological cause for the abnormal behavior. Most of the children he described would probably meet current criteria for diagnosis of ADHD.

ADHD is a common, chronic neurobehavioral syndrome caused by catecholamine dysfunction in prefrontal-subcortical brain systems. Researchers have made tremendous advances in the past decade in our understanding of the underlying pathophysiology of ADHD. This is "one of the best-researched disorders in medicine . . . data on its validity are far more compelling than for most mental disorders and even for many medical conditions."[2] ADHD may affect almost 10 percent of school-aged children[3] and is responsible for up to half of all mental health referrals in childhood.[4] Significant symptoms persist into adulthood in at least half of all cases,[5] suggesting there are approximately 8 to 9 million adults in the United States with ADHD. Most are untreated.

20.2 Symptoms, Diagnosis, and Comorbidities

The core symptoms of ADHD are excessive inattentiveness, impulsivity, and motor overactivity. Labels used over the years to describe children with these problems include *minimal brain damage (or dysfunction), hyperkinetic impulse disorder, hyperkinetic reaction of childhood, hyperactivity, and attention deficit disorder with or without hyperactivity.*

The most widely used current diagnostic criteria are contained in the American Psychiatric Association's *Diagnostic and Statistical Manual of Mental Disorders* (DSM).[6] There are three main subtypes of ADHD: predominantly inattentive, predominantly hyperactive-impulsive, and combined (accounting for most cases). The behaviors are abnormal only if they are developmentally inappropriate, that is, more severe and frequent than expected for age. Symptoms must produce significant impairment in at least two different settings and persist for at least six months. *DSM* criteria require an age of onset before age seven years. However, there is evidence that the predominantly inattentive subtype presents at an older age.[7]

The ADHD diagnosis is made on clinical grounds, essentially by detailed analysis of developmental history and descriptions of behavior emphasizing the *DSM* criteria. There is no simple diagnostic test available. Symptom checklists, behavior rating scales, and neuropsychological assessment are all useful tools in the process but do not replace the history. Various neuroimaging and computerized EEG techniques are promising, but not yet widely accepted as diagnostic tests.

Attentional problems include poor concentration, inability to divide or shift attention appropriately, or difficulty ignoring distractions. Individuals with ADHD are often disorganized. They have trouble setting priorities and structuring complex tasks. There is poor time management, characterized by overscheduling and chronic lateness. Forgetfulness is common and there is a tendency to misplace and lose things. None of these traits is unique or pathognomonic for ADHD. However, compared to someone without ADHD these problems are more pervasive and severe.

Impulsivity reflects an inability to control one's behavior according to the requirements of a situation. ADHD patients tend to speak or act without pausing to consider the ramifications. They have difficulty tolerating frustration, are unable to delay gratification, and tend to overreact. Temper outbursts are not unusual. Hyperactive individuals fidget excessively, are unable to sit still, prefer to be active, and talk excessively. Hyperactivity was once regarded as the key feature of this disorder. However, prominent attentional symptoms can occur without any hyperactivity. With age, the hyperactive and impulsive symptoms tend to improve more than the inattentive symptoms.

ADHD is not a benign condition. Symptoms interfere significantly with school and work performance, family life, and social relationships. Comorbid conditions complicate management of many ADHD patients. In childhood, oppositional defiant disorder and conduct disorders are common. These may be forerunners of substance abuse, academic failure, and adult antisocial personality disorder. Anxiety and mood disorders are common in both children and adults with ADHD. Driving-related problems—accidents, injuries, and traffic violations—are more frequent in individuals with ADHD.[8] Both educational attainment and occupational achievement are impaired.[9]

There are concerns about the validity of the ADHD diagnosis. Though some critics claim this is a uniquely American disorder population studies reveal similar prevalence rates in many other countries.[10] Other critics claim that ADHD is an artifact of symptoms shared by comorbid psychiatric illnesses but, when these conditions resolve or overlapping symptoms are otherwise accounted for, the ADHD diagnosis persists.[11] Finally, several kinds of evidence provide strong support for the validity of ADHD:

- Genetic studies indicate a very high heritability of the disorder
- Laboratory, neuroimaging, and psychological studies provide a pathophysiologic explanation for the symptoms
- There is a coherent symptomatology that clinicians can assess objectively, with consensus rates for the diagnosis comparable to other psychiatric disorders

20.3 Etiologies and Neurobiology

Neurologic disorders that cause damage or dysfunction in frontal-subcortical structures produce symptoms that resemble ADHD. Thus, the differential diagnosis for ADHD includes traumatic brain injury, perinatal encephalopathy, Fragile X syndrome, some developmental disorders, encephalitis, and certain progressive neurodegenerative diseases. Sleep deprivation produces many symptoms that resemble ADHD. Nonconvulsive seizures, especially *petit mal*, can produce diagnostic confusion.

Although the precise pathophysiologic basis for ADHD is not yet known the clinical manifestations indicate that this is a frontal-subcortical syndrome. The symptoms of ADHD reflect impaired dopamine and, to a lesser extent, norepinephrine activity in the pathways that control frontal executive functions. Other neurotransmitters may also be involved. Different core defects are offered as explanations for the clinical problems. One prominent theory holds that defective behavioral inhibition interferes with other executive functions including: working memory; self-regulation of mood, motivation, and arousal; internalized speech; and behavioral analysis and synthesis.[12] Other theories focus on defects in behavioral reinforcement, excessive stimulation-seeking, or impaired cognitive self-regulation. Data from neuropsychological studies provide support for the general notion that ADHD is an executive function disorder.

The medications that improve function in individuals with ADHD typically enhance dopamine and norepinephrine neurotransmission. Dopamine probably mediates cognitive functions such as sustained attention, vigilance, prioritization of behavior, and regulation of behavior; norepinephrine regulates arousal, attention, and motivation.[13] There are extensive dopamine and norepinephrine pathways projecting from brainstem and subcortical regions into prefrontal cortex.

The neuroanatomic basis for ADHD is being unraveled. The underlying circuitry includes prefrontal cortex, thalamus, striatum, brainstem, and cerebellum. Several small neuroimaging studies, mostly utilizing MRI, reveal loss of volume or other anomalies within these structures. Furthermore, a recent larger study indicates that the reduced cerebellar and total brain volumes are not due to treatment with stimulant medications.[14]

There is ample evidence that most cases of ADHD have a genetic basis. Family-genetic and twin studies indicate very high *heritability*—the amount of variability in a trait due to genetic as opposed to environmental factors—with estimates up to 0.8[15] (1.0 is the maximum). Also, the inattentive and hyperactive-impulsive subtypes appear to be genetically separable.[16] Preliminary molecular genetic studies have identified two dopaminergic candidate genes, coding for the dopamine transporter (DAT1) and a dopamine receptor (DRD4).

20.4 Treatment

The first step in successful treatment of ADHD is accurate diagnosis, including identification of any comorbid medical or psychiatric conditions. Management of ADHD usually requires a combination of pharmacologic and nonpharmacologic interventions. Treatment must address each individual's particular concerns and "target" symptoms. If severe coexisting anxiety, mood, substance abuse, conduct, or personality disorders complicate the situation these must be addressed as well, often before attempting to treat the ADHD. This is particularly true for active substance abuse and major depression. There are evidence-based guidelines for treatment of children[17] and adults.[18]

Education about ADHD is essential. Fortunately, there are local and national support groups for individuals with ADHD. Many children will require specialized planning in conjunction with their schools. Various modifications at school and home are needed to minimize the impact of the ADHD symptoms. Psychoeducational testing is often necessary to identify coexisting specific learning disabilities. Some patients will benefit from cognitive therapy or behavioral modification techniques to deal with the wide range of disruptive behaviors and dysfunctional social interactions.

Medications—especially psychostimulants—are the mainstay of treatment for ADHD. Not all patients require medication. The decision to use medication is based on the severity and impact of symptoms on the patient's life. Some patients, or their parents, are satisfied with confirmation of the diagnosis; they then prefer to utilize behavioral techniques to manage their symptoms. Others will choose pharmacologic intervention.

Psychostimulant medications have been used successfully in this disorder for more than sixty years.[19] Several methylphenidate and amphetamine preparations, differing in their delivery systems and durations of action, are now available.[20] The success rate with stimulants exceeds 80 percent if both types are tried.[21] Nonstimulant medications—including the antidepressants bupropion and venlafaxine, the alpha agonists clonidine and guanfacine, modafinil, and the recently introduced selective norepinephrine reuptake inhibitor atomoxetine—are also important in treatment of ADHD.[22]

There are several concerns about the use of stimulants—do they suppress growth, cause tics, or lead to substance abuse? Careful analysis indicates that any growth suppression is transient, normalizing by late adolescence.[23] Tics are very common in children with ADHD but stimulants do not appear to cause significant exacerbations.[24] Finally, a detailed meta-analysis indicates that stimulant treatment of ADHD not only does not lead to substance abuse but actually has a protective effect.[25]

20.5 Medicolegal Concerns
A. ADHD and criminal law

It should not be surprising that a condition characterized by poor impulse control, excessive temper, and impatience is associated with a high risk for criminal activity. For example, in one study of neurologic abnormalities in thirty-one murderers, eleven had evidence of ADHD.[26] ADHD is not often raised as a defense to criminal charges even though it is a form of biological deficiency that could potentially be part of a mental nonresponsibility (insanity) defense or a diminished capacity or responsibility claim.

There are significant hurdles to overcome when raising an ADHD defense. First, many jurisdictions no longer recognize the "irresistible impulse" or volitional form of insanity defense. Instead, the trend is toward a cognitive standard—that a defendant understands the nature of his conduct and its wrongfulness. While impulsive acts are commonplace, ADHD alone rarely produces such severe impairment of cognition that the accused could prevail against a cognitive standard.

If there is a situation where raising the issue of impulsivity secondary to ADHD could be helpful to a defendant, then the attorney must be able to demonstrate a history or pattern of impulsive behaviors and other severe ADHD symptoms. Otherwise, the attorney would be in the difficult position of arguing that the ADHD was so severe that it led to the isolated criminal act yet had never before produced significant problems.

Nevertheless, there have been cases in which ADHD—alone or in conjunction with coexisting conditions—was a successful defense or a mitigating factor. The use of ADHD as a criminal defense is reviewed in greater detail elsewhere.[27]

B. ADHD and education

The need for accommodations and special education services to assist students with severe ADHD—especially when there are coexisting learning disabilities and behavior problems—should not be controversial. However, prior to the 1990 reauthorization of the Individuals with Disabilities Education Act (IDEA)[28] students with isolated ADHD were ineligible for such assistance. Now, there are two possible mechanisms for obtaining special services. Nevertheless, difficulties continue to arise, especially when there is a disagreement between parents and schools about the need for services or the nature of the accommodations being offered.

Although ADHD is recognized as a potentially handicapping condition educational services are not granted automatically. Part B of the IDEA covers children who are "Other Health Impaired." The definition requires a health problem that impairs alertness, thereby adversely affecting educational performance. Under the IDEA, once the student's eligibility is demonstrated by the clinician the school develops an individual educational plan (IEP). This could include placement for all or part of the schoolday in a special education classroom. However, these settings were developed for children with emotional and behavioral problems, learning disabilities, and other serious conditions, and may not be an ideal placement for the child with ADHD. If modifications or accommodations to the general classroom could be effective then that is the preferred course of action. Unfortunately, clear guidelines to determine when special education classrooms are necessary or what modifications are best do not exist.

Special accommodations are also available under Section 504 of the Rehabilitation Act of 1973[29] to children with physical or mental impairments that interfere with academic performance. This is a civil rights statute that prohibits discrimination against anyone with an impairment that substantially limits a major life activity. Learning is one such activity; the clinician must determine whether there is a substantial limitation. It is possible for a child to be eligible for accommodations under §504 without meeting the requirements of the IDEA.

Both IDEA and §504 require schools to provide various accommodations and services. However, there are differences between these two programs. IEPs required under the IDEA provide more safeguards and offer a wider range of possible interventions than §504 plans. Generally, IDEA is the better option for children with more severe problems. On the other hand, §504 is simpler to utilize and has less restrictive eligibility and evaluation requirements. However, services under a §504 plan are implemented by general, not special, education personnel. Thus, this is more appropriate for students with milder impairments who do not need special education.[30]

Endnotes

1. Still GF. "The Coulstonian Lectures on some abnormal psychical conditions in children." *Lancet* 1902;1:1008-1012,1077-1082,1163-1168.

2. Goldman LS, Genel M, et al. "Diagnosis and treatment of attention-deficit/hyperactivity disorder." *JAMA* 1998;279:1100-1107, at 1105.

3. American Academy of Pediatrics Committee on Quality Improvement, Subcommittee on Attention-Deficit/Hyperactivity Disorder. "Clinical practice guideline: Diagnosis and evaluation of the child with attention-deficit/hyperactivity disorder." *Pediatrics* 2000;105:1158-1170.

4. MTA Cooperative Group. "A 14-month randomized clinical trial of treatment strategies for attention-deficit/hyperactivity disorder." *Arch Gen Psychiatry* 1999;56:1073-1086.

5. Faraone SV, Biederman J, et al. "Attention-deficit/hyperactivity disorder in adults: An overview." Biol Psychiatry 2000;48:9-20.

6. American Psychiatric Association. *Diagnostic and Statistical Manual of Mental Disorders*, 4th ed., Text Revision. Washington D.C.: American Psychiatric Association; 2000:85-93.

7. Willoughby MT, Curran PJ, et al. "Implications of early versus late onset of attention-deficit/hyperactivity disorder symptoms." *J Am Acad Child Adolesc Psychiatry* 2000;39:1512-1519.

8. Murphy K, Barkley RA. "Prevalence of DSM-IV symptoms of ADHD in adult licensed drivers: Implications for clinical diagnosis." *J Atten Disord* 1996;1:147-161.

9. Mannuzza S, Klein RG, et al. "Educational and occupational outcome of hyperactive boys grown up." *J Am Acad Child Adolesc Psychiatry* 1997;36:1222-1227.

10. Faraone SV, Sergeant J, et al. "The worldwide prevalence of ADHD: is it an American condition?" *World Psychiatry* 2003;2:104-112.

11. Milberger S, Biederman J, et al. "Attention deficit hyperactivity disorder and comorbid disorders: Issues of overlapping symptoms. *Am J Psychiatry* 1995; 152:1793-1799.

12. Barkley RA. *ADHD and the Nature of Self-control.* New York: Guilford Press; 1997.

13. Stahl S. *Essential Psychopharmacology: Neuroscientific Basis and Practical Applications.* New York: Cambridge University Press; 2000.

14. Castellanos FX, Lee PP, et al. "Developmental trajectories of brain volume abnormalities in children and adolescents with attention-deficit/hyperactivity disorder." *JAMA* 2002;288:1740-1748.

15. Faraone SV, Doyle AE. "The nature and heritability of attention-deficit/hyperactivity disorder." *Child Adolesc Psychiatr Clin N Amer* 2001;10:299-316.

16. Neuman RJ, Todd RD, et al. "Evaluation of ADHD typology in three contrasting samples: a latent class approach." *J Am Acad Child Adolesc Psychiatry* 1999;38:25-33.

17. American Academy of Pediatrics, Committee on Quality Improvement, Subcommittee on Attention-Deficit/Hyperactivity Disorder. "Clinical practice guideline: Treatment of the school-aged child with attention-deficit/hyperactivity disorder." *Pediatrics* 2001;108:1033-1044.

18. American Academy of Child and Adolescent Psychiatry. "Practice parameter for the use of stimulant medications in the treatment of children, adolescents, and adults." *J Am Acad Child Adolesc Psychiatry* 2002;41(2 suppl):26S-49S.

19. Bradley C. "The behavior of children receiving benzedrine." *Am J Psychiatry* 1937;94:577-585.

20. Wilens TE. "Management of attention-deficit/hyperactivity disorder." *CNS News*, January 2004;15-19.

21. Arnold LE. "Methylphenidate vs. amphetamine: A comparative review." *J Atten Disord* 2000;3:200-211.

22. Pliszka SR. "Non-stimulant treatment of attention-deficit/hyperactivity disorder." *CNS Spectrums* 2003;8:253-258.

23. Spencer TJ, Biederman J, Wilens TE. "Growth deficits in children with attention deficit hyperactivity disorder." *Pediatrics* 1998;102:501-506.

24. The Tourette's Syndrome Study Group. "Treatment of ADHD in children with tics: A randomized controlled trial." *Neurology* 2002;58:527-536.

25. Wilens TE, Faraone SV, et al. "Does stimulant therapy of attention-deficit/ hyperactivity disorder beget later substance abuse? A meta-analytic review of the literature." *Pediatrics* 2003;111:179-185.

26. Blake PY, Pincus JH, Buckner C. "Neurologic abnormalities in murderers." *Neurology* 1995;45:1641-1647.

27. Wishik JM. "Attention deficit hyperactivity disorder and criminal responsibility: A guide for attorneys." *Medical Trial Technique Quarterly* 1996;43: 83-128.

28. 20 U.S.C. §§1400 et seq.

29. 29 U.S.C. §794.

30. Rief SF. T*he ADHD Book of Lists*. San Francisco: Jossey-Bass; 2003.

Additional Reading

Attention Deficit Disorder Association: www.add.org, accessed December 24, 2004.

Barkley RA. *Attention-Deficit Hyperactivity Disorder: A Handbook for Diagnosis and Treatment*, 2nd ed. New York: Guilford Press; 1998.

Brown TE, ed. *Attention-Deficit Disorders and Comorbidities in Children, Adolescents, and Adults*. Washington: American Psychiatric Press; 2000.

Children and Adults with Attention-Deficit/Hyperactivity Disorder: www.chadd.org, accessed December 24, 2004.

Solanto MV, Arnsten AFT, Castellanos FX, eds. *Stimulant Drugs and ADHD: Basic and Clinical Neuroscience*. New York: Oxford University Press; 2001.

Chapter 21

Iatrogenic Disorders

21.1 Introduction

Iatrogenic conditions arise from medical treatment. These include adverse reactions to medications, complications from surgical or other therapeutic interventions, and mishaps due to diagnostic procedures. The nervous system can be harmed by treatments directed toward either neurologic or non-neurologic illnesses. Similarly, neurologic interventions can have deleterious effects on other systems. Some adverse events are idiosyncratic and unpredictable, others are well-recognized and potentially avoidable. Iatrogenic conditions can be classified according to the type of neurologic or other systemic complication, by causative agent, or by the disease being treated.

There is great concern about iatrogenic disease. Reportedly, at least 44,000 people die annually because of medical errors.[1] The spectrum of iatrogenic disease is huge. This chapter will highlight only a few iatrogenic conditions relevant to neurology.

21.2 Drug-Induced Neurological Disorders

In the pre-antibiotic era syphilis was regarded as the great imitator, producing a wide variety of neurologic and other symptoms. Now, drug-in-

329

duced neurologic disorders are the great mimics. Almost any class of drugs may affect the nervous system, either directly—*primary neurotoxicity*—or indirectly via drug-induced systemic dysfunction that harms the nervous system—*secondary neurotoxicity*. Known drug-induced conditions include autonomic disturbances, encephalopathies, headaches, movement disorders, myelopathies, myopathies, neuromuscular disorders, neuropathies, pituitary disorders, seizures, and strokes. The exact incidence of such complications is unknown.

Adverse drug reactions are recorded during the drug development process and reported to the Food and Drug Administration (FDA). Clinicians also report adverse events to the FDA and pharmaceutical manufacturers as part of post-marketing surveillance programs. Published case reports are another source of information. However, a report of an adverse reaction does not prove a causal connection. Analysis of causation is complex and requires evaluation of several points including:[2]

- Effect of drug discontinuation and rechallenge
- Prior occurrence of the adverse reaction
- Temporal relation between the event and drug administration
- Whether the manifestations are a natural part of the underlying disease
- Whether there is a plausible mechanism for the reported reaction

If there is a plausible mechanism or a known relationship between a specific drug and a particular neurologic disorder, a drug reaction should be part of the differential diagnosis.

A. Drug-induced movement disorders

These are common occurrences, most often produced by medications used in psychiatric treatment. Some abnormal movements—*dyskinesias*—appear soon after the drug is given whereas others occur only after prolonged administration. Some movements persist after the offending agent is stopped, the *tardive* disorders. There are both *hyperkinetic*—excessive movement—and *hypokinetic*—reduced movement—disorders.

Acute dystonic reaction occurs within a few days, or even a few hours, of starting neuroleptic agents (especially high potency dopamine-blocking antipsychotics) or certain antinausea drugs (such as metoclopramide or prochlorperazine). Even the newer *atypical antipsychotics* can cause dystonia, though the risk is lower. The reaction consists of intense, painful muscle spasms and abnormal postures, especially of head and neck muscles. Breathing can be impaired. Intravenous or intramuscular injections of antihistamines or anticholinergic agents provide rapid relief.

Akathisia is an inability to remain still. Patients swing their legs, repeatedly cross their legs, rock themselves, pace, or fidget. Acute akathisia is the most common neuroleptic-induced movement disorder but is also caused by other drugs, particularly the serotonin reuptake inhibitor antidepressants. Reducing the dose of the drug or complete discontinuation is usually an effective treatment. Anticholinergics and benzodiazepines are also helpful. *Tardive akathisia* persists after discontinuation of the drug. This requires different treatment than the acute form.

Another very common drug-induced movement disorder is *tardive dyskinesia* (TD). This syndrome usually develops after at least three months of treatment with a dopamine-blocking drug. There are reports of TD beginning after shorter exposure to these agents or from non-neuroleptic drugs. Classic TD consists of choreic movements, mostly of orofacial muscles (especially lips and tongue). Patients frequently have rhythmic chewing or pouting movements. Rarer variants include *tardive tics*, *tardive dystonia*, and *tardive myoclonus*. TD needs to be differentiated from the many disorders that cause choreic movements.

TD is more common in older patients and women. Other risk factors and the underlying pathophysiology are not well understood. The risk of TD in a schizophrenic patient treated continuously for one year is 4 to 5 percent,[3] and the overall prevalence in patients exposed to neuroleptic drugs is approximately 20 percent. The best treatment for TD is prevention, either by avoiding high-potency neuroleptics entirely or by using them for the shortest time possible and at the lowest effective doses. When TD develops the neuroleptic dose should be reduced or the drug discontinued. A lower potency agent or one of the newer atypical antipsychotics should be used if necessary. Several different classes of medications may relieve the symptoms.

Unfortunately, TD can be permanent and irreversible. Such cases often lead to litigation against the prescribing physician. Theories for the malpractice action include:

- Inadequate monitoring of the patient
- Inappropriate drug use—either off-label prescribing or misdiagnosis
- Lack of proper informed consent

Neuroleptic malignant syndrome (NMS) is a rare but potentially fatal idiosyncratic reaction to neuroleptic medications that requires aggressive intervention. These patients develop severe muscle rigidity, fever, altered consciousness, autonomic dysfunction, and a massively elevated serum creatinine kinase indicating muscle damage. There are disagreements about classification and diagnostic criteria for NMS. It may occur in up to 2 percent of admissions to acute psychiatric wards.[4] NMS usually develops in patients receiving dopamine-blocking agents but is also seen following abrupt withdrawal of dopaminergic agents. Other medications are rare causes of NMS.

Prompt treatment of the condition is necessary to avoid death. The neuroleptic must be discontinued and supportive care started. The patient should be cooled and electrolyte imbalances corrected. Pulmonary, cardiac, and renal complications need to be addressed. Dantrolene, bromocriptine, benzodiazepines, and amantadine are used to treat NMS.

B. Other drug-induced neurologic disorders

Weakness and fatigue are common presenting complaints in a neurology practice. Most such patients do not have a specific neurologic disorder. Subjective weakness and lack of energy can be caused by many commonly prescribed drugs including analgesics, antiepileptics, beta blockers and other antihypertensives, and tricyclic antidepressants.

However, weakness can be due to drug-induced impairments of neuromuscular transmission. Penicillamine can trigger an autoimmune reaction that produces a form of myasthenia gravis. Most patients recover after the drug is stopped. Some medications exacerbate myasthenia gravis or unmask weakness in previously asymptomatic patients. Frequent offenders are aminoglycoside and fluoroquinolone antibiotics. Many drugs reportedly impair neuromuscular transmission and are blamed for weakness, even in patients without underlying disease.

Weakness may also be due to myopathy. There are several drug-induced causes of myopathy.[5] Many different cholesterol-lowering agents produce muscle cramps and weakness. Chronic corticosteroid use is another cause of myopathy.

Cognitive and neuropsychiatric drug side effects are exceedingly common. These can be produced by direct effects on the brain or indirectly, by drugs that interfere with other systems necessary for normal cerebral function. The elderly and those with preexisting brain dysfunction are most at risk. Alcohol and other substance abuse are important risk factors. Confusion or frank delirium is well-known with anticholinergics, benzodiazepines, narcotic analgesics (opioids), and nonsteroidal anti-inflammatory drugs. Abrupt medication discontinuation is another frequent cause of confusion.

Medications may also produce iatrogenic seizures. Risk factors include previous seizures, family history of epilepsy, other coexisting brain disorders, and high fever. Infants and the elderly are most at risk. Certain antidepressants, chemotherapy drugs, clozapine, particular antimicrobial agents, and theophylline are among the many drugs associated with seizures. Radiology contrast agents and some vaccinations may cause seizures.

Intravenous immunoglobulin is an effective treatment for many autoimmmune neuromuscular diseases such as Guillain-Barré syndrome, chronic inflammatory demyelinating polyradiculoneuropathy, and multifocal motor neuropathy.[6] Thrombotic strokes, probably due to increased serum viscosity, are a rare complication of this therapy.[7,8]

21.3 Complications of Vascular Disease Treatment

Neurologic injuries can occur as a result of surgery to correct cardiovascular or cerebrovascular disease. Coronary artery bypass surgery (CABG) can cause stroke, either from emboli loosened from the aortic wall, from inadequate brain perfusion, or other unidentified processes. Cognitive complaints after CABG are not uncommon but their cause is not clear.[9] *Carotid endarterectomy* is performed to prevent stroke due to occlusion of the artery. Unfortunately, stroke complicates as many as 10 percent of these operations.

Anticoagulants—popularly known as blood thinners—play a major role in stroke prevention in patients with atrial fibrillation and carotid artery disease. Bleeding is a recognized risk in anticoagulated patients. Patients taking anticoagulants must have frequent blood tests to make certain they are neither over- or under-anticoagulated. Subdural hematomas and intracerebral hemorrhages are common neurologic side effects in these patients.[10] Bleeding can also occur in other organs, especially in the retroperitoneal area.

Bleeding is also a complication of thrombolytic treatment—clot-busting—for acute stroke and heart attacks. Thrombolysis for stroke is discussed in §12.3C.

21.4 Iatrogenic Infections of the Central Nervous System

These usually occur as complications of neurosurgical and other invasive procedures including lumbar puncture, intrathecal drug administration, and epidural anesthesia.[11] Bacterial meningitis is a recognized complication of cranial surgery and lumbar puncture. Diagnosis of infection in an unconscious or sedated post-operative patient may be delayed, making successful treatment more difficult. Craniotomy can also cause brain abscess, cranial epidural abscess, and subdural empyema. Spinal surgery or invasive procedures can produce spinal epidural abscess. All of these require rapid diagnosis and appropriate antibiotic treatment.

Creutzfeld-Jakob disease is a human prion disease (see §16.8). It can be spread through introduction of infected tissue. Cases have been described after corneal transplants, with use of electroencephalographic depth electrodes, from dura mater grafts, and in recipients of growth hormone derived from cadaver pituitary glands.[12]

21.5 Neurologic Side Effects of Radiation Therapy[13]

The safe dose for radiation of nervous tissue is unknown. Cognitive dysfunction after brain irradiation is common. Complications of radiation therapy are classified according to time course. Diagnostically, radiation damage must be distinguished from recurrent or progressive tumor growth. Conventional MRI cannot make this distinction. PET and MR spectroscopy are more helpful.

Acute radiation encephalopathy due to cerebral edema occurs within a few days of treatment. Patients develop headache, fever, nausea and vomiting, drowsiness, and increased focal abnormalities. Rarely, severe brain swelling leads to fatal herniation. *Early delayed encephalopathy* develops within weeks of radiation. Focal neurologic signs and the MRI appearance worsen but most patients recover within several weeks. Steroids may be helpful.

Deterioration beginning months or years after treatment is more ominous. This *late delayed encephalopathy* is also known as *radiation necrosis*. It can be diffuse or focal. Clinically, there may be progressive dementia, abnormal gait, and other focal abnormalities. Treatment is rarely helpful.

Radiation can also damage the spinal cord. A transient *early delayed myelopathy* due to demyelination is characterized by paresthesia and *L'Hermitte's sign*—an electric sensation shooting down the spine when the patient flexes the neck. Recovery occurs gradually within a month to a year. *Late delayed myelopathy* begins a year or more after treatment. This begins as a Brown-Séquard syndrome (see §9.3) and slowly leads to paraparesis or quadriparesis. It is irreversible and untreatable. If the radiation damage is below the spinal cord, at the level of the cauda equina, there will be a lower motor neuron syndrome. Patients develop asymmetric leg weakness, atrophy, and areflexia.

Radiation can also damage cranial and peripheral nerves. The brachial plexus is the most common peripheral nervous structure affected. There are *early delayed* and *delayed progressive* brachial plexopathies. Distinguishing this from recurrent tumor is important but difficult. There are at least two helpful features. First, *myokymia*—a particular abnormal electrical discharge—is a common EMG finding in brachial radiation plexopathy, but is rare with recurrent tumor. Second, pain is much less likely with radiation-induced damage than with tumor.

Endnotes

1. Kohn LT, Corrigan JM, Donaldson, MS, eds. *To Err is Human: Building a Safer Health System*. Institutes of Medicine. Washington, DC: National Academies Press; 2000.

2. Jain KK. "A short practical method for triage of adverse drug reactions." *Drug Information Journal* 1995;29:339-342.

3. Gardos G, Cole JO. "Overview of public health issues in tardive dyskinesia." *Am J Psychiatry* 1980;137:776-781.

4. Keck PE, et al. "Neuroleptic malignant syndrome." *Current Opinions in Psychiatry* 1991;4:34-37.

5. Sieb JP, Gillessen T. "Iatrogenic and toxic myopathies." *Muscle Nerve* 2003; 27:142-156.

6. Dalakas MC. "Intravenous immunoglobulin in the treatment of autoimmune neuromuscular diseases: Present status and practical therapeutic guidelines." *Muscle Nerve* 1999;22:1479-1497.

7. Caress JB, Cartwright MS, et al. "The clinical features of 16 cases of stroke associated with administration of IVIg." *Neurology* 2003;60:1822-1824.

8. Okuda D, Flaster M, et al. "Arterial thrombosis induced by IVIg and its treatment with tPA." *Neurology* 2003;60:1825-1826.

9. Newman MF, Kirchner JL, et al. "Longitudinal assessment of neurocognitive function after coronary-artery bypass surgery." *N Engl J Med* 2001;344:395-402.

10. Biller J, Asconapé J, et al. "Neurologic complications of anticoagulant and thrombolytic therapy." *Continuum* 2001;7(2):105-129.

11. Biller J, Asconapé J, et al. "Iatrogenic central nervous system infections." *Continuum* 2001;7(2):8-19.

12. Alter M. "How is Creutzfeld-Jakob disease acquired?" *Neuroepidemiology* 2000;19:55-61.

13. Biller J, Asconapé J, et al. "Neurologic complications of radiation therapy." *Continuum* 2001;7(2):147-159.

Additional Reading

Biller J. *Iatrogenic Disease*. Boston: Butterworth-Heinemann; 1998.

Jain KK. *Drug-Induced Neurological Disorders*. Seattle: Hogrefe & Huber; 1996.

Spencer PS, Schaumber HH, Ludolph AC. *Experimental and Clinical Neurotoxicology*. New York: Oxford University Press; 2000.

About the Author

Jeffrey Wishik, M.D., J.D., is a board certified neurologist and clinical neurophysiologist in private practice in Providence, Rhode Island. He received his medical degree from Rush University in 1981. After neurology residency and a fellowship in clinical neurophysiology at Albany Medical Center he completed a behavioral neurology fellowship at Boston University. He received his J.D., magna cum laude, from Roger Williams University School of Law in 1997, and is a member of the Massachusetts, New York, and Rhode Island bars. He has been practicing neurology in Rhode Island and nearby Massachusetts since 1987, with a special interest in adult attention deficit hyperactivity disorder. Dr. Wishik is also a certified independent medical examiner (American Board of Independent Medical Examiners) and provides medicolegal and consultative services to attorneys. He has published articles in the field of legal medicine and lectures to both physicans and attorneys on clinical and medicolegal topics. Dr. Wishik enjoys birding, chess, nature treks, photography, and mysteries set in Italy.

Index

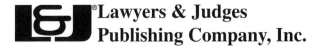

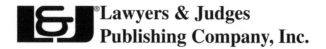

Lawyers & Judges
Publishing Company, Inc.

Drug Injury: Liability, Analysis and Prevention, Second Edition, #6044

James T. O'Donnell, M.S., Pharm.D.

All of us are aware of one or more pharmaceutical and over-the-counter drugs that were pulled from the market because of the injuries they cause to the general public. Yet, every year, thousands of drug injuries occur from human error too. Physicians' ordering mistakes, pharmacists filling the wrong prescriptions, drug administration mistakes, and drug mixing make up a large portion of drug injury litigation.

This book is divided into three useful sections that cover every type of drug injury litigation. The first section deals with the manufacturing and drug-approval process. The second section examines the injuries these drugs caused and the attempted cover-ups by some of the drug companies. You will read about important litigation regarding drugs like Prozac, Accutane, Rezulin, and more. The third section looks at the mistakes that can happen in the pharmacy and malpractice claims. It also includes appendices of FDA regulations relating to drug product liability guidance for industry, use of risk minimization plans, and FDA pregnancy classifications.

You will find this text indispensable because it provides comprehensive information for attorneys, healthcare professionals, pharmacists, and those affiliated with the pharmaceutical industry. 8 $\frac{1}{2}$" × 11", casebound, approx. 1000 pages.

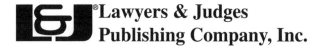

Lawyers & Judges Publishing Company, Inc.

Assessment of Earning Capacity, Second Edition, #6079

Michael S. Shahnasarian, Ph.D.

Earning capacity is quite often underappreciated and not fully understood. All too often in litigated disputes, two vocational evaluators arrive at radically disparate opinions, despite having similar professional backgrounds and analyzing the same set of facts. Who is the jury or judge to believe?

In *Assessment of Earning Capacity*, Second Edition, Dr. Shahnasarian recommends standardization, objectivity, and consistency in vocational evaluations. He begins by introducing you to vocational expert services, guiding you through consultation and the standard methods for determining your clients' earning capacity. From there you will be taken through several comprehensive case studies, examining common situations that may require vocational assessment, such as personal injury cases, family law, employment law, and an all new chapter on long-term disability insurance. Finally, the author presents tips on appearing as an economic expert in court. You will learn what is required for trial preparation, testimony, and be presented with sample deposition questions and tips to aid you in presenting a professional demeanor while undergoing intense cross examination.

This second edition has been extensively revised and contains many examples to help you understand the expert's job. 8 $\frac{1}{2}$" × 11", softbound, 324 pages.

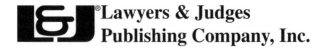

®Lawyers & Judges
Publishing Company, Inc.

Medical-Legal Aspects of Pain and Suffering, #6397

Patricia W. Iyer, M.S.N, RN, LNCC

Written by experienced clinicians and attorneys, *Medical-Legal Aspects of Pain and Suffering* will help you understand how health professionals can better alleviate pain and suffering and how you can more effectively litigate claims. A unique blend of authors have contributed solid material covering a range of concerns on this hot topic. This book is loaded with practical information, medical illustrations, figures and tables, pain assessment forms, and questions for direct examination of witnesses.

Useful for healthcare professionals, claims adjusters, trial attorneys, and legal nurse consultants, this book begins by guiding you through a broad overview of key concepts and assessment tools in pain and suffering. You'll review pain management—covering psychological as well as physical pain—and issues pertaining to specific client populations and healthcare settings. Material is included for attorneys evaluating and presenting a claim involving pain and suffering that explains life care plans and the use of trial exhibits. By combining the clinical information in the first two sections with the legal strategies in the last section, this book becomes a must read. 8 $1/_2$" × 11", casebound, 544 pages.

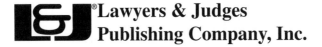

Lawyers & Judges Publishing Company, Inc.

Medical-Legal Aspects of the Spine, #6818

Marjorie Eskay-Auerback, M.D., J.D.

Discover this comprehensive book, complete with a discussion of the medical field, specifically the spine, and the legal implications that surround it.

This text provides beginning and intermediate-level medical information about conditions of the cervical and lumbar spine. Physical examination findings and diagnostic studies are discussed in detail. Explanations of common cervical and lumbar spine conditions, such as disc herniations, degenerative disc disease, and sprain/strain injuries are provided, along with treatment options. Non-surgical treatment, injection therapies, and surgical treatment are discussed with attention to both technique and indications. The goal of this text is to provide the reader with a practical reference to terminology frequently found in medical records and deposition testimony.

Medical-Legal Aspects of the Spine is a must-have for anyone in the field who needs to know about types of treatment, disorders, and studies that involve the spine in the legal arena, backed by accomplished medical and legal expertise. It is a comprehensive text that provides specific, important information that can alter and enhance your case. 8 $\frac{1}{2}$" × 11", casebound, approx. 130 pages.

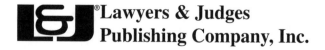

Lawyers & Judges
Publishing Company, Inc.

Biomechanics of Soft-Tissue Injury, #5503

Mark A. Gomez, Ph.D.

Learn about the process of reconstructing an accidental injury in a step-by-step fashion. Discover the mechanisms of injury, based on clinical literature, basic science literature, and experimental data. Differences between muscles and tendons are addressed and depicted in figures and text. You'll read about eccentric loading, range of motions, center of rotation, and the biological response to acute injury.

In addition, you'll encounter the six steps of accidental injury analysis: step one includes a "description of the accident;" step two, an "injury pattern defined;" step three, "define loading conditions that produce injury;" step four, "injury mechanism defined;" step five, "accident reconstruction;" and step six, "accident data consolidation." The last chapter provides you with several case examples from which to work. 8 $\frac{1}{2}$" × 11", casebound, 124 pages.

Topics include

- reconstructing an accidental injury
- cervical spine
- basic components: Ligament, tendon and muscle
- thoracolumbar spine
- shoulder
- knee
- sample case work-ups

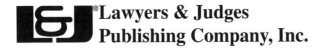

**Lawyers & Judges
Publishing Company, Inc.**

Deposition Dissection: A Handbook for Doctors Facing Deposition, #6559

Susanne Moore, RN, J.D.

Packed with sample questions, strategies, and explanations, *Deposition Dissection* is an essential manual for any healthcare provider facing the looming threat of a deposition. In an easily readable format, the book reveals opposing counsel's specific objectives and tactics, explains how your deposition fits into the big picture of a lawsuit, and empowers you with the tools to give a strong, defensible deposition. Chapters on serving as an expert witness, practicing defensive medicine, and the implications of tort reform, bring you up to date on today's legal trends in medicine. The book contains questions and references from actual cases, and you will notice a shorter, stronger deposition that will stand up during trial. 6" × 9", softbound, approx. 114 pages.

Topics include

- What is a deposition?
- What is a deposition not?
- what topics will be covered at your deposition

- your role
- your attorney's role
- questions and answers

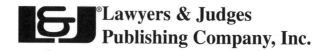
Lawyers & Judges
Publishing Company, Inc.

Workplace Injury Litigation, #6125

Edited by Todd McFarren, Esq. and
Glen J. Grossman, Esq.

Workers' compensation law is a complex field in which even a seasoned litigator may occasionally need the guidance of an expert. The compensability of on-the-job injuries and death varies from state to state, many genuine injuries are subjective (i.e., with little or no physical evidence of damage), insurance companies can and do vigorously resist the payment of benefits, the bureaucracy of the appeals process can be a tangle . . . .

Editors McFarren and Grossman have gathered chapters from leading medical and legal experts in the field. Attorneys and judges—as well as healthcare providers, employers, insurance company representatives and vocational consultants—will find new ideas, fresh perspectives and just plain good advice in this volume. Put their expertise to work for you and order your copy today. 6" × 9", casebound, 510 pages.

These and many more useful products are available through our catalog.
For a FREE catalog, write or call:

Lawyers & Judges Publishing Company, Inc.

P.O. Box 30040 • Tucson, Arizona 85751-0040

(800) 209-7109 • FAX (800) 330-8795
e-mail address: sales@lawyersandjudges.com

Find us on the Internet at:
http://www.lawyersandjudges.com